THE BOOK OF BIRDS

*The First Work Presenting in Full Color All the Major
Species of the United States and Canada*

EDITED BY

GILBERT GROSVENOR, LL.D., Litt.D., D.Sc.

President, National Geographic Society

and

ALEXANDER WETMORE, Ph.D., D.Sc.

Assistant Secretary of the Smithsonian Institution

With 950 Color Portraits by Major Allan Brooks

VOLUME I

DIVING BIRDS, OCEAN BIRDS, SWIMMERS, WADING BIRDS,
WILD FOWL, BIRDS OF PREY, GAME BIRDS, SHORE BIRDS,
MARSH DWELLERS, BIRDS OF THE NORTHERN SEAS

Narrative by Arthur A. Allen, M.A., Ph.D., *Professor of Ornithology in Cornell University;* T. Gilbert Pearson, LL.D., *President Emeritus, National Association of Audubon Societies;* Robert Cushman Murphy, M.A., D.Sc., *Curator of Oceanic Birds, American Museum of Natural History;* Frederick C. Lincoln, *Senior Biologist in Charge, Distribution and Migration of Birds, U. S. Biological Survey;* Alexander Wetmore; Gilbert Grosvenor; Francis H. Herrick, Ph.D., D.Sc.; Henry W. Henshaw, and others.

NATIONAL GEOGRAPHIC SOCIETY
WASHINGTON, D. C.

Table of Contents

A HUDSONIAN CURLEW LEAVES ITS NEST NEAR CHURCHILL, ON HUDSON BAY

Note that the edges of the feathers have been worn away by the long journey to South America and back. In a few weeks the bird will molt and don new plumage.

FOREWORD

By Gilbert Grosvenor
President, National Geographic Society

THIS new *Book of Birds* of the National Geographic Society is the first complete work ever published which portrays with comprehensive detail and illustrations in *full color* all the major species of birds of the United States and Canada.

For a long time naturalists, bird lovers, and sportsmen have badly needed such a work. Excellent volumes on the birds of New England, of New York, of Florida, of Minnesota, of New Mexico, and of California have been published, but, until this National Geographic Society production, no single book printed has covered all the North American Continent north of Mexico.

Our arrangement of picturing side by side in true colors eastern and western varieties enables the owner of the National Geographic Society *Book of Birds* for the first time easily to compare the different forms—the eastern and western bluebirds, the orioles of the Atlantic coast with those of California, etc.

As our members are well aware, few sections of the world enjoy such an abundance and variety of bird life and so many melodious songsters as our continent.

The amazing variety of bird-life studies included in the 37 chapters of the two volumes is partly revealed by the chapter headings. These fascinating accounts, based on a lifetime of observations, adventures, and research discoveries, are the personal narratives of such outstanding authorities as:

> Alexander Wetmore, Ph.D., D.Sc., Assistant Secretary, Smithsonian Institution
>
> T. Gilbert Pearson, LL.D., President Emeritus, National Association of Audubon Societies
>
> Arthur A. Allen, M.A., Ph.D., Professor of Ornithology in Cornell University
>
> Robert Cushman Murphy, M.A., D.Sc., Curator of Oceanic Birds, American Museum of Natural History
>
> Frederick C. Lincoln, Senior Biologist in Charge Distribution and Migration of Birds, U. S. Biological Survey
>
> Francis H. Herrick, Ph.D., D.Sc., Professor Emeritus, Western Reserve University; and others.

In the 748 pages of the two-volume set, there are 204 pages of full color plates showing 950 birds painted by the distinguished artist-naturalist, Major Allan Brooks. When the female differs from the male in plumage (the bluebird, towhee, oriole, etc.) or the immature bird's dress varies from its adult appearance (American eagle, herring gull, etc.), Major Brooks has faithfully pictured each form.

Adding to the permanent reference value of these vivid paintings, biographies set forth the identifying characteristics of each species of bird, its range, breeding habits, and other features of behavior. Six hundred and thirty-three species and scores of subvarieties are thus described.

Two hundred and thirty-two monochrome photographs, the majority by Arthur A. Allen, present various aspects of bird life, while 17 maps reveal the remarkable new developments in the study of bird migration through birdbanding.

The publication of these volumes is undertaken by The Society solely as another contribution to its educational purposes, the increase and diffusion of geographic knowledge. The price set for this colorful album of bird portraits and encyclopedic *Book of Birds* is nominal, because the cost of original color engravings and narratives has been assumed by THE NATIONAL GEOGRAPHIC MAGAZINE over a period of years. Moreover, the books are sold at cost, because The Society is non-profit-making, seeking only to make its works available for the pleasure and information of outdoor enthusiasts, naturalists, sportsmen, students, teachers, and members of all households where young and old find delight in the exciting world of popular science.

July 1, 1939. The demand for this work has necessitated a large second edition.

Photograph by Claude C. Matlack

VOLPLANING ON 7-FOOT WINGS A MAN-O'-WAR-BIRD SNATCHES FISH FROM
THE HAND

Despite their fearsome size and appearance, these birds become tame beggars about ports. This one is receiving a morsel of food from Captain Charles Thompson's hand at Hood Island, Galápagos.

IN MATING TIME THE MALE DEVELOPS A BAGPIPE, BUT, ALAS, HE CANNOT
PLAY A NOTE

Photographs by Claude C. Matlack

THE MAN-O'-WAR-BIRD'S THROAT SWELLS WITH AFFECTION

Photograph by Frank and John Craighead

YOUNG AMERICA, LED BY THE CRAIGHEAD BROTHERS, TAKES UP THE ANCIENT SPORT OF FALCONRY, TAMING AND FLYING THE MOST SPIRITED BIRDS ALIVE

This group of modern falconers of the Nation's Capital comprises (left to right) Frank Craighead, with a trained pigeon hawk; Chestin Eshleman with a trained sparrow hawk; Morgan Berthrong with a trained pigeon hawk; Larry Hufty with a trained Cooper's hawk; Robert Stevenson with a trained pigeon hawk; and John Craighead with a trained tercel duck hawk. Except the pigeon hawks, caught in Canada, all the birds were found at nests within a few miles of the White House. The small hawks are flown at English sparrows, the large falcons at starlings and crows. The hawks have come to know the dogs and so are undisturbed by their presence.

BILLS TO THE WIND, BROWN PELICANS, EMBLEMS OF CHARITY FROM EARLY TIMES, HOVER OVER THEIR ROOKERY IN A FLORIDA
MANGROVE THICKET

A FIRM GRIP WITH THE BILL, A TOSS OF THE HEAD—

Photographs by Eric Fleet

AND THE FISH IS STOWED FOR FUTURE USE

A well-equipped fisherman is the pelican, for it carries its own net in the form of the capacious pouch under the bill. The fish are stowed in the stomach (page 5). These birds become so tame about Florida resorts that they remind the traveler of the beggars of the Far East.

IF THE BIRD WERE ABSENT, THE EGGS MIGHT ESCAPE NOTICE AS "PEBBLES"

A Wilson's plover returns to the slight hollow in the sand of the beach which constitutes her "nest" near Ponce de Leon Inlet, Florida.

Photographs by Arthur A. Allen

A LEAST BITTERN DEFENDS ITS NEST AGAINST AN AGGRESSOR

"SAILING, SAILING, OVER THE BOUNDING MAIN"

Resembling a monster pterodactyl in miniature, the brown pelican of our eastern seaboard fishes for its meals as much as fifty miles from home. It alternately flaps its wings, and sails, glider fashion, usually from 30 to 60 feet above the water, diving for menhaden when it sights a school of these fish. Although awkward in appearance, it has a marvelous mastery of the air.

THE PELICANS, CORMORANTS, LOONS, AND GREBES

Birds That Cruise the Coast and Inland Waters Once Gave Rise to Sea Serpent Legends

By T. Gilbert Pearson

THE warden patrol boat, *Royal Tern*, had come to anchor for the night in the shelter of the Chandeleurs, against whose outer beaches the waves were pounding in from the Gulf of Mexico. Off to leeward a long, undulating line, like a many-humped caterpillar, moved slowly to the southward. It looked like the movement of some gigantic sea serpent.

Early explorers told of such monsters disporting themselves along the surface of the sea. In fancy this was what I saw, but my notebook merely records that forty-eight brown pelicans passed in single file. They were returning from a fishing excursion and were headed for the little Louisiana possession known as Isle Grandgosier (Errol), where numerous hungry young awaited them.

HABITS OF THE BROWN PELICAN

At various places that day we saw pelicans catching their prey. Flying above the surface of the water, usually at a distance of from 30 to 60 feet, a bird would abruptly plunge with a mighty splash into the sea. Often it would turn as it descended, to get the wind at its back, but it would always rise from the water with head toward the wind.

The bill of a brown pelican is from 9 to 13 inches in length, and beneath it is a pouch capable of great distention. Once, while a man held a dead pelican, I poured three and one-half gallons of water into the pouch before any of it spilled over the sides of the bill.

This pouch is used, not as a carrier of food, but as a dip net or scoop with which to capture fish. When, after a plunge, the bird rights itself on the water, it slowly raises its head.

From between the mandibles the water streams out as the pouch contracts. Then the bill is pointed upward, the fish is swallowed, and the bird is ready to fly in quest of another quarry.

Once I cruised with a naturalist who collected a number of brown pelicans for his museum. We weighed all the specimens and found that they varied from seven and one-half to eleven and one-half pounds. I have measured many of these birds and have noted that their length runs more than four feet and that the wing-spread of some individuals is nearly seven feet.

The pelican belongs to a suborder of birds known as Pelecani, which includes also the cormorants and darters, to be referred to later. One peculiarity they possess in common is the form of the foot. The web extends to all four of the toes.

The force with which a diving brown pelican strikes the sea is amazing. The fact that these repeated percussions do not injure or disable the bird may be due to the mass of air sacs beneath the skin, which form, it would seem, an effective pneumatic cushion.

Brown pelicans accumulate in colonies to breed on small, isolated islands in the sea, never far from the mainland. The nests are of twigs, among which leaves and weeds sometimes are mingled. They are built on the ground or in mangrove trees. The eggs are white, usually three in number, and incubation of about one month's duration is required.

The largest breeding assemblage of these birds on the Atlantic coast of the United States is on an island in the southern end of Mosquito Lagoon, Florida. Formerly this colony occupied Pelican Island, in Indian River, near Sebastian, but the encroachments of civilization caused the birds to move to their present nesting site.

WAR ON THE BROWN PELICAN

A much smaller colony often collects to breed on an island in Bull Bay, South Carolina, but high tides frequently sweep away the eggs. A few years ago some nested on Royal Shoal, near Ocracoke, North Carolina.

There are other nesting places of these birds along the Gulf coast between Key West and the Mexican border.

In 1918 the States bordering on the Gulf

Photograph by Lewis W. Walker from Eastman Kodak Company

"LUNCHEON IS READY"

This picture of a brown pelican over its nest was a prize-winning amateur photograph from the Salon of the 1936 Newspaper National Snapshot Awards. Brown pelicans nest in trees as well as on the ground (see page 1). Pelicans, gannets, cormorants, anhingas, tropic-birds, and man-o'-war-birds differ from all other swimming birds in having four-toed feet fully webbed. Their large webbed feet are powerful swimming instruments (see page 39).

vestigation had revealed a million pelicans along the Florida coast, and that they ate nine hundred and fifty thousand dollars' worth of food fish every day. Certain newspapers joined in the clamor and denounced the Federal Government and the Audubon Societies for having created reservations for these birds.

On the night of May 10, 1918, men landed on Pelican Island Government Bird Reservation in Indian River and, while the warden slept, clubbed to death 400 young pelicans in their nests.

So many complaints reached the Federal Food Administration that investigation was deemed necessary, and the writer was asked to ascertain if the estimate of 5,-000,000 pelicans for the Gulf

were swept by hysterical denunciations of the brown pelican. Our country was at war, food was growing scarce, Herbert Hoover, directing the Food Administration, was calling upon the people to eat fish, and fish dealers were complaining that the fish supply was diminishing because of depredations of the brown pelican.

From Texas came reports from officials that there were thousands of pelicans along the shores, and that "every day they consume more food fish than the people of Texas get in a year."

A Florida observer declared that his in-

coast was correct, and if the birds were destroying the fishing industry. I undertook this work in June, 1918, when the pelicans were gathered on their nesting islands, all of which were situated in Texas, Louisiana, and Florida.

The interest of those States was such that I readily obtained State coöperation and was able to make my cruises on State patrol boats. By the simple method of counting two old birds for each nest and adding 30 per cent of this count for non-breeding birds, I found that there were about 65,000 in the 1,500-mile stretch of coast between Key West and the mouth of the Rio Grande, on the Mexican border.

Both young and old pelicans disgorged quantities of fish as we walked about the rookeries. In Texas and Louisiana every fish disgorged by a pelican, or found in or about the nests, was the Gulf menhaden, an oily fish never used for human consumption. On the Florida coast we collected 3,428 fish which we saw pelicans disgorge, and only 27 were species used for food by mankind—mullet, pigfish, pinfish, and crevalle. No high-priced, valuable forms, such as mackerel, pompano, or trout, were found. Identifications were made by the United States Bureau of Fisheries in Washington, where I shipped various tanks of formaldehyde containing fish collected in the breeding colonies. In every case a State representative was present when these collections were made.

Basing its decision on these findings, the Federal Food Administration ruled adversely on requests to destroy the pelicans as a war measure; so the Audubon Association and the Biological Survey went on with their work of protecting them.

THE GREAT WHITE PELICAN

The pelican family (Pelecanidae) numbers eight species and four additional forms, distributed throughout the warmer parts of the world. Three are found in North America. Of these the white pelican is one of the largest of all North American water birds. It has a wing expanse of from 8 to 10 feet, and adults vary in weight from 15 to 20 pounds. A battalion of these immense birds, soaring in the sky above one of our western lakes, presents a picture not easily forgotten, and a flock at rest is a most conspicuous object, which may be seen from afar.

The methods which this bird employs in fishing are strikingly different from those of its smaller relatives, the brown pelicans, one form of which lives along our Pacific coast. Whereas the brown pelican secures its prey by plunging from aloft, the former scoops its food into its capacious mouth as it swims majestically along the surface of the water. Now and then it feeds while wading in the shallows.

Lower Klamath Lake, which formerly stretched across the boundary of Oregon and California, constituted an excellent area for studying the habits of this bird. Here some years ago I observed a scene which

Photograph by Hugo H. Schroder

A BULL'S-EYE AT FIFTY FEET

Dropping like a plummet, a brown pelican strikes the water with a splash and deftly captures a fish in its scooplike pouch. Taking off, it scatters spray like the wash from an amphibian's propeller.

WHITE PELICANS FLOCK LIKE DOMESTIC GEESE

Seen from a distance through the shimmering haze of marshlands adjacent to Upper Klamath Lake, Oregon, they resemble lingering patches of snow, or billowing sheets of Monday's wash. Fresh water attracts them in summer, though in winter they prefer southern coastal regions.

my companions told me was a good example of the fishing methods at times employed by the white pelican.

PELICANS STAGE A FISH DRIVE

Perhaps 150 of these birds were engaged in what, to all appearances, was a communal undertaking. They had formed a semicircle and were all swimming toward the shore. Many flapped their wings at intervals, evidently to beat the water and create a commotion. The fish were being driven in from all sides. Frequently birds struck with their 12-inch beaks, and their subsequent actions indicated that their fishing enterprise was being attended with marked success.

We noted that other eyes than ours were watching the fish drive, and that their owners understood what was going on. From three directions Farallon cormorants hastened up eagerly. Passing over the line of pelicans, they alighted in the water and instantly dived beneath the surface. Such an opportunity to be in the midst of an abundant food supply was not to be overlooked by the hungry and sagacious cormorants.

At that time white pelicans to the number of fully 5,000 to 6,000 were breeding on Lower Klamath Lake. In at least 20 places colonies had been established, these ranging from 50 to about 600 inhabitants. The birds had built their nests on the nu-

"LOOK OUT BELOW, YOU POOR FISH!"

Frequently companies of white pelicans beat their wings on the water, herd their victims in front and scoop them up. Unlike their brown brothers, they do not dive for food. These birds are flying over Williamson River, a popular feeding ground near Klamath Falls, Oregon.

merous floating islands of massed tule reeds, which were extremely abundant in and about the lake. This is the only place that I have ever seen white pelicans nesting in such a situation. Elsewhere they have built on the earth, gravel, or rocks. I have never seen a white pelican nest in a tree; islands in all cases are used by these birds. With a single exception, they have never been known to breed any place other than on lakes in the interior.

Lower Klamath Lake is no longer the nesting haunt of the myriads of water birds of numerous species that once frequented its broad expanse. The water is all but gone and the former lake bed is now an area of weeds and alkali dust, with here and

there a ranch of limited productivity. This change was brought about by man in the relentless march of civilization.

In Oregon is the Malheur Lake Bird Refuge. Both Malheur and its sister lake, Harney, are shallow bodies of water and undergo extreme changes in area from season to season. Both are practically dry during the nesting season. From September 1 to December 1 Malheur's water area is about 3,000 acres, and Harney is dry, except for a 500-acre expanse on the west side. There is no pelican colony in the refuge, but some 200 pelicans arrived in the spring of 1932, and occasionally 40 or 50 visit the refuge during the summer.

Complaint has arisen that white pelicans

"SAY IT WITH FISH," FOR THE BEGARS

So tame and unsuspicious do eastern brown pelicans become near Florida seaside resorts that visitors are amused by throwing them small fry. The absurd antics of these awkward-looking birds as they fight for such titbits resemble the splashing sport of the brown-skinned boys who dive for copper coins in Caribbean ports.

Photograph by Arthur A. Allen

A RED-THROATED LOON GOES HOUSE HUNTING

From its winter home in the United States this bird flew to the coast of Labrador, thence inland, when the snow melted, and built a nest on the edge of a fresh-water pond. John James Audubon, the famous naturalist, studied these birds during his summer visit to Labrador in 1833.

Photograph by W. L. Finley and H. T. Bohlman

"HOME, SWEET HOME," AMONG THE RUSHES

Graceful western grebes, the "swan necks," build moundlike nests of water-soaked vegetation so close to the surface that the eggs lie just above the water. Like other grebes, they eat their own feathers, which perhaps act as strainers for fishbones or other hard substances.

11

THE NIGHT SHIFT TONES UP WITH A MORNING SPLASH

The Japanese, with the aid of trained cormorants, usually fish in the dark, using flaming torches as lures. Each angler manipulates a flock of a dozen birds by means of collar-attached reins held in his left hand and untangled skillfully with his right. With full gullets the live "dip nets" are pulled aboard and forced to disgorge. Undaunted, they then dive back into the water for more. Distinguished visitors often come in boats, such as those in the background, to watch the sport.

are destructive to game fish, and that their numbers should be reduced. It is true that they eat trout, but they consume also species of fish not used by man. In any event, their numbers are not so large as to constitute any serious danger to the game fish of America.

As far as we have been able to learn, there are about thirty breeding colonies of white pelicans. The total population to-day may be anywhere from 30,000 to 60,000. The birds are so conspicuous that they attract attention whenever seen and their numbers are constantly overestimated by untrained observers. Flocks of thousands are often reported, which, upon investigation, prove to contain only a few hundred individuals.

The largest breeding colonies of white pelicans in the United States are those in Great Salt Lake, Utah; Pyramid Lake, Nevada; Clear Lake, California, and Chase Lake, North Dakota. These, together with the colony in Yellowstone Lake, are under the care of State or Federal guardians and appear to be in a flourishing condition.

THE COMMON LOON

Another large waterfowl is the common loon—a heavy, stocky bird with thick neck and strong, sharp beak. The first living specimen I saw was brought to me in North Carolina many years ago. It was nearly three feet in length. A man had picked it up in his dooryard one foggy morning. So far as we could discover, it was uninjured. Probably it had become bewildered during migration, and, tired out, had at length made a forced landing. It flopped its wings and dragged itself along the ground, but seemed totally incapable of taking flight. Only upon being liberated on a pond was it able to mount aloft after much flapping and splashing along the surface, to acquire the necessary momentum.

The summer range of the common loon extends throughout the Northern States and much of Canada. In many regions there is scarcely a sequestered lake not inhabited by one or more pairs of this splendid bird. Its loud, far-carrying cries have suggested to many the demoniacal laughter of a madman; hence the expression, "crazy as a loon."

The novice who thinks this saying refers to the mentality of the bird soon learns his mistake when he attempts to catch one of them. In summer the birds are seen usually singly or in pairs. If one is approached it will dive before the canoeist has arrived within shotgun range. There is no way of predicting accurately at what point of the compass it will come to the surface. One thing is certain, however: it will appear at a spot much farther away. Paddle toward it and it will again disappear.

A man may thus follow a loon for half a day if he wishes, but will find himself at the end not one bit closer to the object of his quest.

Loons pass the winter in open waters throughout much of the United States. They occur in the Great Lakes, in broad rivers, and in large ponds, and are especially common on the coastal waters of the South Atlantic and Gulf States. In spring

Photograph by Arthur A. Allen

"AND WHAT I DIDN'T SAY TO HIM!"

This colony of European and double-crested cormorants clings to a guano-covered cliff on the Labrador coast. Sometimes the latter species decorates its basket nest, two feet across and often a foot high, with sprigs of evergreens, gulls' feathers, and dead crabs; also with pipes, combs, pocket knives, or other salvage from wrecks.

migration they often move north in scattered flocks, many passing over a given point in the course of a day or night.

In traveling along the coast they do not always follow closely the curvatures of the shoreline, but often cross over the capes or headlands. Many fly this way every year over the outer sand banks along the North Carolina coast. Some years ago it was the custom to shoot them from the dunes near Cape Lookout, where men gathered in the spring for that purpose. "War loon" is the name by which it is known to the people of that region.

There are four species of loons, with four

Photograph by Arthur A. Allen

"SAY AAH, MOTHER!"

This European cormorant is feeding its young by regurgitation in a nest on the Labrador coast. The baby at first sips half-liquid food from its parent's bill. Later it thrusts its head and neck far down the feeder's throat for the predigested food. When the youngster is old enough to "eat what is on the table," the parent birds bring him whole fish.

The grebe which is probably better known to more people of the Western Hemisphere than is any other member of the family is the pied-billed, locally known by various names, as "dabchick," "didapper," "water witch," and "hell diver." It breeds locally from British Columbia and Nova Scotia south to Florida and Mexico. In winter it remains throughout much of its summer range, if the lakes do not freeze, although many move southward, some going to Cuba.

When I was a boy in Florida a negro told me that he had seen an alligator's nest at the side of one of the reedy ponds on Kanapaha Prairie, so I went to look for it. I found that it would be a much nearer way to reach the designated spot if I waded my horse across an arm of shallow water. There, amid a scattered growth of small reeds, I noticed a little raft of decayed water plants anchored to a few stout reed stalks. Dismounting in the shallow water, I found on this raft five dull white eggs covered with some of the nesting material. It was the nest of a pied-billed grebe.

Leaving the structure as I found it, I proceeded about 40 yards and found the eggs of the alligator. After tying the horse in the woods, I returned, sat down on the alligator's nest, the only dry spot in the vicinity, and awaited the return of the grebe. About every five minutes I arose cautiously, to look over the intervening reeds.

I must have been there an hour when suddenly I saw the bird sitting on her

geographical forms, all belonging to the family Gaviidae. The group is circumpolar in distribution, six of the known forms occurring in North America.

THE GREBES ARE WIDELY KNOWN

Closely related to the loons are the grebes (family Colymbidae). Their distribution is world-wide. Six of the 39 known forms inhabit North America. Like the loons, they are proficient divers. Casual observers sometimes mistake them for ducks, but the superficial resemblance vanishes when one is taken in the hand or observed closely with a field glass.

eggs. It discovered me at about the same moment. Rising instantly, it gave two or three swift pecks at the nest, slid into the water, and disappeared from view. Wading out to the nest, I found that at the moment of leaving the bird had completely covered its eggs. They were left safe from the searching eyes of the egg-eating fish crows, ever seeking food about the ponds and lakes.

So quickly can the grebe disappear when alarmed that it occasions comment wherever the bird is known. It is a common remark among country boys that no one can shoot a didapper when it is watching. The bird will dive at the flash of a gun and be safely beneath the surface when the shot arrives (page 27).

This grebe haunts especially the reedy shallows of ponds, lakes, and quiet backwaters of rivers. Though it is often seen swimming about in open water, much after the manner of ducks, I seldom have observed it in swift-running streams. There are comparatively few suitable regions in most of the Eastern States where it may not be seen. The whitish beak, crossed by a dark bar near the tip, is a mark which readily distinguishes it from other grebes. It is fairly safe to assume that any grebe seen in the Eastern or Southern States in summer is a pied-billed.

Among other members of this family, the large western grebe is one of the most interesting. In a sheltered bay of a California lake I came upon a colony containing at least thirty nests. The antics of the birds, as they bowed to each other or chased their mates or rivals over the water, were different from those of any other species of which I have knowledge. I have seen them going about their daily activities in many places, such as Klamath and Malheur Lakes, the Carson Sink country of Nevada, and in the vast marshes at the mouth of Bear River, in Utah.

The young frequently clamber upon the backs of their parents, where they may rest and doze in safety. If startled, the old birds, of course, dive and swim away beneath the surface, often taking the young with them. Soon, however, the little ones appear, bobbing up one at a time, like small animated balls of gray and white cotton.

THE WATER TURKEYS OR "SNAKEBIRDS"

Inhabiting the lakes and swamplands from North Carolina and Arkansas southward through tropical America, we may find that peculiar bird, the water turkey. It belongs to the family Anhingidae, or darters.

There are only four species of this group, one of each being found in Africa, Australia, southern Asia, and the warmer parts of America. The African species has three geographic races, one of which extends to Mesopotamia.

Water turkeys are silent birds, capturing their prey while swimming beneath the water, and are fond of spreading their wings in the sunshine to dry after each submarine voyage.

Often they swim with bodies submerged and with only their small heads and long necks protruding. Thus the bird has in some regions acquired the name "snakebird."

The water turkey builds a substantial nest of sticks and twigs, often with green leaves attached, in stout bushes and trees. I have visited at least a hundred of their nesting colonies, and the largest number of nests I have counted in any one place was seventy-five, although I was sure that some colonies contained many more.

This was in a swamp perhaps twenty miles south of Natchez, Mississippi, and known as "The Burn." I had finished my observations in a flourishing colony of egrets and other herons, and with the guide was making my way out of the swamp, when unexpectedly we came upon the water turkeys.

Their nests were on the horizontal limbs of fairly large cypress trees which surrounded an opening of about an acre in extent. It was quiet in this sultry, sequestered spot, that day in May, 1920. Only now and then a few sounds reached us from some nest, as a parent returned with food for its young.

The birds were not greatly alarmed by our presence. As a rule, they did not fly away, but thrust out their necks curiously at different angles to look down at us, as we sat in our frail pirogue, viewing the daily life of a water-turkey settlement.

White Pelican

(Pelecanus erythrorhynchos)
Average Length, Sixty Inches

The settlement of the country has driven white pelicans from many of their former dwelling places. As nesting birds, they have deserted the lakes they once occupied in Minnesota, Wisconsin, Colorado, and elsewhere, although they frequently are seen as nonbreeders in these regions. When a nesting colony is disturbed by visitors, the old birds desert their eggs and young without the slightest protest. If alarmed too often, they have been known to leave the region and select a nesting place in another part of the country.

In 1920 the writer discovered that a small colony had established itself on an island in Laguna Madre, on the lower Texas coast, and he photographed the birds, together with their eggs and young. The colony thrived and was probably joined by others migrating from their former haunts, for ten years later J. J. Carroll visited the island and estimated the colony at 5,000 birds. They were disturbed frequently by visitors, and trips to the island of late years have revealed the fact that the birds have gone away.

There were two interesting facts about this Texas group. The nearest neighboring colony is in Utah, 1,400 miles away, and it is the only case where the white pelican has been known to breed on an island surrounded by the waters of the sea.

The present breeding territory covers several of the far western States and extends north in the Canadian Provinces to central British Columbia and the Great Slave Lake. In autumn white pelicans move south and pass the winter from California to Panama and along the Gulf coast of the United States and Mexico. It is not uncommon in summer to find flocks of unmated birds far to the east and south of their present breeding range.

The sexes are alike in appearance, and in the spring both carry on the upper bill a curious horny plate, which later falls away. The whitish eggs are three or four in number and are covered with a chalky deposit. This heavy bird rises laboriously from the ground, but once in the air it sails with apparent ease and dignity. Often a flock will circle upward until it is no longer visible to the watcher below.

Eastern Brown Pelican

(Pelecanus occidentalis occidentalis)
Average Length, Fifty Inches

Brown pelicans feed entirely upon fish. In taking food to the young, the parent does not carry it in the great pouch beneath its bill, but in its stomach. Small semidigested particles are regurgitated into the pouch and run down to a point near the tip of the bill. The recently hatched young thrust in their bills and secure the nourishment. Later, whole fish are handled in much the same way.

When partly grown pelicans are disturbed, they usually disgorge their last meal. I have examined many hundreds of fish thus placed within my reach, which were in as perfect condition as when swallowed. Fish that had been in the stomachs of the young for some time showed that digestion began at the nose of the fish and proceeded toward the tail.

I have visited all the breeding colonies of these pelicans along the South Atlantic and Gulf coasts, several of them more than once, and have never known the adult birds to show the intense fear of man exhibited by white pelicans. One day I sat on a drift log for a little time holding one beside me. When liberated, it waddled away a few feet and deliberately picked its feathers several times before taking leisurely flight.

In his beautifully illustrated and most interesting *Florida Bird Life,* Arthur H. Howell writes: "Small companies of brown pelicans may be seen at almost any time along the sea coasts, winging their way in single file over the surf, sometimes almost touching the waves with their wings, again rising to a height of 20 feet or more. They fly steadily, flapping their great wings slowly in unison and varying the flapping with short periods of sailing. When fishing, they usually ascend to a height of 15 to 30 feet and when a fish is spied set their wings at an angle and plunge beneath the water with a great splash, emerging again at once with a fish in their bill. The plunge is made *down wind* and the bird emerges *up wind*. The pelicans are often robbed of their catch by man-o'-war-birds or by laughing gulls, the latter species sometimes alighting on the head of a pelican and snatching a fish from its pouch."

The eastern brown pelican nests from South Carolina and Texas to Brazil, and is found also in the Galápagos Islands and on the coasts of Colombia and Ecuador.

California Brown Pelican

(Pelecanus occidentalis californicus)
Average Length, Fifty-four Inches

The western form of the brown pelican inhabits the Pacific coast as a summer bird from San Francisco Bay to Cape San Lucas, in Baja California. In winter it wanders far, having been recorded as far north as British Columbia and southward to Central America.

These birds breed on steep hillsides on islands from the Santa Barbaras south. The nests are usually built on the ground, but sometimes in trees. A. B. Howell writes: "They are noisy little fellows, clucking to themselves continuously and with a flirt of the wings at each cluck. In spite of their tender age, they are very pugnacious, . . . even though this does not do them much good when the western gulls take a notion to peck out their brains."

A QUEER-LOOKING BIRD IS THE PELICAN

Florida visitors marvel at this ungainly inhabitant, the **Eastern Brown Pelican** (lower). Soaring above it are **White Pelicans** flying in line formation like airplanes. These snowy-plumaged heavy-weights, one of the largest of the North American water birds, summer in our western lakes and winter in coastal waters of the South and West.

Double-crested Cormorant

(Phalacrocorax auritus)

Average Length, Thirty Inches

In the sounds and shallow bays dotting the southern coast of the United States, the channels are marked with many stakes and buoys, and these are popular perching places for the double-crested cormorant. When a boat approaches, the big black bird leans forward, raises his wings, then hesitates as if loath to leave his comfortable position. When finally he launches forth in a clumsy, awkward fashion, he seems unable to keep from striking the water before he can get well under way. With heavily pounding wings he departs to seek another perch, or perhaps comes to rest at a distant point on the surface of the bay.

Sometimes cormorants take food fish from nets, but their usual diet consists of fish of no known value to man. On several occasions I have collected sculpins and other nonedible varieties which excited cormorants have disgorged in my presence.

For many years fishing clubs situated along streams flowing into the Gulf of St. Lawrence offered a standing bounty of 25 cents a head for every cormorant brought to them. Clubmen and their guides contended that the birds were destroying salmon. At length the Geological Survey of Canada obtained the services of one of the Dominion's ablest ornithologists to study the food of cormorants in these waters. Numbers of them were killed and the contents of their stomachs examined. Not a single bird was found to have eaten a salmon. Instead, many sculpins, "a few herrings, one capelin, an eel, and some tomcod were brought to light"; consequently the bounty offers were withdrawn.

When flying, the cormorant's neck is stretched to its fullest extent and its feet point out straight behind. While the bird is swimming on the surface, the large, webbed feet paddle alternately, but when it is pursuing prey under water both of the feet strike backward at the same time. As with all cormorants and pelicans, the feet of this bird have all four toes united by a web. The crests on the side of the head, which give this species its name, disappear soon after the nesting season begins, and on many of the birds they are never very conspicuous.

While I was visiting a colony of cormorants in North Carolina, a downy young bird fell from a cypress limb along which it was clambering. With waving wings it struck the water lightly and began swimming away. An alligator gave chase, and twice I thought the bird had been caught; but, by diving, it had in both cases escaped the enemy's jaws. We replaced the bird among the limbs of its cypress tree.

Of the Florida cormorant, Arthur H. Howell writes: "The abundance of the birds has led to the erection for many miles along the Gulf coast of a series of racks to catch the excrement of the birds, which is collected and used for fertilizer. During the greater part of the year long lines of cormorants may be seen flying in single file along the coast, many of them alighting on the racks, and others in the sea to fish. Their food is obtained by diving from the surface or swimming under water. They are able to remain under for long periods, and when in pursuit of their prey they sometimes use both feet and wings in swimming and are then capable of great speed. The birds, when alarmed, utter a hoarse, guttural croak like that of a bullfrog."

This species is divided into four subspecies, as follows: double-crested cormorant (Phalacrocorax auritus auritus), Florida cormorant (P. a. floridanus), white-crested cormorant (P. a. cincinatus), and the Farallon cormorant (P. a. albociliatus).

The combined geographic territory frequented by these four varieties gives to the species a range extending from Alaska, James Bay, and Newfoundland to Florida and Mexico.

In many places the birds build their nests on the ground or on rocky cliffs, but in Maine, as well as in North Carolina, Florida, and other southern States, trees are selected.

European Cormorant

(Phalacrocorax carbo carbo)

Average Length, Thirty-six Inches

The European cormorant is seen in the United States in winter, but even during that season one may expect to find it only along the Atlantic coast north of New York. It is casual south to South Carolina. Once known as the "common cormorant," it is no longer common on the Atlantic coast.

Although the bird at one time probably bred as far south as Maine, the most southern colony known today is on an island off Big Bras d'Or, Cape Breton Island, Nova Scotia. In company with Dr. Gilbert Grosvenor, in the summer of 1930, I examined this assemblage of one hundred or more birds and photographed them on their nests at close range. They inhabited a high, rocky cliff and their nests were placed on the narrow ledges. They kept careful watch of their eggs, for there was a pair of great black-backed gulls in the neighborhood, to which fact the breeding terns of the island from time to time gave vociferous testimony. The colony is now protected and is increasing.

Other forms of this cormorant occur in Europe, Asia, Africa, and Australia. I found these cormorants common on the Farne Islands, off the east coast of England, in 1922, and, two years later, along the Scottish coast. Their croaking notes and their nesting and feeding habits do not differ materially from those of other cormorants.

MAN HAS ENLISTED THE CORMORANT'S AID IN FISHING

The Japanese and Chinese put a cord, ring, or strap on the neck of each bird to keep it from swallowing the fish. The two head tufts of the adult **Double-crested Cormorant** (right) disappear in winter, and are not present on the immature bird (upper left). The handsome **European Cormorant** shown in breeding dress (lower left) nests from Nova Scotia to Greenland and in northern Europe.

Mexican Cormorant

(Phalacrocorax olivaceus mexicanus)

Average Length, Twenty-five Inches

On the prairie of Cameron Parish, Louisiana, there is an area of many acres where trees grow in shallow water. This place, known as "Bird Island," is a nesting haunt of roseate spoonbills and many herons. Here, too, accumulate several hundred cormorants about equally divided in numbers between two forms, the Florida and Mexican.

The latter is slightly the smaller bird, being three or four inches shorter than the former; also, in the breeding plumage, it shows a white U-shaped line running under the throat.

The nests of the two species are very similar, being composed of twigs and sticks and placed on horizontal limbs from 20 to 40 feet from the ground. When, in May, 1930, I last visited this place, I was greeted with many guttural grunting sounds made by the birds as they alighted at their nests, took flight, or sparred among themselves.

Near Brownsville, Texas, I fought my way through tangled, thorny bushes and waded for a mile in a brush-grown shallow lake, hunting for a colony of Mexican cormorants of which a trapper had told me. Many birds were seen, but I had to content myself with examining the nests from photographs made by my guide the following week. In this colony all the nests were in low trees, hardly more than bushes, scattered at intervals of several yards apart.

The Mexican cormorant has a hooked beak nearly two inches long, and its wing-spread is about three feet four inches.

This form nests from southern Louisiana to Cuba, the Bahamas, and Nicaragua.

In THE NATIONAL GEOGRAPHIC MAGAZINE for September, 1924, Dr. Robert Cushman Murphy describes the Peruvian cormorant, a relative of the Mexican cormorant. Of it he says: "Figuring in dollars and cents, and with reference to effect upon human life and human geography, we beg to present our candidate for the post of king among avian benefactors— the Peruvian cormorant or *guanay*, known to science by the ponderous name of *Phalacrocorax bougainvillei*.

"The guanayes are strictly creatures of the Humboldt Current; their huge flocks move up and down the coast as the birds forage among migrating schools of fish; they breed, likewise in vast numbers, upon the many islands lying from one to a score of miles from the coast; but they do not stray outside the field of the current, to the northward, the southward, or offshore.

"The islets of the Humboldt Current, which are most thickly distributed along the northerly two-thirds of Peru, partake of the same desert character of the opposite continental mainland. This climatic fact is the secret of the guanay's economic importance, for the guano or excrement of sea birds is preserved on the nesting grounds without loss of fertilizing efficacy such as would be caused by moisture.

"From prehistoric times guano from these islands has been used in the agriculture of the native peoples of Peru, but the importance and money value of this natural fertilizer and of its chief producer are greater today than at any time in the past" (see page 346).

Water Turkey

(Anhinga anhinga)

Average Length, Thirty-four Inches

Of all the nests that one may find in the populous water-bird colonies of the Southern States, those built by the water turkeys are pretty sure to be the most substantial. In cypress trees, large or small, or in stout buttonwood bushes, or perhaps in scraggy old willows, they construct cradles for their young that are so bulky as readily to be noticed among the other nests of the rookery. Often one may count the blue eggs in a heron's nest by looking through the twigs from below, but the white eggs of the water turkey are not so exposed. Sticks and twigs, often with leaves attached, are used in abundance. Usually green, freshly picked leaves are used for lining the cavity where the eggs and young are to rest.

When hatched, the young birds are naked, but gradually they become covered with buff-colored down. Their food consists of leeches, shrimps, tadpoles, insects, fish, and young alligators.

The most northern record of this bird, breeding in eastern United States, was made June 7, 1898, when the writer found a nest with four eggs in Brunswick County, North Carolina. It was thirty-four years before a second nest of this species was found in that State. This second nest was in a small cypress tree growing in the same lake where the first one had been discovered.

The anhinga is resident from Texas, Arkansas, and North Carolina to northern Argentina. In winter it is also found in the lower Colorado River region of California and Arizona.

Mexican Grebe

(Colymbus dominicus brachypterus)

Average Length, Nine and One-half Inches

The bird is by far the smallest and least known of all our North American grebes.

It is known to occur in the United States only in southern Texas. It inhabits also the region of southern Baja California and from Texas southward to Panama. Like the pied-billed grebe, this species lives in quiet ponds and slow-moving, fresh-water streams and builds a floating nest of decaying vegetation. Mud is often used in nest construction. Closely allied forms are found in the West Indies and South America.

HE MIMICS THE SNAKE WHEN FRIGHTENED

If alarmed while swimming, the **Water Turkey,** or darter (center right, and flying), frequently will submerge, leaving only his snaky head and neck protruding. The "snakebird," as he is popularly called, is strong and graceful in the air. The **Mexican Cormorant** (lower) is a relative of both species shown in the preceding plate. The **Mexican Grebe** (left) is North America's smallest grebe.

Brandt's Cormorant
(Phalacrocorax penicillatus)
Average Length, Thirty-three Inches

Cormorants inhabit the coastal waters of nearly all countries of the world and are found also about many of the lakes and larger rivers of the interior. They usually gather in flocks to roost and nearly always nest in colonies, often in association with other species of water birds. They swim beneath the surface to procure their prey. Thirty species are known, six of which inhabit North America.

Amid the teeming bird life that gathers to breed on various rocky islands along the Pacific coast from Alaska to Baja California, the big Brandt's cormorant occupies a conspicuous place. Many a high rocky ledge shows white sides and crest due to guano deposits made by the roosting cormorants.

At times large rafts of them accumulate in bays or in the open sea to feed where the running tides have brought in schools of fish. The bird is maritime, loving the salt sea and its rocky shores and its fish. One need not expect to find it about the shorelines of quiet lakes.

In seeking their food these birds do not hesitate to dive to great depths.

On the sloping sides of rocky islands they gather in numerous colonies to rear their young. At times the nests are placed very close to one another. Seaweeds and moss are generally used as nesting material and make substantial cradles for the blind, black, naked young soon to appear. Nests, as a rule, are nearly two feet wide, with a circular hollow about ten inches across. The bluish eggs, washed with chalky white, number three to six.

Frank M. Chapman, in his *Camps and Cruises of an Ornithologist*, writes of their nest building near Point Lobos, California: "The cormorants were now gathering grass for their nests, from an island almost within a stone's throw of the mainland. They appeared as a rule from the south, alighted at the edge of the island, a cliff some thirty feet in height, waddled awkwardly to the unclipped grass, pulled a bill-full, waddled back to the cliff border, threw themselves into the air on outstretched wings, and, flying toward the north, returned to their nesting rock, which was immediately back of the one on which they were 'haying.' Throughout the day feathered mowers were rarely absent from the field, sometimes as many as nine birds being present. The denuded area from which the grass had been removed was as bare and as sharply defined from that portion of the crop which the cormorants had not yet gathered as though it had been mowed and raked by a human harvester."

Western gulls prey upon the helpless young and eat quantities of eggs. Some observers have wondered how it is possible for the cormorants in certain localities to rear any young, so constantly are their nests rifled by the fierce and audacious gulls. However, when parent cormorants are robbed of their eggs or young, they philosophically construct another nest and try again.

Among the important nesting places of this species may be mentioned Point Carmel and Seal Rocks near Monterey and the Santa Barbara Islands of the California coast.

Pelagic Cormorant
(Phalacrocorax pelagicus pelagicus)
Average Length, Twenty-five and One-half Inches

This bird, formerly called the "violet-green cormorant," is an inhabitant of the Arctic and subarctic regions. It breeds locally along the coast and on the islands of Bering Sea, in Siberia, and in the Kurile Islands of Japan. Along the Aleutian Islands it is found also, as well as down toward southern Alaska. It winters from the Pribilof Islands to Puget Sound, on the American side of the Pacific, and as far south as China, on the Asiatic coast.

It is almost indistinguishable from Baird's cormorant, which breeds from British Columbia to Baja California. From the other cormorants of the northern Pacific there are two characteristics which distinguish these two. One is their small size; the other is the large patch of white feathers on the flank.

I found the Baird's cormorant on one of the Three Arch Rocks lying off the coast of Tillamook County, Oregon. Up the steep, rocky cliffs we climbed, disturbing murres by hundreds. Looking around a projecting cliff, we saw a cormorant climb awkwardly to a slightly higher elevation. As it moved its wings the white of the flanks was visible.

No others were seen near by, and, since this species is not inclined to breed in closely associated groups, we suspected that this solitary bird had just risen from its nest. However, no creature without wings could reach the cranny from which it had come, and I was unable to discover whether or not there was a nest there.

The violet-green cormorant is wise to begin sitting as soon as the first egg is laid, for if an egg is left uncovered, even for a short time, it may be pierced by one of the ever-hungry gulls which keep watch from the air or from near-by crags. The breeding season begins in May, and eggs are found as late as July 15. The number varies from two to six.

The birds place their nests on the same rock ledges year after year, so that sometimes the structures may be built up to a considerable depth by the new material added during successive seasons. The grass used in construction is bound by layers of lime from the excrement of the birds as if by mortar.

Baird's cormorants often fish in the wildest waters where waves dash on rocks and bowlders in a tumult of foam and spray. They dive deeply, as C. I. Clay of Eureka, California, has recorded them caught in fish nets at depths of twenty fathoms. The water pressure at such depths is necessarily tremendous.

BEAU BRUMMELLS OF OUR PACIFIC WATERS

Brandt's Cormorant when immature wears dull brown (left), but when full-grown dons a resplendent summer coat of greenish black (right). The bulky birds perch lazily on rocks or piles and, when fishing is good, congregate in huge flocks on the water. The **Pelagic,** or **Violet-green Cormorant** (adult in summer plumage, center), is a showy bird when he circles around a boat.

Photograph by W. L. Finley and H. T. Bohlman

THEY SMILE FOR THEIR PORTRAITS

Before learning to fly, white pelicans waddle about the nesting grounds in groups, perhaps hoping to inveigle parent birds into feeding them.

Photograph by Arthur A. Allen

A BABY "HELL DIVER," OR PIED-BILLED GREBE, LAZILY EXTENDS A LOBED FOOT

Instead of having a webbed foot, the toes of the grebe are bordered with broad flaps. When swimming, the bird brings its feet forward with the lobes folded against the toes, and on the backward stroke it extends them. Young grebes can leave home as soon as their down is dry. Within a few hours after birth, they swim and dive (see pages 26-27).

Photograph by J. C. Dowding

CHINESE USE DOMESTICATED CORMORANTS INSTEAD OF ROD AND REEL

Fishermen deploy their boats in line or crescent formation and, advancing, drive their flocks before them upon a school of fish. Each man recognizes his own birds, and each bird knows its boat and even its particular station on board. If a fish proves too large for one to handle, others will come to its aid. Some firms breed and train cormorants commercially.

Photograph by W. L. Finley and H. T. Bohlman

FARALLON CORMORANTS TAKE TO THE SEA ON A FISHING EXPEDITION

They breed in vast numbers on San Martín Island, Baja California. On a visit to this island in 1913, an observer estimated that there were more than 300,000 nests.

"HELL DIVERS" AND "WATER WITCHES" ARE DIVING CHAMPIONS OF THE BIRD WORLD

In diving, grebes spring partly from the water to plunge head first, or sink back silently, with scarcely a ripple. In summer regalia are: **Pied-billed Grebe** (lower left), which especially has earned these popular names, and a downy striped chick; the **American Eared Grebe** (center); and the **Horned Grebe** (lower right). Winter garb is portrayed by the horned grebe in gray and white plumage at the upper right, and the pied-bill above, at the left.

Pied-billed Grebe

(Podilymbus podiceps podiceps)

Average Length, Thirteen and One-half Inches

The "water witch," to use one of several local names, inhabits a range the extent of which is exceeded by that of few other American birds. In summer breeding pairs may be found throughout all the southern Provinces of Canada and southward over the continent generally into Florida and Mexico. The species is not found in winter in the extreme northern part of its range. Then many go south as far as Cuba and lower Mexico.

The call notes of the pied-billed are difficult to describe, but are easily remembered if once heard and identified. In sluggish and stagnant ponds the bird is much at home. When undisturbed, it swims buoyantly, but may submerge gradually until only the head is visible. It has remarkable power to submerge its body to any desired depth. I have often seen one disappear at the flash of a gun fired at it and be completely under water before the shot reached the spot where it had been swimming. On land it is awkward, usually moving along by flapping its wings and striking with its feet as if swimming beneath the surface of the water.

The nest, a floating mass of decaying vegetation, such as reeds, grass, and whatever other water plants are easily available, is from one foot to a foot and a half in diameter and several inches in thickness. Generally it is anchored among reeds and usually in water from one to three feet in depth. The eggs number from 5 to 8, rarely 10, and are about one inch and three-quarters long and a little more than an inch in thickness.

Eared Grebe

(Colymbus nigricollis californicus)

Average Length, Twelve and One-half Inches

Although allied forms of this species are scattered widely in Europe, Asia, and Africa, the American form is confined to a range that may be roughly described as the western half of the North American Continent from British Columbia and Manitoba to Mexico.

In general habits it is not greatly unlike the pied-billed grebe, but its nesting is in one respect quite different. I have watched these handsome birds on various lakes from North Dakota westward, but have never had an opportunity to observe one of their nesting colonies. I shall, therefore, quote a paragraph from the account given by B. F. Goss. Speaking of one of their nesting communities, he said:

"The nests were built on floating débris about 15 rods from shore, where the water was perhaps three feet deep. Old flags, rushes, reeds, etc., had been driven by the wind into a point of a bay, forming a mass two or three inches deep and several rods in extent. This mass was firm enough to hold up the birds in most places, but was full of holes where they could dive through. There were at least 25 nests on an area of 10 by 20 feet. They were made of partly decayed moss and reeds brought up from the bottom and were small, not more than a handful of material to a nest."

Horned Grebe

(Colymbus auritus)

Average Length, Thirteen and One-half Inches

The summer range of the horned grebe extends from Maine, Minnesota, and northern Nebraska to Iceland, the Arctic coast of Canada, and Siberia.

The winter range is amazing. At this season of the year the species occurs over nearly all of the territory of the United States, and inhabits also southern Europe, northern Africa, and regions of the coasts of Japan and China.

In the United States most observers are familiar with this grebe only in its gray and white winter plumage. Occasionally, in late spring, I have seen it in the bright summer plumage, especially in North Carolina and Georgia.

Singly or in flocks ranging from a dozen to two hundred or more, they feed on our lakes, estuaries, and along the coast just outside the breakers. The food of the birds consists of small fish, shrimps, other crustaceans, beetles, and various insects. Mr. W. L. McAtee reports finding large quantities of feathers in the stomachs he has examined for the Bureau of Biological Survey.

Though fishes are important in the diet, especially of birds taken during fall and winter, most of the species eaten are of no particular value for human food. Crawfishes form an important source of food, and in destroying them the horned grebe does a certain amount of good. Some of the shrimps taken are palatable to man, but are not present in great numbers in the grebe stomachs studied. The insects eaten represent varied groups, part of them aquatic in habit and part individuals that by chance have fallen into the water. When these facts are carefully considered, the horned grebe cannot be called injurious in any way. As a harmless species it merits protection for the good it may do in destroying crawfishes.

Although this species flies more readily than other grebes, sometimes it shows the usual grebe reluctance to fly when approached. I have rowed a boat directly toward a flock scattered about the water and have not been able to get one of them to take wing. They have preferred to seek safety by submerging and swimming away under the water.

Although strongly inclined to be gregarious in winter, these birds appear never to colonize in summer like the eared grebe. They seek privacy furnished by the numerous ponds and sloughs of their summer habitat.

Allen Brooks.

LOONS RIVAL THE GREBES AS CHAMPION SWIMMERS AND DIVERS

They are clumsy on land, and use bill and wings to assist them in walking. The **Red-throated Loon** (left) bears his red triangular throat mark only in summer. The **Pacific Loon** (right) has lost his handsome black and white summer markings when he flies south along the coast in autumn.

Red-throated Loon

(Gavia stellata)

Average Length, Twenty-five Inches

As a breeding bird, the red-throated loon is an Arctic and subarctic species throughout Europe, Asia, and America. In the Western Hemisphere its summer range extends from the coast and islands of the Arctic Sea, including Alaska and Greenland, southward into British Columbia, Manitoba, and Quebec. In autumn it migrates southward and may be found along the Pacific coast from the Aleutian Islands to Baja California, and in the waters of and near the Atlantic from the Gulf of St. Lawrence to Florida. At this season it also inhabits the Great Lakes and occasionally lakes and rivers of some midwest States.

Several ornithologists, including Audubon, have studied this loon in its summer habitat. It reaches the coast of Labrador in spring, before the snows have disappeared. When the snow melts, innumerable ponds and small lakes are formed and the permanent lakes lose their ice. The red-throated loons which have been gathering in the open coastal waters and the adjacent sea take possession of these quiet fresh-water areas, and the birds, already mated, begin to build their nests. At this period they are extremely active and their flights, splashings, and various call notes are among the most animated sights and sounds of the Arctic waste.

On the numerous pools and shallow sloughs of the Alaskan tundra these loons are among the first birds to appear, and they are much in evidence until the return of cold weather causes them to move far to the southward.

Many descriptions of their notes have been given. Bent speaks of the "harsh, gooselike honking calls or the weird, shrill cries." Macgillivray wrote: "On being deprived of their eggs, they may be heard for several evenings lamenting their loss with loud, melancholy cries." Nelson gave us this description: "Their arrival (in spring) is at once announced by the hoarse, grating cries which the birds utter as they fly from place to place or float upon the water."

One writer has made a record of the method employed by this bird to preserve its young: "When danger threatens, the old bird sinks her body below the surface, with only the head and neck stretched up above it; the young bird climbs upon her back, and she swims away with him to safety."

The red-throated loon occurs rather uncommonly in winter in the northern half of Florida. Worthington, who made observations of its activities on Amelia Island in the winter of 1905 and 1906, reports that the last one seen by him that season was on April 20 and that in the fall of the same year the first migrant appeared on November 17. Howe recorded a specimen in the winter of 1899 at Lemon City,

Florida, the most southerly record in the State. Scott reports seeing the bird frequently on the Gulf coast in December and January near the mouth of the Anclote River; and one was taken near Clearwater Harbor in February, 1880.

During its stay in the southeastern States, the bird is found on the ocean and in the Gulf. In habits it is so much like the common loon that the two species are distinguished with difficulty. Some observers report that the red-throated loon rises more easily from the water than the common loon and gets away more quickly.

Pacific Loon

(Gavia arctica pacifica)

Average Length, Twenty-three Inches

During the colder period of the year nearly all of the individuals of this species are found in the Pacific Ocean, along the North American coast. Its name, therefore, is very appropriate. It is abundant in many sections along the coast of southern California and Baja California. During migration the birds sometimes stream northward past a given point for hours, not in compact flocks, but singly, as a rule. While such flights are in progress there may be scarcely a minute when at least one of the birds is not in sight.

When swimming under water they move with swiftness. Not only do they use their feet to propel their bodies, but their half-folded wings also are continually in action as auxiliary means of locomotion. When these actions become observable, by a watcher favorably situated for the purpose, one gets the impression that the loon is actually flying through the water.

The birds breed in the region of Hudson Bay and along the Arctic coast westward to Point Barrow, Alaska, and southward to Great Slave Lake and the Alaska Peninsula. The nests are built on islands and on the shores of sloughs and ponds. They are substantial structures of water plants and rushes. The eggs, two in number, are covered with spots and blotches of various shades of drab, brown, and lavender.

The parents visit the seacoast to secure fish for their young. This prey is carried crosswise in their beaks, as they fly swiftly over the intervening miles. When the young are old enough to accompany their parents to the coast, the birds become a common sight in the shallow bays along the shores. In September they commence moving southward, and when the Arctic winter settles down, the regions that so recently resounded with the cries of loons become the great "white silence" of the North.

The smoky gray markings of the head, the glossy, greenish black of the throat, and the white bars of the back disappear with the approach of autumn, and therefore the bird is of much less striking appearance at this season, when it journeys down the Pacific coast to its winter feeding grounds.

THE PIERCING SCREAMS OF THESE BIRDS JUSTIFY THE SAYING "CRAZY AS A LOON"

The adult **Common Loon** (left) wears his summer suit of black-and-white checks, stripes, and spots, but his chick is somber. The immature bird (upper right) is similar to the adult in winter.

Common Loon

(Gavia immer)

Average Length, Thirty-two Inches

To one whose duties or pleasures have taken him into the northern wilderness, the sound of the word "loon" brings to memory visions of quiet lakes, with shores bordered by firs, spruces, and the gleaming white trunks of clustered birch trees.

To the voyager in these regions, whether in quest of trout or salmon or merely seeking the enjoyment of being where Nature has been unmarred by man, the weird, mournful cry of the loon is an inseparable part of the world about him. The far-reaching, trembling wail comes across the lake with a quality of unutterable melancholy. One may hear it at dawn, at evening, at any hour, day or night, and rare is the person who does not pause to listen when this cry comes down the wind.

I never tire of watching loons. Sometimes a pair swims close to camp on the lake side, where they move back and forth, turning their heads from side to side and peering around with evident curiosity. From the porch of a little camp on Lake Champlain I have watched them day by day swimming slowly about, diving and coming up, and now and then sparring mildly with each other.

It seems that sometimes they lose all desire for motion and exhibit a feeling of indolence by lying on their sides, thus exposing one foot, which occasionally moves in a feeble manner. At such times the white breast is revealed so extensively that one might readily suppose the bird to be floating flat on its back.

Loons were common summer birds in many of our Northern States a hundred years ago, but people would not leave them alone. The nests were robbed of their eggs, either to be taken home to be boiled or to be set under hens, or maybe they were picked up just to be thrown far out into the lake as a test of somebody's prowess.

Often the birds were considered good moving targets for rifle practice. A man once told me that he had shot them all his life, but had never eaten one. When I asked why he did this, his only reply was, "Why not? They are no good for anything." Since the Audubon laws have been enacted to protect them, and civilized man has acquired more interest in the living bird, the loons have not been persecuted so extensively as formerly.

The loon lays two eggs, usually in a substantial nest constructed of grasses and rushes. A favorite location for the nest is a tiny island. In all cases it is very close to the water, for the loon is no pedestrian and can only crawl or flop along in a most laborious manner.

The young when hatched are completely covered with down, as is the case with many water birds. They are, therefore, ready to begin cruising very soon after the sun has dried their brownish-black down, although they may linger in or about the nest for a day or two. At this stage they get about on the land better than their parents, progressing by little jumps or leaps.

If the family is approached, the young dive and make short trips under the water. Upon rising they again disappear in the same manner. Meantime the parents, in alarm, flop about in the water, showing distress and making obvious efforts to lure the intruder away from the direction taken by their young.

Late in August or September the old ones pass much time upon the wing, calling as they circle about the lake where they have passed the summer. Perhaps this is to encourage the young to acquire strength in flying. The time for migration to the southward is approaching, and soon the young must be led away to the open waters of the sea, where they will have to shift for themselves.

In coloration the sexes are indistinguishable, and in the winter plumage the adults and the young of the year are almost identical. During migration, loons sometimes strike against lighthouses in foggy weather. In the tower of Cape Hatteras Light I was shown a lens from which a piece had been broken by a loon which one night crashed through the outer window.

Arthur H. Howell, in *Florida Bird Life*, writes: "During the winter season common loons may be found, singly or in scattered flocks, in the bays and lagoons along the coasts of Florida, as well as in the Gulf and on the ocean. Usually they are wary, and at the approach of a boat dive and swim a long distance under water. Their weird laughing notes are sometimes heard at this season.

"The loon feeds chiefly on fish. Thirty-five stomachs have been examined in the Biological Survey, and all but four contained fish remains. Much of this material was so mutilated as to be unrecognizable, but in a few cases the contents were identified as mullet, pickerel, horned pout, smelt, black bass, a large minnow, one of the surf fishes, and seven killifishes. Commercial food fishes furnished about 11 per cent of the total food of the 35 birds examined, nonedible varieties comprised 20 per cent, and about 47 per cent was made up of unrecognized fish bones, scales, and flesh. Crabs were eaten by five birds, and crawfishes by three. A loon taken in Pensacola Bay in April, 1926, had in its throat a menhaden four inches long."

The common loon breeds from Labrador and Nova Scotia south to northern New York and in Iceland. It is found in winter from the Great Lakes to the Gulf coast and on the eastern side of the Atlantic to the Mediterranean and Black Seas.

A related form *(Gavia i. elasson)* nests from northern California and northern Wisconsin to British Columbia and is found in winter on the coast of California.

Allan Brooks.

STRIPED CHICKS EXPLORE THE CHANNELS OF REEDY LAKES ON THE BACKS OF EITHER PARENT

Holboell's Grebe (center) has a chestnut-red neck during the nesting season, but in winter this plumage turns to brown or ashy (rising at upper right). A black-capped head tops the swanlike neck of the graceful **Western Grebe** (left), largest of the family, but not its grayish chick.

Holboell's Grebe

(Colymbus grisegena holboelli)
Average Length, Nineteen Inches

In the estuary of the Neuse River where it flows into Pamlico Sound, North Carolina, I have watched in winter the Holboell's grebe sink slowly from sight until only the head was visible. Again, when frightened, they would plunge forward and downward, disappearing with amazing swiftness. As they swam along with heads held in a horizontal position, they resembled the loons, which frequent these waters at this season of the year. Their smaller size, however, usually renders it an easy matter to distinguish between the two species.

Here, as well as at points as far north as Cape Cod, they were feeding probably on fish and crustaceans. In the lakes and reedy marshes of their summer homes in the far north their food consists in the main of fish, crayfish, other crustaceans, and insects.

They are unusually wary birds. The only case that has come to my attention in which any of them overcame their fear of human beings was in Long Island Sound. Here a man who lived alone on an anchored boat was considerably entertained by a number of them which daily fed near by, coming sometimes within six feet of his vessel. Even in summer, on their breeding grounds, they are extremely shy, and ornithologists have reported that it was an easier task to find the nest than the bird itself.

The nest is a floating mass of decaying reeds and other vegetation. The eggs, generally three to five in number, are bluish white. About twenty-three days are required for them to hatch.

Holboell's grebe occurs in Florida occasionally as a rare winter visitor. Arthur H. Howell writes of it: "This grebe is found mainly in the salt-water bays along the coasts. It is an expert diver, obtaining all its food under water; when pursued, it escapes usually by swimming rapidly away, or in some cases by diving. It is able also to sink its body deeply, so that only its head is above water. It cannot take flight from the land, but in rising from the water uses both feet and wings to assist it in getting under way, and when fairly launched flies swiftly and strongly a few feet above the water, with its long neck stretched out straight and its feet projecting behind like a rudder.

"Wetmore, who has studied the food of grebes, finds that about half the food of this species consists of fishes, chiefly of species of no commercial value; one-fifth of the food in the 36 stomachs examined was composed of crustaceans, and 21.5 percent of insects."

All grebes produce peculiar sounds, heard chiefly during the nesting season. The cries of the Holboell's grebe are loonlike in their long-drawn wailing.

This bird breeds from Hudson Strait westward through Ungava, northern Mackenzie, northwestern Alaska, and northeastern Siberia, and southward to northern Washington, North Dakota, and New Brunswick. It passes the winter mainly in the coastal waters of the Atlantic and the Pacific to southern California and North Carolina. It is also found in limited numbers in the central States as far south as Tennessee.

Western Grebe

(Aechmophorus occidentalis)
Average Length, Twenty-six Inches

A young western grebe escapes from the shell in which it has developed by pecking a ring, which causes the end of the shell to drop off like an unattached cap. With the other little grebes, which have appeared in the nest about the same time, it seeks a resting place on the back of its father or mother, and so is borne away among the channels of the reedy lake so loved by these birds. The parent covers the young with its inner wing feathers. Often the head protrudes, as the swanlike grebe sails along with its tender burden. Food is picked up here and there and it is a simple matter for the parent to turn its head and feed its offspring.

Mr. William L. Finley, who has studied the nesting habits of this species more than any other man of whom I have knowledge, tells us of watching young grebes slide from the back of one parent and board the back of the other. The second old bird, upon being approached by its tiny young, "lowered his body slightly in the water and the youngster floated aboard."

During the days when fashion demanded feathers of birds as millinery decorations, the western grebes suffered greatly from plume hunters. When a hunter killed a bird, it was customary to remove the head, wings, and feet, and then, after slitting the skin at one end, to pull this back over the body, as one removes a glove. The skin, thus turned inside out, quickly dried and was ready for shipment to market. The hunter received about twenty cents for each "grebe breast."

The National Association of Audubon Societies secured laws prohibiting the killing of these birds, got their largest breeding colonies established as Government bird reservations, helped provide funds for wardens to guard them, and thus saved the birds in important sections of their range.

This species is the largest of our grebes. In characteristic grebe fashion it builds a floating nest of stems and leaves of aquatic plants, and many are often found in close proximity. It breeds from British Columbia and Manitoba to northern California and North Dakota. In winter many migrate as far south as central Mexico.

THE OCEAN BIRDS

Albatrosses and Petrels; Gannets, Man-o'-war-birds, and Tropic-birds

BY ROBERT CUSHMAN MURPHY

CURATOR OF OCEANIC BIRDS, AMERICAN MUSEUM OF NATURAL HISTORY

"They . . . that do business in great waters" (Psalm 107:23)

BIRDS of only a few groups inhabit the high seas. Over the vast, far, oceanic reaches of a world surfaced mainly with water, the winged wanderers are likely to belong within one of three or four comprehensive orders.

THE "TUBE-NOSED" SWIMMERS

Among pelagic birds the Procellariiformes, or members of the order of albatrosses and petrels, stand first. They are present in all salt waters from the Arctic basin to the uttermost shores of the south polar continent, including even such land-encompassed bodies as the Mediterranean Sea and the Gulf of California.

They belong to the marine environment more fully than any other birds, for, like sea turtles and fur seals, many of them come ashore only for reproduction, remaining at other seasons permanently in the wastes of waters, and even shying away from coasts so thoroughly that they may scarcely sight land other than their annual breeding stations.

Not all of these creatures are far-roaming, but some of them make yearly migrations that are among the longest known.

More and more it has become evident that each kind of these birds, like organisms living beneath the surface, is specialized in one way or another for particular types of ocean water.

The curved expanse of the sea is not "boundless," as tradition holds. On the contrary, it is rather sharply divided by lines of temperature, wind belts, zones of varying rainfall and evaporation, and other agencies into regions of different physicochemical characteristics, respectively inhabited by different types of the surface life which constitutes bird "pasturage."

SARGASSO A WATERY "DESERT"

Thus the famed Sargasso Sea, and corresponding areas in the central parts of other oceans, are watery "deserts." The underlying depths may be rich in life, but the surface is warm and hence poor in oxygen, extremely salty because the water has been long exposed to the evaporating influence of sun and trade wind, and deficient in nutrient chemicals because of the great distance from land and the bounty of rivers.

In such centers, moreover, the highly saline and dense surface waters tend continually to sink, thus preventing decomposition products held in "cold storage" far below from rising to the upper layers.

On the other hand, the encircling ocean-current regions, particularly those close to continental coasts, are constantly or periodically enriched by the phenomenon known as "upwelling." Whenever a current diverges from a shore line, under the influence of a land breeze or for any other reason, the surface water removed must be replaced from below.

OCEAN "PASTURAGE" ZONES

The ascending masses are cool, usually rich in oxygen, and almost invariably teeming with food products such as stored nitrates and phosphates, plant cells living and dead, and small animals such as copepod crustaceans which, by being eaten themselves, carry on the marine "key industry" of converting microscopic pasturage into fish, sea birds, and gigantic whales.

For such reasons the boundaries between the ranges of sea birds are no less definite than those formed on the continents by such more obvious barriers as mountain crests, deserts, forested lowlands, or wide rivers.

In other words, the entire face of the ocean is "zonal" no less than the land.

Since many birds are highly specialized in their food habits (some kinds get practically all their subsistence from a single type of organism, such as squids), it is easy to understand how in the agelong course of evolution certain petrels have become conditioned to restricted oceanic areas, from which they never voluntarily stray.

Food chains may not, of course, offer the whole explanation, for even among species that travel during their nonbreeding season across successive belts of highly varying climate, it appears that the route and rate are by no means haphazard.

Illustrative examples are offered by three common Southern Hemisphere birds that enter the North Atlantic during our summer. These are Wilson's petrel, which nests on many Antarctic islands; the sooty shearwater, which comes from the subantarctic continental islets of the Cape Horn neighborhood; and the greater shearwater, the only known breeding grounds of which are at the extremely isolated Tristan da Cunha group in the middle of the South Atlantic.

PETRELS FOLLOW REGULAR CYCLE

All three of these petrels follow a cycle that seems to be as regular as most other phenomena operated by the cosmic clockwork. Their seasons and stages are not exactly the same, but they all appear to cross very rapidly the broad band of tropical water, which is relatively poor in food resources. Once in the Northern Hemisphere, all three species pass up the American side of the Atlantic, skirting the extensive Sargasso area.

The greater shearwater is the first to reach our latitudes in spring, perhaps because it has the shortest journey from its place of origin. By early June the vanguard reaches Davis Strait and Greenland waters, but prior to August there are no records for the eastern North Atlantic.

By mid-September the hordes have spread out so that they are generally distributed all along the cooler parallels between North America and Europe. Later, the southward migration is concentrated largely in the eastern Atlantic, with huge flocks reported off the westernmost extension of Africa.

The sooty shearwater puts in a slightly more tardy appearance, but it is likewise much commoner on the American than the European side of the Atlantic until late August. At all times it seems distinctly scarcer in mid-ocean than the greater shearwater. It is more a bird of the "offshore" zone of continental shelf and fishing banks than of the deep pelagic reaches.

Finally, the tiny Wilson's petrel follows much the same Atlantic circuit as its larger cousins, but goes the sooty shearwater one better by becoming an "inshore" visitor, plying its investigative way into every bay and cove between southern New England and Newfoundland. The ornithologist is astonished to see no trace in these littoral waters of Leach's petrel, which at the time is nesting by hundreds of thousands on the local grassy or spruce-grown islands. But all the while Wilson's petrel, from the other end of the world, is flitting everywhere!

ODDITIES OF DISTRIBUTION

Just why the Wilson's petrels check their northward movement at about latitude 50° north is another mystery of the ocean. They come from icy Antarctic waters; yet they do not penetrate the similarly cold regions of the north. Instead, they swing eastward and southward just before reaching districts particularly rich in food that would seem to be best suited to their needs.

Possibly the competition of abundant Leach's petrels preëmpts the more northerly waters. The rareness of Wilson's petrel in the temperate North Pacific, where there are so many other kinds of Mother Carey's chickens, would lend weight to such a theory.

The orderliness of the grand-scale rotary movements is well confirmed by scattered information relating to petrels of the South Atlantic and several parts of the Pacific.

The facts offer not only an indication of the rigid control exercised by oceanographic and meteorological conditions over birds of the sea, but they also go far toward suggesting an explanatory mechanism for the marvelous precision with which these seeming waifs of the great waters find their way back, at the appointed time, to the bourns whence they started.

"Homing," in such migratory examples, might be defined as a fixed circulation, the track of which is largely determined by successive climatic effects upon the birds throughout their journey.

Much remains to be learned about the extent to which cycles or vagaries of weather affect the annual routine of the migrants. The summer of 1937 offered striking suggestions as to the possibilities for research in this obscure field. For three months the greater part of the North Atlantic, according to all oceanographic records, displayed abnormally high surface temperatures which, in turn, produced curious effects upon oceanic life. One of these was a very extraordinary shoreward movement of several kinds of petrels all along eastern North America.

No precedent is known for the observed abundance of the birds during that season in Hampton Roads and the bays to northward, Long Island Sound, and the littoral waters of New England and the Maritime Provinces of Canada.

"GREEN PASTURES OF PETRELDOM"

About 115 species or other distinct kinds of albatrosses and petrels are known, a list considerably swelled by additional geographic forms. In general, the bigger the ocean, the more kinds, for which reason the nearly landless belt of the Southern or "water" Hemisphere, from the Roaring Forties to the polar edge of the pack ice, supplies the true green pastures of "petreldom."

The North Pacific is next best endowed, and is the only part of the Northern Hemisphere rejoicing in native albatrosses. Of the 21 forms of petrel-like birds in Major Brooks' accompanying paintings, nine are to be found only on the Pacific side of America. These are the short-tailed and black-footed albatrosses, the pink-footed, slender-billed, and black-vented shearwaters, the black, fork-tailed, ashy, and least petrels. The Socorro petrel might be added, except that it is probably only a subspecies of Leach's petrel.

The exclusively Atlantic species in the plates number only four: namely, Cory's and greater shearwaters, the black-capped petrel, and the Old World storm petrel.

The following seven are common to the two oceans, though not all of them are to be encountered along both coasts of North America: fulmar, sooty and Audubon's shearwaters, Leach's and Wilson's petrels, the Cape pigeon, and Bulwer's petrel.

Despite their abundance and universal distribution, the petrels and their allies occupy an increasingly precarious position in the modern world. Islands once afforded them the safety of perfect isolation, but man and his domestic and parasitic animals have turned security into special vulnerability and still constitute a hazard which has already caused immeasurable destruction. Several species are supposed to have become extinct and others are seriously threatened.

Seventeenth-century French accounts of the nocturnal raids upon the breeding grounds of the West Indian black-capped petrels, or *diablotins,* as the colonists called them, make entertaining but rueful reading for the modern generations deprived of the opportunity of meeting these birds alive.

Small petrels are in jeopardy wherever cats, dogs, or hogs have been introduced, and house rats have probably wiped out practically all such birds at many nesting stations, including the main island of Tristan da Cunha. The other two islands of this group are happily still free from the curse.

It is exciting to speculate that for millions of years, perhaps, the Laysan and black-footed albatrosses were "cocks of the roost" at the tiny but sufficient nesting grounds of Wake and Midway Islands, in the Pacific. Then, in the 18th and 19th centuries, came explorers and whalemen, in sailing vessels months or years from home, to make occasional forays for fresh eggs. But today passengers in unruffled and immaculate clothes step calmly out of the China Clippers, walk right among the amazing—and doubtless amazed—albatrosses, and watch to their hearts' content some of the most astonishing performances known in the whole field of bird behavior!

These albatrosses are, of course, fully protected from undue interference at the seaplane stations. Furthermore, their dancing and "singing" are so extremely entertaining that they can hardly fail to awaken a sympathetic interest which may redound to the ultimate welfare of their relatives all over the seven seas.

THE GREATEST SIZE RANGE AMONG BIRDS

The Procellariiformes are an ancient and primitive group, doubtless more abundant, and certainly more widespread, during former geologic ages. We know from fossils that there were once albatrosses in the North Atlantic.

All the species share many common traits, in both anatomy and behavior. All, for instance, possess tubular nostrils, and all are so strictly maritime that no one has yet succeeded in keeping them long alive in captivity, whereas penguins, cormorants, gulls, and other oceanic fowl have lived for years in suitable aviaries.

In at least one respect, however, the petrel-like birds exhibit unique diversity: namely, in size range. In no other feathered group is there a discrepancy in bulk equal to that between a storm petrel, scarcely larger than a swallow, and the wandering albatross, which attains a wing-spread of 11 feet 4 inches (not 17 feet, as some encyclopedias allege!).

The birds of the order fall into four families, of which one comprises the albatrosses, a second the more varied aggregation of medium-sized petrels, fulmars, and shear-waters, a third the little storm, Leach's and Wilson's petrels, and a fourth, the peculiar diving petrels, which are birds of auklike form confined wholly to the Southern Hemisphere.

Since certain species are closely woven into the lore of all human seafarers, a few words on the English group names may be of interest.

"Albatross" proves to have had an especially checkered career. The root of the word is Arabic and refers to the bucket on a water wheel. In its Moorish-Spanish form, *alcatraz*, it was applied to the pelican, which has a "bucket" in its pouch. Subsequently, the Spanish and Portuguese mariners bestowed some form of the name upon the *largest* sea fowl of any particular region —sometimes a frigate bird or booby, sometimes one of the wide-winged creatures upon which the corruption "albatross" eventually became fixed.

PETRELS "WALK UPON THE WATER"

"Petrel" is no less interesting. According to a pretty legend, it arose from the fact that the bird, like Saint Peter, "walks upon the water." But both the current form of the word and the explanation are alike very young, dating only from a yarn by Dampier published in 1703.

Earlier English usage, as in Flawes's *Voyage to Nova Zembla* (1676), employed the spelling "pitteral." I suspect, therefore, that the term was derived either from the chattering voices of the sea sprites or from the fact that they "pitter-patter" on the surface of the sea, and that the link with Saint Peter was an afterthought.

"Mother Carey's chicken" may, however, have a medieval religious origin. The name of this vague demigoddess—no doubt the wife of Davy Jones—has been traced by some to prayers addressed by storm-tossed Mediterranean sailors to the Virgin, the *mater cara,* or "dear mother."

Broadly similar in history and specialization to the Procellariiformes is another ancient and widely distributed group of waterfowl, characterized by having all four toes of the foot connected by a common web. In modern scientific parlance they are known as the Pelecaniformes. They comprise the tropic-birds, pelicans, gannets, cormorants, snakebirds, and man-o'-war-birds.

This assemblage is far more diversified than the petrel-like birds; it includes not merely several families but nearly as many distinct suborders. The structural difference between a tropic-bird and a man-o'-war-bird, for instance, is incomparably greater than that between an albatross and a Mother Carey's chicken.

Not all of the Pelecaniformes are oceanic; certain cormorants and pelicans have become birds of interior continental waterways. At the other extreme, the tropic-birds are nearly as pelagic as the petrels. The gannets and boobies, too, are maritime and seem for the most part to be repelled by continental coasts.

The man-o'-war-birds are in a sense supremely specialized sea fowl, although they are creatures of the atmosphere far more than of the water. They never swim and must roost ashore. They show no repugnance toward land, flying freely from sea to sea over the Isthmus of Panama, or even across high islands such as Cuba.

Although they have established themselves at the most faraway islands throughout the world's warmer oceans, the man-o'-war-birds tend, nevertheless, to be sedentary rather than nomadic. If they are often seen out of sight of land, it should be remembered that the home island may still be within view of the lofty bird.

Records of man-o'-war birds at a great distance from any land are rare, except as regards individuals transported by hurricanes, and in the existence of many distinct species and subspecies at islands or archipelagoes, we see a biological reflection of their penchant for clinging persistently to the vicinity of home and shore.

The decreasing extent to which the several groups of salt-water Pelecaniformes are "tied to the land" is expressed by the following sequence: pelicans, cormorants, man-o'-war-birds, boobies, tropic-birds.

Pelicans practically never lose sight of the coast, and have occupied no remote islands except the Galápagos. Of the other families, only the tropic-birds, which resemble terns except for their long, streaming tail plumes, are to be looked for in the most distant stretches of blue water, unbroken by rock or sand.

© Niall Rankin

LIKE A HUGE SQUADRON OF BOMBERS, HUNDREDS OF GANNETS SOAR OVERHEAD IN THE TEETH OF A HIGH WIND

Wings and feet work in perfect unison to keep the birds on an even keel as they give an exhibition of their superb flying skill over Bass Rock, off the east coast of Scotland. Fully extended wings supply the supporting surface and the tails are employed as elevators, regulating altitude.

© Niall Rankin

PUTTING ON THE BRAKES!

So great was the speed of the gannet as it swept toward the ledge that it seemed the bird would smash against the rocks. Instead, bringing wings and feet well forward, it checked momentum and alighted safely. In a flash it had offered maximum resistance to forward motion, permitting an almost vertical landing. Strikingly illustrated are the gannet's powerful four-toed, webbed feet. The membranes extend to the tips of the toes (see page 6).

© Ronald M. Lockley

A STORM PETREL REARS A "FAMILY" OF ONE

The dainty bird, met with by sailors everywhere on the North Atlantic, is one of the kinds known as "Mother Carey's Chickens." It breeds in vast numbers in the crevices on Skokholm Island, off the southwest coast of Wales. Stones were removed to show the single egg. Fifty days must elapse before it will hatch, and then it will be many weeks more before the lone offspring is ready to take wing.

Short-tailed Albatross

(Diomedea albatrus)

Average Length, Thirty-seven Inches

Swift, wheeling, effortless flight is associated with the very name of albatrosses, and the sighting of these birds at sea is an experience never to be forgotten. The structure of a perfect glider and the subconscious technique of a master pilot are jointly responsible for the supreme result, for no albatross is a highly muscular bird. Its ends are gained by balance, finesse, and economy of energy rather than by main strength.

The adult short-tailed albatross, with its white body, tawny crown, black wings, and narrowly black-tipped tail, is readily distinguishable from any other species of the North Pacific. The immature bird, however, wears a completely dark plumage, and is to be separated from the black-footed albatrosses chiefly by its pinkish bill and feet.

The bird was familiar along the Alaskan steamship routes until the nineties of the last century, and its bones are abundant in the kitchen middens of the California coastal Indians. But none had been definitely reported from our Pacific waters for a generation until the summer of 1937 when a half dozen were seen near the Aleutian Islands.

The decline of Arctic whaling, and other reasons put forward to explain its disappearance are probably specious. It is greatly to be feared that this most impressive and magnificent of all North Pacific ocean fowl may be exterminated by man's wantonness at the Bonin group and other islands toward the Asiatic side of that ocean, which furnish its only breeding grounds.

Black-footed Albatross

(Diomedea nigripes)

Average Length, Twenty-eight Inches

The black-footed albatross, or "gooney," which Audubon first made known to science, nests at a relatively large number of islands from the Hawaiian region westward to Japan, and has thus far escaped the probable fate of its larger cousin. It is the common albatross of the California coast, though to be seen chiefly along the edge of the continental shelf rather than inshore.

Like its many relatives in the Southern Hemisphere, this and other North Pacific albatrosses breed at the beginning of the northern winter instead of in our proper springtime. In early November the goonies arrive at Laysan Island, of the Hawaiian sea bird reservation. Once ashore they begin their dancing, a performance for which all albatrosses are famous. In the black-footed species this, however, is more stately and deliberate than the dance of its neighbor, the Laysan albatross. The latter may be readily distinguished, since its abdomen is white instead of sooty brown. The black-foots try on occasion to join in the antics of the other albatross, only to have their ritual thrown out of kilter by a too rapid tempo!

Although the ceremony just referred to has always been called a "courtship dance," it has now been learned that the birds indulge in similar amenities while they are far away at sea during the nonbreeding season. Furthermore, youthful as well as adult members of the tribe take part in such pastimes. The custom is probably in the nature of general social community behavior, which at the breeding season becomes heightened and specialized as part of a stimulation necessary for reproduction.

The vocal aspect is as notable as the terpsichorean, for while the ardent albatrosses are posturing and crossing beaks they also groan and gabble and utter muffled, abdominal, bell-like notes. These sounds are hardly musical, though they may be accepted by the females of the species as ardent love songs.

Goonies regularly follow ships for refuse tossed overboard, and they are often seen scaling about and feeding well into the night. Their sense of smell may help them in finding the malodorous, long-dead fish sometimes found in their stomachs along with squids, masses of fish eggs, and bits of kelp.

The goonies have only a seven-foot spread of wings, which is considerably smaller than in some of the other species. They seem to have the same expert control over rising air currents, however, for it is a common experience to see them alight far behind a ship at sea for some bit of refuse, and then, rising directly into the wind, without a single stroke but with a rapid pattering of the feet on the water, overtake the vessel and wheel circles about it.

With the establishment of trans-Pacific flying, the goonies are likely to become a much more familiar subject of conversation, for near the seaplane station on Midway Island they go about their dancing and domestic duties more familiarly than the sparrows of our city streets. Here they are associated with Laysan albatrosses, a much friendlier species.

Like other albatrosses, these goonies pass most of the year on the open sea, but arrive at their nesting islands on almost exactly the same day each year. So nearly are they on schedule that men at the Commercial Cable Company at Midway have betting pools based on the exact time they will arrive each year. Once they make their appearance, they assume cocky airs and are not above taking a nip at anybody who passes too close to them. They show absolutely no fear of the parvenu human inhabitants.

The single large white egg, laid on the bare sand, needs constant sheltering to prevent its cooking. Young albatrosses have two coats of down, a light coat at hatching followed almost immediately by a dark curly coat which pushes out the former, just as, in turn, it is pushed out by the incoming juvenile plumage.

FLAWLESS FLYERS WHEEL ABOVE THE SHIP'S WAKE

The **Short-tailed Albatross** (above, adult left, young right) and the more familiar "gooney," or **Black-footed Albatross** (below, adult right, young left) breed only on certain islands in the central and western North Pacific, but may appear during migration anywhere on the American coast from Alaska to Baja California. A half dozen of the short-tailed species, now extremely rare, were observed in the vicinity of the Aleutian Islands in the summer of 1937.

Cory's Shearwater

(Puffinus diomedea borealis)
Average Length, Twenty Inches

Cory's shearwater was described from the shore waters of Cape Cod. It was imagined to have come from the Arctic—hence the name *borealis*—and it remained a bird of mystery until, years afterwards, it was discovered to be the common breeding shearwater of such easterly Atlantic islands as the Azores, Madeira, and the Canaries.

Eggs are laid in April and May. When the young reach the fledgling stage they are abandoned, as is the custom among all Procellariiformes, and large numbers of the parents then work westward across the ocean to feed along our temperate shores. In September they sometimes enter New York Bay together with the greater shearwaters, from which they can most easily be distinguished by the uniform brownish appearance of the head and neck. The other species is distinctly "capped," with a sharp line between dark and white plumage.

Greater Shearwater

(Puffinus gravis)
Average Length, Twenty Inches

Although first described from Greenland waters, the greater shearwaters all come from far-off Tristan da Cunha.

How such tiny islands can account for the staggering numbers of these birds that seasonally make the North Atlantic "grand tour" would be hard to explain; for to the observer who sees them in seemingly endless procession of huge flocks, they seem numerous enough to cover like a blanket many times the area of the territory from which they come. Possibly their breeding rhythm is not annual; if a large part of the population remained at sea over alternate nesting seasons, a multiple use of the limited grassy areas in which the birds burrow would become possible.

The greater shearwater follows whales and porpoises for excreta or for scraps from their tables. Moving in loose bands, and yet working strictly as individuals, the birds likewise pursue shoals of surface-swimming fishes, as well as the squids that come to the uppermost layers of the ocean on dark days or during the hours of half-light.

North Atlantic cod fishermen formerly took advantage of the great numbers, audacity, and insatiable appetite of the "hagdons," as the shearwaters were called, to use the birds both as food and as bait. They were lured within range by the simple expedient of "chumming up" the Mother Carey's chickens with fish entrails. The small birds quickly attracted the larger, which sailed in, scattered the lesser gluttons, and proceeded to snap up the food. They were then caught on mackerel hooks, and it was not unusual to see as many as 500 hanging from the rigging of a Grand Banker.

Fulmar

(Fulmarus glacialis)
Average Length, Nineteen Inches

The "foulmart," that is, the stinking-marten or polecat, has had its name transferred to this pearly sea bird. The reason has to do with the rank, musky oil discharged from the stomach—not only, however, by the fulmar but by every Procellariiform species.

Petrel oil has been exploited by many peoples in as many parts of the world. An old-time visitor to St. Kilda, of the Hebrides, where "the cliffs dissolve into birds" when the fulmars take flight, wrote: "The Kildeans use the oil afforded by the stomach as a catholicon for diseases, especially for any aching of the bones, stitches, etc." Here, too, thousands of fledgling fulmars are collected in August and salted as winter food.

Breeding on precipices from the British Isles northward to Greenland and other arctic lands, and migrating southward beyond the zone of floating ice, the fulmar is perhaps the most familiar ocean bird of the Northern Hemisphere.

It is the species which leads travelers to believe that "gulls" follow steamers between America and Europe. Its numbers are frequently overpowering; the Dutch whalemen of Spitsbergen called fulmars by the same name as the teeming midges of the polar grasslands—*mallemugge,* and Darwin, in the *Origin of Species,* refers to them as the most numerous birds in the world. During recent years or decades there has been a steady southward extension of the fulmar's breeding range in the British Isles.

The fulmar is *par excellence* pelagic. Except at the nesting season, it shies away from all land. When an outbound ship passes off soundings, fulmars often magically appear within a mile or two of the hundred-fathom line. In California, where the coastal shelf is narrow, they more frequently approach the beaches than in eastern North America.

The flight of the fulmar resembles that of albatrosses rather more than that of shearwaters. In ghostly silence the birds glide and scale tirelessly on their stiff, somewhat blunt-looking wings, in which the process of molt and growth can easily be observed from shipboard. That the molt brings no loss of aeronautic efficiency is due to its symmetry and to the fact that the two outermost or leading quills are retained until the inner ones are nearly full grown.

Like many other petrels, the fulmar has two plumage phases, of which the pearl gray is by far the commoner. Dark birds are more numerous in the western part of the North Atlantic than in European waters, but even off the Labrador coast, where most in evidence, they probably make up not more than one in twenty of the whole population.

RESTLESS SHEARWATERS STAY FAR OFFSHORE

During the northern summer they frequently congregate in the vicinity of vessels on the various fishing "banks," alert for discarded scraps and offal. The Atlantic's **Greater Shearwater** (upper right) "coasts" on stiffly held wings between flurries of rapid wing beats. Its only known breeding grounds are in the isolated Tristan da Cunha group in the South Atlantic. Another summer visitor to American shores is the **Cory's Shearwater** (lower left). The circumpolar **Fulmar** (lower right, light phase on the water, dark phase flying above) winters as far south as the fishing grounds off Massachusetts.

Black-capped Petrel
(Pterodroma hasitata)
Average Length, Eleven Inches

The black-capped petrel dwells on the Atlantic hurricane track, which is the principal reason why so many examples have been picked up in the interior of the United States and other odd places. Its nesting ground, however, is only on islands of the West Indies, where it was generally exterminated, soon after the introduction of slaves, by being yanked from its mountain burrows for human food. What the black men missed, the introduced mongoose, or one or two kinds of opossums likewise brought from other places, finished.

There is evidence, however, that at least a few of these birds still exist in Haiti, as well as in the little island of Dominica of the Lesser Antilles. Recently, several have been identified in the Gulf Stream.

Two phases apparently once occupied the Antilles, the second being a blackish form usually known as the "Jamaican petrel."

Sooty Shearwater
(Puffinus griseus)
Average Length, Seventeen Inches

Here we have a petrel that is unique in being abundant throughout the length of the oceans on both sides of the Americas, from the latitude of Cape Horn northward to subarctic fishing grounds. A hundred thousand birds is a low estimate of the number one may see in a day along California shores.

The sooty shearwater breeds in New Zealand, where it is one of the famous "muttonbirds" of Maori feasts, and also in the Magellanic region of South America. Nests near Cape Horn have been found at the New Year season, the single egg lying in a chamber at the end of a long tunnel excavated through wet ground. The sitting birds fight savagely when hauled into the daylight.

One January day, when some 15 miles off the coast of Peru, I sailed through a raft of sooty shearwaters that covered many acres of the ocean. The air was calm, and the birds in the vessel's path flopped to either side, making frequent and frantic dives. I noted that they literally "flew" while submerged.

Audubon's Shearwater
(Puffinus lherminieri lherminieri)
Average Length, Twelve Inches

Belonging to a group of cosmopolitan distribution in warm seas, the typical form of Audubon's shearwater inhabits the Caribbean region, with a northern breeding outpost at Bermuda. It is the only small, sharply black and white shearwater of southeastern North American waters.

At certain islands these birds occupy natural cavities in the coral limestone, while at others they burrow in grassy ground or even beneath the shade of forest trees. The nesting season appears to be nearly continuous. In the West Indies courtship and nest construction have been observed between July and November, eggs between January and May, and newly hatched young between May and July.

At home, these secretive beings are nocturnal and eerie. All night during the nuptial season mournful cries, some of which resemble cat-calls, ring out in the free air or come as a muffled chorus from tunnels.

Leach's Petrel
(Oceanodroma leucorhoa)
Average Length, Eight Inches

Leach's and Wilson's petrels look substantially alike, yet I have learned to tell them apart instantly, as far as the eye can reach, because their *movements* are so unlike.

Words can hardly give the key, but the flight of the stormy petrel has been called batlike, that of Wilson's swallowlike, and that of Leach's nightjarlike. The last is springy, bounding, and erratic, strongly suggesting a whippoorwill under way. Leach's petrel shows little interest in ships, while its two relatives are notorious wake-foragers (Vol. II, p. 364).

Leach's petrel nests at islands on both sides of the great northern oceans, from about the latitude of Massachusetts to the Arctic Circle. In winter it migrates as far as the Equator.

Wilson's Petrel
(Oceanites oceanicus)
Average Length, Seven Inches

Wilson's petrel, a famous surface-dancer, comes to us in summer from islands east and south of southern South America, some of them beyond the Antarctic Circle.

Life conditions are so severe at the nesting grounds that one often finds frozen chicks and eggs of previous years in the rock crevices where the birds rear their single offspring.

Storm Petrel
(Hydrobates pelagicus)
Average Length, Five and One-half Inches

The storm petrel was rather vaguely reported by Audubon from the Grand Banks of Newfoundland. Recently it has been found to be an occasional visitor in spring and autumn to high latitudes off eastern North America. In summer it nests at Old World islets between Iceland and the Mediterranean; in winter it migrates southward as far as the Cape of Good Hope.

Incubation of the egg requires 50 days and the whole term of brooding and feeding, by parents which alternate in the task, about twice as long. Small wonder that some abandoned fledglings fail to take to sea until snowfall!

Formerly the Faeroe islanders converted storm petrels into candles by drawing wicks through their oily bodies.

YOU CAN TELL SOME OF THEM BY THEIR FLIGHT

The flight of the **Storm Petrel** (lowest figure) has been called batlike, that of the **Wilson's Petrel** (with yellow-webbed feet) swallowlike, while that of the **Leach's Petrel** (left foreground) suggests a whippoorwill on the wing. The very rare **Black-capped Petrel** (upper) and **Audubon's Shearwater** (lower right), both inhabitants of the West Indies, are occasionally blown into northern latitudes by hurricanes. Abundant on both coasts of both Americas, the **Sooty Shearwater** (center) breeds in New Zealand and on the southern tip of South America.

Cape Pigeon

(Daption capensis)

Average Length, Fourteen Inches

The best known sea bird of the southern oceans, mentioned by all voyagers since the earliest days, might perhaps never reach the North Atlantic were not sailors so fond of hooking it and—sometimes—of letting it go. One ship's crew freed eleven just before making Southampton! In the Pacific, however, the Cape pigeon occasionally crosses the narrow warm-water belt under its own power, to enter the cool California current.

The name of this antarctic petrel is sufficiently explained by its appearance. At home it is almost inconceivably abundant, especially about whaling stations, where the cantankerous birds squabble noisily for blubber scraps. Lincoln Ellsworth and Sir Hubert Wilkins have both found that the rafts of Cape pigeons on the crater harbor of Deception Island constitute the most serious hazard when taking flight in a seaplane or attempting a landing.

Pink-footed Shearwater

(Puffinus creatopus)

Average Length, Nineteen Inches

The pink-footed shearwater is so closely related to the Cory's shearwater that it may be regarded as a representative of the same group. Its range comprises the waters along the entire Pacific coast of the Americas, from south-central Chile to Alaska.

The species was described in 1864 from a specimen collected near San Nicolas Island, California, but not until some years later was it discovered that the birthplace and center of origin of the great armadas which come as summer visitors to our coasts is at Robinson Crusoe's Island, the inner member of the Juan Fernández group. Still later the species has been found to inhabit also Mocha Island, which is farther southward and much nearer the Chilean shore.

At Mas a tierra Island, Juan Fernández, the pink-footed shearwaters burrow in the steep hillsides from near sea level up through the woods and the fern belt to an altitude of 1,500 feet or more. The burrows fairly honeycomb the ground in certain places near the tops of successive ridges, from which the outcoming birds can most readily take flight. Many of them penetrate from 6 to 10 feet from the entrance, and in the enlarged nest chamber the single egg lies on a bed of straws and sedges.

During the day the shearwaters remain silent and concealed, but at nightfall they make a terrific noise as they come and go in countless thousands, reminding the observer of the clouds of bats that issue from the mouth of the vast bat cave near Carlsbad, New Mexico. They are true creatures of darkness, for a bright moon will delay their arrival or even cause them to skip a night at home.

Slender-billed Shearwater

(Puffinus tenuirostris)

Average Length, Eighteen Inches

This species is confined to the Pacific, breeding chiefly at islands close to southern Australia and reaching the west coast of North America only as a rather rare migrant. In the field it is difficult to distinguish from the slightly larger sooty shearwater. Perhaps the darker wing lining of the present species would make the best distinguishing mark.

The slender-billed shearwater is the "muttonbird" of Bass Strait. A petrel of ancient fame and great economic importance, it is protected by Tasmanian law, but an open season begins on March 20, and the young may be legally taken thereafter until the surviving fledglings leave the breeding grounds in May. About half a million of the chicks were captured and prepared as food in a single season a few years ago. Formerly the adults as well as the young were slaughtered in great numbers for the feathers, oil, and flesh.

The young hatch in January. After dusk there is a rush of adults from the sea. This influx is conducted in silence, but presently the burrowed ground begins to emit extraordinary gurglings, groanings, and laughter as the numberless chicks are receiving their one meal of the day. About 10 o'clock the muffled clamor ceases, while the young are digesting and the adults resting from their labors. Some of the parents come forth to sleep in the open air. At 2:30 a.m. a rising murmur announces the awakening of the rookery, and the old birds scramble like land crabs to the higher ridges of their isle, where they stretch their wings over their backs and launch into the air.

Black-vented Shearwater

(Puffinus opisthomelas)

Average Length, Thirteen and One-half Inches

The black-vented shearwater reverses the ordinary direction of migration. It nests on islands off Baja California, and in August passes northward along the Pacific coast of the United States. The return flight is equally conspicuous in early spring.

At Guadalupe Island, south of San Diego and about 65 miles offshore, the black-vented shearwater breeds in burrows or niches, with such sea fowl as auklets and murrelets for neighbors. The love-song is unflatteringly described as a series of wheezes resembling steam escaping through a partly clogged pipe!

This species is in the main a fish-eater, and correlated with this is its indifference toward ship's refuse, which sometimes draws many kinds of petrels into the wake of a vessel. When pursuing their prey, the shearwaters are inclined to describe a circle or an ellipse, which may be either in a horizontal or a vertical plane. In the latter case, a flattened ring of birds rolls along after the moving shoal.

A MOTTLED CAPE PIGEON TAGS ALONG ABOVE PACIFIC SHEARWATERS

At Deception Island in Antarctica, Lincoln Ellsworth found that rafts of the **Cape Pigeon,** or "pintado petrel" (upper), constituted a serious hazard in taking off or landing in a seaplane. Best known sea bird of southern oceans, this petrel rarely visits the North Pacific. Below, from left to right, fly three sea birds: the **Pink-footed Shearwater,** the **Slender-billed Shearwater,** and the **Black-vented Shearwater,** which nest in widely separated corners of the Pacific and only occasionally mingle on the west coast of the United States during the northern summer.

© Niall Rankin

MASTER OF THE AIR IS THE GANNET, OR "SOLAN GOOSE"

These birds are endowed with remarkable powers of flight, and have been known to traverse 100 to 200 miles a day in search of food. They are power flyers, and in addition show proficiency in gliding, soaring, and diving at great speed. The wings are so shaped as to permit their being used in propulsive effort, and in consequence, there is some lack of the special qualities necessary for the prolonged soaring flight of the albatross. Compare to page 347.

Photograph by H. Armstrong Roberts

LONG-BILLED GANNETS HUDDLE TOGETHER, SHELTERED FROM HARM ON THEIR ISLAND SANCTUARY

Driven from one breeding site after another by advancing civilization, these interesting and curious birds have been given a nesting home at last on Bonaventure Island, off Percé, Gaspé Peninsula, in the Gulf of St. Lawrence. In such inaccessible cliff rookeries thousands rear their young in saucerlike nests of seaweed (see page 58). The strange factor of evolution which sealed the nostrils of gannets and boobies as early as the Miocene period saddled these birds with a comic bill expression.

"MOTHER CAREY'S CHICKENS" SAILORS CALL THEM

The **Bulwer's Petrel** (left center) frequents the eastern Atlantic and the western Pacific. Strictly Pacific species are the other somberly clad little mariners. To the right of the lovely pearl-gray **Fork-tailed Petrel** (upper) hovers the **Black Petrel,** one of the few birds that migrate north after the breeding season. Water drips from the feet of the rising **Socorro Petrel** (lower right). Smallest of the all-dark species is the **Least Petrel** (left foreground), which half faces the pert **Ashy Petrel.**

Bulwer's Petrel

(Bulweria bulweri)

Average Length, Nine Inches

This petrel claims inclusion in the fauna of North America upon the grounds of a single accidental Greenland record. It has long been famous, however, for an extraordinary type of distribution, for it occurs in the warmer latitudes of the eastern Atlantic and the central and western parts of the Pacific. Between these two widely separated areas of its range there is, so far as known, no connection.

Some ornithologists have supposed that the distribution of Bulwer's petrel antedates the present land connection between North and South America, but this is highly speculative.

Bulwer's petrel stands betwixt the Mother Carey's chickens and the larger petrels. It resembles the former, and yet is more closely related to the latter.

Black Petrel

(Oceanodroma melania)

Average Length, Nine Inches

The black petrel nests on Baja Californian islands and, as in the case of the black-vented shearwater, its numbers spread northward to our Pacific coast after the breeding season. However, the black petrels also migrate across the Tropics, for they are well known in Peru. They are exclusively American.

During the winter the black petrels come close to west coast ports to feed upon garbage. They are at times given to "rafting," forming in calm weather dense black patches a hundred yards or more in diameter.

Fork-tailed Petrel

(Oceanodroma furcata)

Average Length, Nine Inches

This species is unique in its light-gray plumage, which renders it easily identifiable among the puzzling black or black and white forms that make up the bulk of the family.

The fork-tailed petrel belongs to the northern part of the North Pacific, where it nests on many islands from the Kurile and Commander groups on the Siberian side, across the Aleutian chain and southward in North American coastal waters to northern California. Its range during the nonbreeding season extends to southern California and also northward through Bering Strait into both Asiatic and Alaskan Arctic waters.

The fork-tailed petrel is not narrowly limited as to the nature of its breeding ground. Its burrows have been found on grassy, treeless slopes of the Aleutian Islands, among basaltic rocks at Copper Island of the Commander group, and in the soil under a dense forest of huge firs and hemlocks at St. Lazaria Island, near Sitka, Alaska.

The nesting season comes in June and July. At St. Lazaria the nesting petrels do not come in from sea until the tail end of the late summer twilight makes the woods gloomy. Thereafter their calls and the wind from their wings can be heard throughout the hours of darkness. The birds frequently fly against the face of an observer, and they have actually extinguished a campfire by flying into it. They become fewer and quieter, however, at the first sign of dawn, and by sunrise disappear.

Socorro Petrel

(Oceanodroma socorroensis)

Average Length, Seven and Three-quarters Inches

Described from near Socorro Island, Mexico, this petrel was saddled with a misnomer, for it nests only at the San Benito and Los Coronados groups.

It closely resembles Leach's petrel, of which, indeed, it is probably only one of the several geographic forms that have developed at distinct breeding stations along the Pacific coast of North America. Most examples are all blackish, but about three per cent have more or less white on the upper tail coverts.

Ashy Petrel

(Oceanodroma homochroa)

Average Length, Seven and One-half Inches

The Mother Carey's chickens that visit the Atlantic coast of the United States have white patches above the tail, but along our Pacific shores there are several forms which are dark-rumped and which are extraordinarily difficult to distinguish one from another in the field.

The more closely such birds are observed, the more apparent their individualities become, but unfortunately not enough seems yet to have been learned to enable the distinctive traits of the ashy petrel to be put into print. We can say only that it is the smallest of the all-dark species of its genus *(Oceanodroma)*, that its range seems to be limited entirely to the cool waters of the California coast, and that its breeding grounds are restricted to the Farallon Islands and to San Miguel and Santa Cruz Islands.

At the Farallons, where this petrel is said to be the last bird to return for nesting in the spring, the sites are mainly between and under stones. The creatures have become so well conditioned to man's presence that they ignore the ear-splitting blasts of the siren, repeated every 45 seconds in foggy weather.

Least Petrel

(Halocyptena microsoma)

Average Length, Five and One-half Inches

Breeding at San Benito Island, off Baja California, this species has been collected at sea from Ecuador northward to Point Loma, California. Little has been recorded of its appearance or habits. It nests in midsummer, seeking crevices under slabs of rock, rather than burrowing as do its relatives.

ABOVE TRANQUIL SEAS, WIDE-WINGED HIGH DIVERS SOAR

The inspiring **Gannet** fills the place in the North Atlantic which the albatrosses occupy in the Pacific. Plunging spectacularly from high in the air, it seizes fish in its bill and often makes spray shoot up ten feet. It breeds on both sides of the ocean as far south as the British Isles and the Gulf of St. Lawrence. One of its principal American nesting grounds, Bonaventure Island in the Gaspé region of Quebec, is now a carefully guarded reserve for many kinds of sea birds. In spite of increased conservation, this magnificent species is still in need of vigilant protection.

Gannet

(Moris bassana)

Average Length, Thirty-five Inches

The gannet is the most inspiring inhabitant of the North Atlantic, to which ocean it exclusively belongs, although it has a close relative in South Africa and another in the Australasian region. The magnificent bird is a sort of symbol of the maritime pioneers of our race. In the *Anglo-Saxon Chronicle*, of the 10th century, the ocean itself is called the "Gannet's Bath." The name gannet is of the same origin as "gander," and solan goose, derived from the Scandinavian *havsula* (sea goose), is still current in the British Isles.

The specific name of the gannet *(bassana)* comes from Bass Rock, at the entrance of the Firth of Forth, a historic nesting ground. The bird's stations are by no means numerous, for outside the British Isles it is known to breed today only at islands off Iceland, and at several in the Gulf of St. Lawrence and near Newfoundland. The names "Gannet Ledge" and "Gannet Rock" are reminiscent of a time in which it also covered like snow certain islets nearer the borders of the United States, off Nova Scotia and New Brunswick, but it has now left these localities.

When Jacques Cartier entered the St. Lawrence he sighted, according to Hakluyt's early translation, "islands . . . as full of birds as any medow is of grasse, which there do make their nestes; and in the greatest of them there was a great and infinite number of those that wee cal margaulx, that are white and bigger than any geese."

For three centuries the gannets of Bird Rock remained in happy security, so that when Audubon visited the colony in 1833 he rubbed his eyes in amazement at the host of white birds covering the "roof" as well as the ledges of the island. Subsequent ravages of cod fishermen, who used gannet flesh for bait, reduced the population from a hundred thousand or more to less than three thousand. Fortunately, the gannets are now well guarded by the Canadian Government, and their slowly increasing colonies on the ledges of Bonaventure and other islands, where the birds can be seen at close range courting, nesting, and feeding their young, furnish delightful entertainment to tourists visiting the Gaspé region.

Although occasionally seen far from land, the gannet is not a truly pelagic bird. Its distribution is largely regulated by that of herrings, pilchards, and other shoaling fish, which mainly frequent the offshore zone of the continental shelf. On daily feeding excursions its stately and purposeful flight may carry it away, however, a hundred miles or more. Its winter migration takes it southward along our eastern coast as far as Florida and the Gulf of Mexico. On the Old World side of the ocean it ranges to North Africa, but the great intervening stretches of water between these ranges appear to be without gannets.

The gannet weighs about 7 pounds. It feeds by plunging from high in air and seizing its prey, making the spray shoot up ten feet. Among peculiar structures correlated with such a violent mode of life is its equipment of subcutaneous air cells, which form a cushion against the impact of the bird's streamlined body with the water. This cellular layer is connected with a series of larger air sacs and indirectly with the lungs. So extensive, indeed, is the entire respiratory system of the bird that at least three full inspirations of a man's lungs may be successively blown into the windpipe of a freshly killed gannet.

In having this system of air-filled buffers to protect them from the impact of the water, gannets are like the pelicans, whose heavy bodies would likewise suffer in their plunges from on high were it not for similar pneumatic structures.

The gannet's single egg, which is more than three inches long, but exceptionally small-yolked, is pale bluish-white overlaid with limy material, but with no dark spots whatsoever. The nest on the ledge overlooking the sea is usually small and insignificant when the egg is first laid, but it grows larger during the 42 days of incubation because it is a common practice for one bird, upon returning to take its place on the egg, to present its mate with a piece of nesting material which is ceremoniously tucked into the nest.

When first hatched, young gannets are dull black and nearly as bare and as handsome as short sections of garden hose. Down begins to appear, however, when they are 24 hours old and, within two weeks, they are clothed in a thick covering of white or yellowish down; then they could pass for old-fashioned powder-puffs. Soon, however, their dark juvenile feathers begin to push out the down and by the time they are 12 to 13 weeks old they are heavier than the adults and clothed in a plumage of dark grayish brown, spangled above with white.

At this age they are abandoned by their parents and, like young petrels, they starve and lose weight for ten days or more before finding their way to the sea, where for a time they lead an exclusively swimming life.

The change to the adult plumage is gradual through successive molts, two-year-old birds having white heads and underparts, but dark backs. Fully adult plumage is not attained until at least the third year. The gannet's eyes, which are brown at first, likewise undergo a change to gray and finally to white when the bird is two years old, though the ring about the eye becomes blue when the youngster is only seven months old.

Despite the fact that gannets are usually classed as surface feeders, they have been captured in nets set as deep as 14 fathoms.

BUSINESSLIKE FISHERMEN OF THE TROPICS

On their breeding grounds, boobies partly live up to their name, but on the wing or in power dives for fish their grace and mastery of air currents excite only unqualified admiration. The **Red-footed Booby** (adults, left center and flying above; young below) is the only member of its family to nest in trees, the others always selecting ledges or flat ground. Probably the first New World bird seen by Columbus, the **White-bellied Booby** (right, adult above two young birds) fishes patiently just outside the breakers along its home-island shores.

Red-footed Booby

(Sula piscator)

Average Length, Twenty-nine Inches

Boobies are tropical relatives of the gannets and have the same curious feet, with all four toes connected by webs, that are characteristic of the members of the order of pelicanlike birds. The red-footed species is of cosmopolitan distribution in warm seas, but its presence in any particular district depends upon suitable trees or shrubs for nesting, because, alone in its whole family, it prefers to construct its twig-built platform only in woody vegetation, growing or dead. At certain arid islands a single surviving tree, perhaps supporting a dozen red-footed booby nests, represents the favored local home of the species. When such a tree disappears, the boobies either depart or, if they remain, are driven to nest on the low elevation of clumps of grass.

The red-footed booby is famous for its little understood color phases. Not all adult birds are white; in certain regions a large proportion may be grayish brown, with either a gray or a white tail.

This species feeds upon fish, and probably still more upon squids. It usually flies far beyond the broken water of its own island shores, seeking an area of peaceful ocean swell, where flying fish break the surface, and where squids approach it when the sky darkens.

In flight this booby, particularly birds in the white color phase, resembles its northern cousin, the gannet, giving several quick strokes of the wing followed by a short glide. The birds ordinarily plunge into the sea from a height of thirty feet or more, but they sometimes catch their prey in air when flying fish have been driven from the sea by predators below.

While incubating their single eggs on their flimsy nests of twigs, these boobies are either unsuspicious or stupid and permit themselves to be pushed from the nest, though an occasional individual strikes a cruel blow with his sharp bill. The name booby comes from the Spanish *bobo*, meaning a dunce, and the lethargic behavior and stupid expression of the bird make the name seem appropriate.

White-bellied Booby

(Sula leucogaster leucogaster)

Average Length, Thirty Inches

After crossing the greater part of the mysterious, endless ocean, Columbus recorded in his journal a joyful sign—an "alcatraz" had perched upon the *Santa Maria*. In the English version this word is usually rendered "pelican," which is, of course, entirely wrong. Pelicans neither fly far offshore nor alight upon vessels under way. The white-bellied or brown booby does both. Furthermore, and unknown to the translator, this particular species is called "alcatraz" in all those parts of the Spanish-Portuguese world *where there are no pelicans.*

The brown booby is found in most warm oceans. Like other boobies, however, and unlike pelicans and man-o'-war-birds, it never flies across even so narrow a wall between oceans as the Isthmus of Panama. As an effect of the resulting isolation of bird communities, we find the interesting biological fact that the true white-bellied booby is restricted to the Atlantic or Caribbean side, whereas just over the mountains, in the Gulf of Panama, is a quite distinct sub-specific relative called the Colombian booby.

The white-bellied booby is a ground-breeder, making the merest pretense of a nest in a shallow scrape, laying two or three eggs but usually rearing only one chick.

It is a businesslike fisherman, doing much of its plunging just outside the breakers of its home island, varying its altitude according to the depth at which fish are moving, and keeping for its own sustenance whatever the man-o'-war-bird does not subsequently steal.

The depredations of the man-o'-war-birds cause the boobies to return to their home island later than most sea birds, even after their enemy has gone to roost. At times, likewise, they do some of their fishing at night.

The eggs of this booby resemble those of other species in being bluish-white and unspotted, but overlaid with a white, chalky deposit. They do show, however, much more variation in size and shape than those of most species. The youngsters when first hatched are naked and have to be carefully sheltered by their parents lest they be cooked outright by the sun. Very soon, however, they become completely covered with pure-white down. Their parents bring back fish in their gullets, if they are successful in evading the man-o'-war-birds, and merely open their mouths and let the little ones help themselves. This is a simple matter for the first course, but when it comes time for dessert a small youngster may almost entirely disappear down its parent's throat for the last tidbit.

The breeding season of the white-bellied booby is apparently more irregular than that of most sea birds, so that fresh eggs and full-grown young are likely to be found from the first of February to the middle of August.

Female boobies are somewhat larger than males, even to their feet, but their plumages are almost identical. First-year birds, however, do not have white underparts, being uniformly grayish brown. On calm days boobies have much more difficulty in flying and in rising from the water than during the most severe storms. At such times they often travel single file, and their measured wing-strokes are almost gull-like.

RED-THROATED PIRATES SOMETIMES MAKE AN HONEST LIVING

The **Man-o'-war-bird,** or "frigate bird" (upper pair, young above), of floating, tireless flight, steals fish from swift boobies and other bird neighbors, but is also an expert fisherman on its own, nose-diving from great heights to pluck juicy fish or squid from the ocean surface. Sailors know tropic-birds as "boatswains" because of their shrill whistles and marlin-spike tails. The **Red-tailed Tropic-bird** (left center pair, adult below), frequenting warmer waters of the Pacific and Indian Oceans, is a rare straggler off southern California. Ternlike except for its tail plumes is the common West Indian **Yellow-billed Tropic-bird** (lower right-hand pair, young with the barred back).

Man-o'-war-bird

(Fregata magnificens)
Average Length, Forty Inches

In many languages much has been stated and sung of the man-o'-war-bird. "Thou art all wings," cried Walt Whitman, with substantial truth. When, however, he placed the same individual at eve in Senegal, at morn in America, the poetic flight vastly exaggerated the choice, if not the ability of the bird.

A seven-foot wing spread to three and a half pounds of weight, speaking in average terms, is a unique relation in the animal world. Together with extraordinary fusing and strengthening of the bones of the shoulder girdle and breast muscles which make up a quarter of the body weight, it gives the man-o'-war-bird unequaled powers of sleepy, floating flight in the light tropical air, as well as of the relentless swift pursuit by means of which it despoils the fast-flying boobies and other sea fowl.

Man-o'-war-birds are expert fishers on their own account, nose-diving with a rush of air from great heights, and deftly seizing prey from the surface which their easily water-soaked plumage never touches. Much of their living is gained, however, by forcing their neighbors to disgorge. Rarely does a fish dropped by a booby reach the water!

There are numerous species and subspecies of man-o'-war-birds, which is indicative of the seldom realized fact that they are not great wanderers. Probably the world's islands have become peopled with them largely through the agency of birds carried at rare intervals by severe tropical storms.

The habits of the several sorts are very similar, and most of them agree with our American bird in the general pattern of coloration. The dark, iridescent male has a throat sac which is red and expansible during the breeding season. It is his love-symbol. He sits and guards the nest with this balloon blown up, while his somewhat larger but more plainly colored mate brings lumber. The two then posture and gabble before each other, but from beginning to end, the major share of homebuilding, incubation, and guarding of the young seems to fall to the lot of father.

Red-tailed Tropic-bird

(Phaëthon rubricaudus rothschildi)
Average Length, Eighteen and One-half to Thirty-six Inches; Tail, Three and One-half to Eighteen and One-half Inches

Considered by many to be the handsomest of all the tropic-birds, the red-tailed is by far the rarest near the coast of the United States. Its range is confined entirely to the warmer waters of the Pacific and Indian Oceans, and it is only a straggler off southern California.

The red-tailed tropic-bird has the thinnest and most wiry central tail plumes of all species within its family. These were highly prized as ornaments by the Polynesians and other savages of the South Seas, who made them into headdresses, or even stuck them as ornaments through their noses.

Herman Melville, author and hero of the classic Marquesan tale, *Typee*, describes the chief, Mehevi, as wearing a crest of such plumes upon his noble head. Incidentally, the tropic-birds were not killed in this primitive millinery traffic. During the period of brooding they cling closely to the nest, and it was the custom of the islanders to attract the attention of the sitter's eyes and sharp beak with the left hand, while deftly plucking out the one or two long red tail feathers with the right.

This species differs from other tropic-birds in that it nests on the ground of low islands, instead of seeking lofty niches in cliffs. In keeping with this habit it has considerable agility in rising into flight from a level surface, which it does by scurrying along foot after foot, rapidly beating its wings.

Yellow-billed Tropic-bird

(Phaëthon lepturus catesbyi)
Average Length, Fifteen and One-half to Thirty-two Inches; Tail, Four to Twenty-one and One-half Inches

The tropic-birds are extremely ternlike members of the Pelecaniform group, the resemblance extending even to their boldly marked eggs, which are totally unlike those of boobies, pelicans, or man-o'-war-birds.

They are practically as pelagic as the petrels, traveling vast distances in remote seas as soon as the breeding season is over. Even in the heart of the barren Sargasso area one may see the winged comets with their streaming tails, and hear the shrill whistle which has led sailors to call them "boatswain-birds." They feed by hurtling like arrows into the ocean, a fact commemorated by their generic name, which they take from the ill-fated son of Apollo who fell from his badly managed chariot into the deep. Squids appear to make up the bulk of the tropic-birds' diet.

The yellow-billed species—which, incidentally, has a red bill during the breeding season—is found the world over between the Tropics. In the West Indies, and at Bermuda where the bird is known as the "longtail," is a form named by the Russian zoölogist, Brandt, in honor of Catesby, who wrote in colonial days a famous book on the birds of Carolina.

The longtails come to Bermuda in April, after their winter wanderings, lay the single egg in cavities of the cliffs, and about three months later abandon their fledglings, which must thereafter rely upon instinct and their own initiative to shift for themselves. It has only recently been learned that such Spartan procedure in the rearing of the young is a trait common to many oceanic birds.

Photograph by H. Armstrong Roberts

TEEMING THOUSANDS OF GANNETS FEATHER THE FACADE OF BONAVENTURE ISLAND

When strangers intrude, white clouds of these winged fishermen take off from the narrow shelf ledges, uttering a chorus of harsh cries. Black-tipped wings and snow-white bodies identify them quickly. As they dive headfirst for prey, folded wings and pointed bills give them the appearance of swift arrows (see pages 48, 49, 52, 53).

THE LARGE WADING BIRDS

Long Legs and Remarkable Beaks, as Well as Size, Form, and Color, Distinguish the Herons, Ibises, and Flamingos

By T. Gilbert Pearson

HAUNTING the solitudes of the marshlands, the tule regions of the West, the winding streams and muskegs of the North, and the moss-hung cypress swamps of the South, are found those birds we may call the large waders. Their size, their grace, the snowy whiteness of some, the striking colors of others, their unusual forms and attitudes, immediately arrest the attention.

Their lonely surroundings enhance their appeal to the lover of the wilderness, for a glimpse of one suggests the days of the pioneer, before steam shovels dug canals that took the water from seventy million acres of our picturesque regions. Their presence brings to the imagination other forms of wild life that one might see—an otter sliding from the bank, a bright-eyed mink darting to cover, or a turtle sunning itself on a log. This environment, years ago, was the haunt of the Indian seeking the bear, the beaver, and the white-tailed deer. In fancy, these are the things I see when a heron rises and wings its way into the shadows of the swamp.

LONG LEGS AND REMARKABLE BEAKS AID IN GAINING LIVELIHOOD

What influences in the evolution of life caused these birds to develop their long legs and remarkable beaks of varied shapes, one can only conjecture. Nature has provided them with specialized equipment that serves them well in their daily lives. Their bills are of use not only in oiling and preening their feathers, in carrying sticks for their nests, and in turning their eggs, but serve also as weapons of defense, and, when the birds are young, as hooks with which to support their weight when falling from a limb. Each species possesses a beak especially adapted for gathering the kind of food upon which it subsists. The sharp dagger of the heron spears fish, the curved bill of the ibis explores nooks and holes for crawfish,

and the peculiar bill of the flamingo makes it possible to gather mollusks from the mud.

As these birds collect virtually all their food from shallow water, their long legs, bare of feathers to a point near the body, make wading easy.

Members of this group are distributed over nearly all parts of the globe, but are especially numerous in tropical and temperate zones.

HERONS ARE ONLY REMOTELY RELATED TO CRANES

This article treats of the 18 species and 11 varieties that have been found in North America from Mexico to the Arctic seas (Canada and southern Alaska). They are classified under the Order Ciconiiformes and are placed in four separate families.

The herons and bitterns (family Ardeidae), because of their large necks and legs, bear a superficial resemblance to cranes, but are only remotely related to that group.

The storks (family Ciconiidae) are distributed through the warmer parts of the earth, though only one species, the wood ibis, reaches the United States.

The ibises and spoonbills (family Threskiornithidae) are of large or medium size, resembling storks. The ibises have the long bill decurved at the tip instead of straight, as in the storks, while in the spoonbills the bill is greatly broadened and flattened at the tip.

The flamingos (family Phoenicopteridae) have certain characters that ally them to the ducks and geese, with which they were formerly grouped, but more modern studies place them with the storklike birds. The form of the bill, which is abruptly bent downward at the middle, is found in no other bird. While at first glance this may seem a deformity, it is an adaptation required by the long neck and the method

Photograph by Hugo H. Schroder

WHITE IBIS, AMERICAN EGRETS AND OTHER HERONS TAKE OFF FROM A LARGE MARSH WEST OF VERO BEACH, FLORIDA

Florida visitors are amazed by the huge flocks of these birds that congregate in the perfect weather of the winter months. The swampy land of the Everglades, and the extraordinary number of coastal lagoons, shallow fresh-water lakes and streams, make Florida the ideal habitat for these large wading birds.

Photograph by James E. Stanley

AMERICAN EGRETS AND SNOWY EGRETS RANGE IN COMPANY IN A FLORIDA MARSH

Photograph by S. A. Grimes

WITH A ROAR OF BLACK-TIPPED WINGS, WOOD IBISES (LEFT) ACCOMPANY AMERICAN EGRETS (RIGHT) TO A FLORIDA ROOKERY

61

of procuring food. As the neck is lowered, the bent portion of the mandibles is held parallel to the surface of the ground, so that thin sand can be passed through the bill and the small shells and other food that it contains be strained out and swallowed.

Though flamingos ordinarily are considered a tropical species, in South America they range into Patagonia and to lakes at high altitudes in the Andes. In the latter localities they nest in colonies of many thousands. Natives procure their eggs, roast them to preserve them, and transport them for sale into the lowlands.

THE ROSEATE SPOONBILL FACES EXTINCTION

One July day in my boyhood, when the tide was low and the greasy mud lay bare under the mangrove bushes, I crawled along behind a man with a gun. My hands were cut by shells, and mosquitoes and stinging flies swarmed over my face, but these meant little in the excitement of the moment. From behind the broken stub of a mast, which the Gulf had cast ashore, we were listening soon to the contented guttural notes of a flock of feeding roseate spoonbills.

As the birds waded, their long bills skimmed the bottom, swinging from side to side as a mower's scythe reaches for the timothy stalks in the meadow. My companion raised his gun and fired. Familiar with the habits of his prey, he reloaded quickly and bade me remain quiet. Within two minutes the flock had returned and was swinging low overhead. Seven roseate spoonbills were carried back to the boat at the edge of the Florida key.

On other keys, about shallow ponds of the pineland prairies, up nameless streams of the Everglades, or in the depths of the Big Cypress, many such killings were going on, for other men and boys were abroad with guns. Curio stores in St. Augustine, Tampa, and Jacksonville displayed fans of wonderful pink feathers, which thousands of tourists bought to take north as souvenirs of their sojourn under sunny skies.

The spoonbills were also esteemed as food. Back in the Everglades, Indians cooked them in steaming pots beside their palm-thatched lodges, and fishermen, alligator hunters, and orchid collectors broiled them in charcoal buckets.

Mankind has wrought great havoc upon these birds in the United States. From hundreds of thousands, two generations ago, they have dwindled to a pitiful few hundred. Even yet some men seem determined to hunt out and slay the last survivors of one of the most striking birds of our country. Within the United States, there are still a few hundred in Florida, one breeding colony in Louisiana, and two or three nesting places in Texas; but that is all, and it is a question whether or not the race can be saved north of the Rio Grande.

My most recent experience with nesting spoonbills was on May 22, 1932, in a populous heron colony occupying a cluster of trees and bushes on the prairie of Cameron Parish, Louisiana. There were fifty birds, perhaps half of them being in the full pink plumage assumed only after two years' growth. In constructing their nests, ten of which were located, I noticed that the birds had used not only dead twigs, but also liberal supplies of small branches bearing green leaves. The nests contained freshly laid eggs which would require 28 days of incubation before the young would appear.

WOOD IBISES MUDDY THE WATER, MAKING FISH APPEAR

Once, upon emerging from a cabbage-palm hammock, I reined my horse to a sudden stop. Before me, amid the scattered slender pines and clusters of scrub palmettos, was a shallow pond crowded with wading birds moving rapidly about and making a great commotion. Scratching with their feet, they were muddying the water so that the fish were obliged to rise to the surface to breathe. I had come suddenly upon a flock of wood ibises, birds closely related to the storks. They were gathering their food in the peculiar, communistic manner they sometimes employ, for when many thus work at the same time they can so pollute the water that their victims quickly appear.

Wood ibises do not stab their prey as do herons, on occasion, but seize it between their large and powerful beaks. A bill I once measured was nine inches long and seven and a half inches around at the base.

The head of this bird is without feathers, lying bare to the beating sun and to the sweep of every wind that blows. "Flintheads," the native Floridians call them. In Arkansas the hunter speaks of the "gourdhead," and chuckles with anticipation as

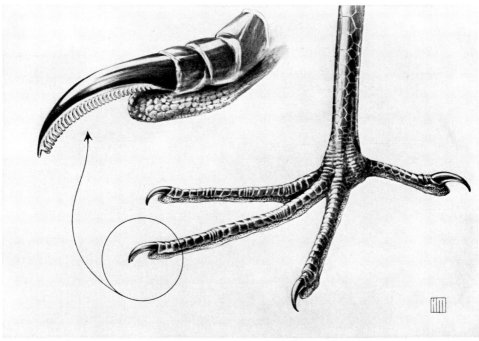

Drawing by Hashime Murayama

RIGHT FOOT OF GREAT BLUE HERON, SHOWING THE PECULIAR COMB, OR PECTEN, ON THE CLAW OF THE MIDDLE TOE

This curious structure, found in herons and also in whippoorwills, nighthawks, barn owls, and some other birds, is supposed to be useful in cleaning and dressing the plumage and may be of assistance in removing the bird lice known as mallophaga. The foot is shown one-half natural size, with the inset of the claw enlarged two and one-half times.

he prepares it for dinner. When, in summer, they appear in the low country of South Carolina, the Gullah boatman points across the marshes and says, "De gannets come, enty?"

The Corkscrew is a great yoke-shaped bend of the Big Cypress 30 miles south of Fort Myers. Here the trees are old and many of them are very tall. To this spot come wood ibises in great numbers, when the season arrives for them to lay their eggs and rear their young. Long, gray moss hangs from the trees, and air plants decorate the limbs in great profusion, while here and there an orchid adds its brilliant touch to the somber solitudes. In large part the water, hidden by a massed growth of floating wild lettuce, is from knee to shoulder deep.

I have never seen a place where cotton-mouthed moccasins were so numerous, grew so large, or were so exasperatingly tame. They decorated nearly every log or fallen limb. For protection I carried a stout club, for these snakes are not always inclined to retreat at the approach of an intruder. In wading across one strip of the swamp, 200 yards wide, I felt obliged to kill 14 of them, one with a length of more than five feet. There were many others in sight. I counted seven at one time that I did not molest. The moccasins had collected in such unusual numbers to feast upon the dead fish falling day by day from the hundreds of nests far overhead.

For perhaps two miles the bird encampment extended along the sides and around the curves of the Corkscrew. Between swamp and pines is a strip of glade, and as far as one could see, fish crows were traversing this open space. In nearly all cases each of those returning from the cypresses carried a large white egg transfixed on its bill. This little crow is the greatest natural enemy with which the big wood ibis has to battle in its annual efforts to reproduce its kind.

I never tire of traveling the Tamiami Trail, which, south of Lake Okeechobee,

Photograph by C. P. Martin

HUNDREDS OF TREETOP NESTS FORM A HERON COLONY NEAR SPRINGFIELD, OHIO

Cradled in the topmost branches of tall beeches, poplars, and red oaks are the rough, basketlike nests of the great blue heron and its neighbors, the black-crowned night herons. Often a dozen of these nests are found in one tree. The view shows nearly a hundred nests, and in this one small wood lot there are more than three hundred others.

Photograph by Alvin R. Cahn

THE LEAST BITTERN: A STUDY IN EXPRESSION

Photograph by C. P. Martin

IN FLIGHT THE GREAT BLUE HERON IS A SPECTACULAR FIGURE

Photograph by Oscar E. Baynard

AN EGRET MAKING ITS TOILET

traverses our attractive southern peninsula from coast to coast. When water conditions are favorable, 20,000 large wading birds may readily be seen in a few hours. One is almost certain to find wood ibises, sometimes thousands of them. They may be sitting on trees 200 yards from the trail or flying across the saw-grass wastes of the Everglades. Now and then a flock soars aloft. In wide circles it continues to rise with scarcely a movement of the black-tipped wings. Silently and with infinite grace the great birds go up and up until their white bodies seem to vanish in the far-away heavens.

There was a report that a man employed to guard a large nesting colony of birds had proved untrue to his trust. It was alleged that he was taking hundreds of eggs and selling them to collectors. The informant had passed the bird island and had seen many limbs that had been broken from the trees, he said, by the unfaithful warden, as he climbed about collecting eggs. Going to investigate the matter, three days later the prow of my boat came to rest on the muddy shore of that island. Everywhere small branches and twigs lay on the mud or hung from limbs above, as if a gale had swept the region.

The trees were of a kind that have very brittle limbs. Several hundred white ibises had appeared on the lake and had caused the damage by deciding to roost and build their nests in company with the herons and egrets here. Birds generally possess keen judgment as to the supporting strength of limbs on which they attempt to alight. Only in rare cases have I seen a branch break under the weight of a bird, and this was the first instance I had ever known where a whole flock made so many miscalculations.

WHITE IBIS SURVIVES PERSECUTION

In Florida the white ibis is more abundant than in any other State, despite its long persecution by hunters. For fifty years and more it was the custom for men to go in boats into the uninhabited Shark River country to shoot the "white curlews" in great numbers. Reports are common that several thousand have been killed in a season, their bodies salted in barrels and taken to Havana and elsewhere for food. In recent years wardens employed by the Audubon Society have camped on the river bank or lived in a houseboat, from where they could warn away those who would destroy the ibises and other water birds.

Photograph by L. W. Brownell

TWO YOUNG BLACK-CROWNED NIGHT HERONS IN THEIR NEST

Like several others of the large white birds of our country, the white ibis has black-tipped wings. Plumage with such striking contrasts, combined with the flash of red from their long, down-curved bills, makes a picture that, once seen, cannot readily be forgotten. As they come to roost in the evening, rank after rank sweeping low over great areas of green lily pads, then rising sharply to perch in trees lighted by the rays of the setting sun, they make one of the most pleasing pictures of bird life.

"BLACK IBISES" RARE IN AMERICA

Sometimes with them, but more often alone, glossy ibises appear. The iridescent, bronze-tinted plumage of the fully adult bird is discernible only on close inspection. Usually it is merely "black ibises" that one sees flying across the marsh. In America these are extremely rare birds.

West of the Mississippi is found a very similar species, the white-faced glossy ibis. To study it, go to the brackish marshes of western Louisiana, to the tule regions of Texas or California, or, better still, to the Bear River marshes of Utah, and to the great reaches of the little-known Carson Sink of Nevada. This ibis feeds in shallow water and usually builds its nest with others, among the tall rushes. It flies with its long neck stretched forward to the utmost, in true ibis fashion.

Over much of North America the great blue heron is known by sight to more people than any other of our large wading birds. Standing about four feet in height, it is the tallest of our common water birds. It is known by various local names, such as "poor Joe" and "old cranky," but as a rule people refer to it as the "blue crane."

Its prowess as a fisherman is such that anglers often express a dislike for the bird, which they regard as too successful a competitor for the game fish which they like to consider their own particular property. Many overlook the fact that this heron often feeds, in large part, upon fish of no special value to mankind, and that it destroys countless water snakes, which are among the greatest natural enemies of game fish.

BLUE HERONS COLONIZE IN FORESTS

In some of the Northern States and in Canada, it is a common experience to find great blue herons colonizing in forests, often at quite a distance from a lake or stream. Some of these colonies are very old. The big nests of twigs are in the tallest trees, and the location chosen is at least a mile from any body of water. I have seen such nesting colonies in dry, wooded regions in Maine, in the Carolinas, in Georgia, and elsewhere. In the Gulf States the nests are built usually in trees or in bushes growing in the water.

On islands along the Texas coast where trees are scarce, the nests are placed in mesquite bushes or on cacti. I found on North Bird Island, south of Corpus Christi, 75 occupied nests, every one of which was on the ground. In a tule marsh in northern California I counted nearly as many nests of tule reeds, built to a height of from two to three feet. The intervening rushes were trampled down, so that the nesting area appeared as an extended flat surface covered with numerous tree stumps.

Gilbert Grosvenor reports visiting in early July a colony of several hundred great blue herons nesting in a yellow-birch and maple forest near Baddeck, Cape Breton, Nova Scotia. The honking of the birds and the stench of rotting fish were noticeable for a long distance before the colony was reached. Under the trees mounds of decomposing fish bones and droppings, several feet high and five to seven feet in diameter, indicated that the birds had nested on the same limbs for many years. Ospreys were also nesting in the area.

"A helpless young heron that tumbled off a tree was carried home. As it paid no attention to fish placed beside it, and after two days without food seemed in danger of starving to death, I forced its beak open while one of the children dropped small pieces of fish down its throat. Soon the bird revived and began to gain rapidly. At first we had to be careful not to feed it too generously, for in that case it would vomit all the contents of its stomach.

"Presently it learned to pick up and swallow dead fish and developed a ravenous appetite, requiring eight or ten large perch daily.

"It was a savage creature that always flashed a rapier beak furiously and dangerously against any who approached.

"After several weeks of careful tending, it had so gained in strength that it could easily capture large, vigorous fish swimming in a tank.

"In mid-August we opened the door of its wire enclosure and it sailed away with a happy honk to join its fellows feeding down the shore, who had occasionally cautiously investigated the enclosure during the several weeks of its confinement."

Similar to the great blue heron in size is the great white heron, which is confined to the extreme southern tip of Florida and the adjoining keys and mud flats. In single pairs or in small groups, it nests on the tiny, mangrove-covered islands of Florida Bay and southward.

The seepage from the marl was milky white in the shallow hole which my guide had dug near camp. Here, at sunrise, we filled our canteens, for we had a long day ahead and the spring drought of 1913 lay upon the land. For hours we traveled through open pinelands and skirted dried-up swamps. Once I was shown the nesting hole used the year before by a pair of the almost extinct ivory-billed woodpeckers. At times our thirsty horses turned hopefully to openings in the landscape, only to find that the ponds were dry. On the caked mud lay hundreds of small dead fish, warped by the heat of the sun.

At noon we reached our destination, a small cypress "head" where my guide had found a flourishing colony of nesting egrets, "long whites," as he called them. To our chagrin, we discovered that others had preceded us by a few days, for a flattened pile of dry palmetto fronds showed where blankets had been spread. Nibbled grass, broken weeds, and tracks indicated various places where horses had been tethered. The remains of numerous white egrets, torn and dragged about by vultures, revealed the success of the plume hunters' raid. The parent birds had been shot as they came to bring food to their young, and the skin bearing the aigrettes had been stripped from their backs.

Up in the cypress trees were the nests, dozens of them, but not a sound of young birds came to our ears. Their last faint calls for food had died away. In what had been a populous, clamorous egret rookery, nothing was left but sickening odors, dancing heat waves, and the silence of death.

Far away in some great city, fashionable women would wear on their hats those long, white, airy feathers which Nature had given as nuptial plumes to the birds whose pitiful remains now lay about us. The aigrettes adorn the birds only in the nesting season, and to collect them for the millinery feather trade it was most profitable to shoot the birds at the time of year when they were caring for their young.

Photograph by Arthur A. Allen

AFTER AN UNEXPECTED TUMBLE INTO THE WATER
The young green heron is an awkward but efficient swimmer.

I have visited egret breeding colonies since 1886, and with others have worked to protect them. Our pleas before committees of State legislatures and of Congress during a period of 15 years finally brought laws making it illegal to kill egrets or to sell their feathers.

Twenty years ago it seemed almost certain that a losing fight was being made, and that white egrets would disappear from our country; but restrictive laws and an awakened public sentiment in time began to have their effect, and today they exist by tens of thousands. There are numerous breeding colonies, especially in the South Atlantic and Gulf States. In summer some individuals wander up the Atlantic coast, the Mississippi Valley, and the Pacific coast almost, if not quite, to the Canadian border.

REDDISH EGRETS FIND A HOME ON GREEN ISLAND

The history of the smaller snowy egret parallels closely that of the larger species. It inhabits the same general regions, gathers its food, and conducts nesting operations in the same manner, often in company of its larger neighbor. In spring it bears beautiful, recurved aigrettes. For a time it was threatened with extermination by plume hunters for the millinery feather trade, but now it, too, is gaining rapidly in numbers.

In Laguna Madre, Texas, perhaps 40 miles above the mouth of the Rio Grande, lies Green Island. The greater part of its area is covered with a thick, tangled mass of thorn trees, so compact that a heron could walk upon their tops almost from one side of the island to the other. In 1920, quite by accident, I discovered that this was the summer home of the largest percentage of reddish egrets in the United States. When notice of this came to the attention of the Legislature of Texas, that body enacted a law authorizing the State Land Commissioner to lease it to the Audubon Association as a bird sanctuary. Since then a guard has lived on the island several months each year.

A tower was built where visitors may look out over the 25 acres of low trees and view the 8,000 reddish egrets and perhaps 4,000 other larger waders that resort here throughout the summer months. Of all the heron family, this species is the least shy. So tame have the birds become on Green Island that they permit a visitor to approach within 15 or 20 feet and photograph them at leisure.

STUDYING FLAMINGO NESTS ON ANDROS ISLAND, BAHAMAS

At the right is the late artist-naturalist, Dr. Louis Agassiz Fuertes, who, with Dr. John Oliver La Gorce, led an expedition for the National Geographic Society to make a photographic study of the flights of flamingos in the Bahamas. The party made the first successful motion pictures of a flock in the air.

The hoarse squawk that comes out of the darkness when a black-crowned night heron flies overhead may in some cases have been "the cry of the night bird," which fanciful writers have been wont to refer to as an evil omen. Seldom are night herons seen abroad on a bright day except during the warmer months, when the demands of their young force them afield in quest of food. They may be encountered in suitable localities from the waterways of southern Canada to the savannas of South America.

In trees or bushes, in secluded ponds, on islands, or among sand dunes, or in the rank growths of marshes, this bird seeks its abode, often with hundreds of its kind and sometimes in company with other herons. It lays greenish-blue eggs, which require about 21 days to be hatched. So common is this night heron that almost any bird student with field experience can name one or more places where it congregates to rear its young.

The bittern has long been heralded by writers as a bird of mystery and its name associated with the owl and the bat in scenes of desolation. It inhabits marshes and

bogs, where it skulks in the shelter of rank vegetation. Usually it prefers to hide when danger is near, and unless surprised in an exposed position is loath to take wing. Although it breeds throughout the Northern and Central States, nowhere is it found in numbers, and it never gathers with others in colonies, as do most of the herons.

In solitary pairs they pass the spring and summer, with their nests usually hidden in a section of the marsh most likely to be free from intrusion. Sometimes the nests are made in salt marshes, but thickets of bulrushes and cattails growing in fresh water are more to their liking. Now and then a nest is discovered on dry ground, showing that, although a somber, meditative, retiring individual, the bittern nevertheless possesses an imagination which permits it to deviate at times from its customary habits.

THE BRILLIANTLY PLUMED FLAMINGO

One of the world's largest birds of brilliant plumage is the American flamingo. The studies of C. J. Maynard, made at a flamingo colony on Andros Island in 1884, first brought to general public attention the

Photograph by Capt. Albert W. Stevens

HUNDREDS OF FLAMINGOS IN FLIGHT OFF THE ORINOCO DELTA COAST

The black shadows of the birds are seen on the still surface of the clear, shallow water, beneath which is visible a vast expanse of tidal sand ridges. White clouds are also reflected in the mirrorlike surface, giving a dappled effect to the remarkable photograph, which was taken on the National Geographic Society's 1930 aërial survey of Latin America.

fact that here, at our door, is to be seen one of the most stirring sights in all the ornithological world. Two thousand great flame-colored birds of unusual form, gathered on a white and leafless plain, is a spectacle of the first magnitude. In such a place I have seen fully a thousand of their mud nests in a single group.

From a veranda on Turiguano Island, off the north coast of Cuba, my host at sunrise pointed to a mass of red a mile away and said: "There are the birds you are looking for."

A few minutes later a great company of flamingos arose and, with legs and neck outstretched, streamed through the sky, their scarlet wings flashing in the early sunlight. In a semicircular course they followed the shore line around the end of the island and alighted in a shallow lagoon. Sheltered by a few mangrove bushes, we approached close enough to the feeding host to determine that about 1,100 flamingos were in action only a few hundred yards from us.

This was in 1924. I was taken by a Cuban boat captain to near-by Cayo Coco and shown the site of a former flamingo colony from which, two years previously, he had taken 1,500 of the young. In his schooner they were transferred to Cuba, herded through the streets of Morón like so many geese, and sold for food to the residents.

Wood Ibis

(Mycteria americana)

Average Length, Forty Inches

The wood ibis inhabits the low wet country of the Southern States and is more abundant in Florida than elsewhere. As a rule, the birds are shy and wary and sentinels are posted when a flock is feeding. About their rookeries they are loath to leave their young, and when frightened away will soon return and give the hidden observer opportunity to view them at leisure.

The best place I have seen to get near to wood ibises is on Alligator Lake, near the extreme southern tip of Florida. Here the limbs of some clusters of low, wide-spreading mangroves were thickly covered with their nests when I visited the region, early in May, 1929. Young of various sizes were standing with their parents all over the dome-shaped trees. In February, 1930, while many young were in evidence, eggs still remained in some nests.

None of the nests was over 20 feet above the water. Some were so low and so easily accessible that one could photograph their contents from a horizontal position while standing in a small launch lying alongside.

One who has been repeatedly disappointed in attempts to photograph young great blue herons in the nest, because they lie down when one comes near, will find in the young wood ibis a very satisfactory subject for his art. I have watched them at a distance of eight or ten feet for many minutes, during which they stood erect and moved only occasionally.

The nest of the wood ibis is not particularly large for a bird which weighs from 11 to 12 pounds. However, it is about 15 inches across and is a substantial structure of small limbs and twigs. The white eggs are two to four or five in number. The shell is lightly pitted and is sometimes covered with blood stains.

Wood ibises like company and as a rule are seen in flocks. I have found them nesting in colonies ranging from 100 to fully 5,000 birds. Usually the nests are built in cypress trees, often 80 feet or more above the water of the swamp in which the big cypresses grow. Under ordinary circumstances this bird is difficult to approach, which argues well for its preservation.

Food is sought in marshes, in shallow ponds, or along the margins of grassy lakes. Here, to the accompaniment of clattering bills, the birds gather their diet of fish, snakes, frogs, tadpoles, water insects, and, according to Audubon, young alligators.

When a flock takes wing from its feeding ground the roar of wings may be heard afar.

In the United States this bird breeds in the coastal country from South Carolina to Florida, in Utah and Texas. Beyond our borders it extends to Peru and Argentina. After the nesting season some individuals migrate northward, rarely as far as Montana and Massachusetts.

Roseate Spoonbill

(Ajaia ajaja)

Average Length, Thirty-two Inches

Roseate spoonbills live in flocks, the number in a company ranging anywhere from five or six individuals to as many hundreds. If a group becomes scattered by hunters, storms, or other agencies, single birds will for a time join flocks of other waders encountered in the neighborhood. As evidence of this habit I have noticed particularly single spoonbills in company with wood ibises.

These birds feed in shallow water, where they sift the sand or silt in their long, flat beaks. Often the head and sometimes the entire neck is submerged for brief periods. Examination of stomachs has revealed the remains of fish, shrimps, and insects. Audubon says the birds grind their food by moving their partly open mandibles laterally to and fro.

The bone near the tip of the spoonbill's beak is perforated by numerous tiny orifices for nerves, which perhaps aid the bird to select its food by the sense of touch.

In taking wing, spoonbills fly in a more or less confused group, but if the flight be prolonged they often assume a rank formation.

When the breeding season approaches, they collect with other birds of the order Ciconiiformes. Their nests are scattered among those of herons, but are more substantial structures. They have many larger sticks, and, being made for heavier birds, are placed in secure positions among trees or bushes. The eggs vary from three to five, and are covered with dots and blotches of varying shades of olive brown. The shell is granulated, without any gloss.

The breeding season of the roseate spoonbill varies in different parts of the country. Those in Alligator Lake, Florida, had newly hatched young on January 1, 1930. On Big Vingt-une Island, Texas, young two weeks old were found in nests on June 25, 1931. At first the bodies are covered with white down, through which a vivid pinkish skin is revealed. The young in the nest get their food by inserting the bill deep into the mouth of the parent. They do not attain full plumage until at least two years of age.

The beak of the newly hatched bird is short, with little resemblance to that of the parents, but very soon the spoonbill shape of the tip begins to develop. By the time the bird matures, the beak has become very flat, is much widened, and is from 6 to 7 inches long.

Near Aransas Pass, Texas, in the spring of 1920, I observed at intervals during a period of two days a spoonbill whose body was black—a most unusual occurrence of melanism.

This species breeds from the Gulf States, Cuba, and Mexico southward to Argentina and Chile. On rare occasions it has been known to come northward as far as Pennsylvania, Illinois, Wisconsin, Utah, and California.

A WOOD IBIS POSES POMPOUSLY ABOVE A SPOONBILLED COUSIN

The wary **Wood Ibis** (upper) frequents marshes, ponds, and inlets of the Southern States. It is most easily observed about its rookeries when caring for its young. The nest of sticks and twigs, placed in a bush or low tree (usually in cypresses), resembles that of the **Roseate Spoonbill** (lower). Great colonies of the superb aviator, the wood ibis, which is a stork, abound in Florida, but the beautiful spoonbill has almost disappeared in the United States (see page 62).

White-faced Glossy Ibis

(Plegadis guarauna)

Average Length, Twenty-four Inches

The white-faced glossy ibis is the most widely distributed of the ibises of our country, being an inhabitant of open marshes, where it ranges in flocks often of considerable size. As ordinarily seen, it appears as a dull silhouette, the striking colors of the adult being visible only under unusual circumstances.

It breeds in colonies in growths of rushes, bending the stalks down for a foundation and on this placing a nest of similar materials with a well-marked depression to contain the two to six dark bluish-green eggs. Young ibises are ungainly creatures, scantily covered with black down with a whitish patch on the back of the head. About their colonies the birds make strange grunting calls (see p. 208).

In the air, ibises fly in lines or open wedges. Although these birds are not particularly shy when unmolested, they will not allow too familiar an approach.

They feed mainly in wet, marshy ground, and in the West come often into freshly irrigated fields, particularly where earthworms are abundant. These form part of their food, which includes also frogs, crayfish, aquatic insects, small fishes, and similar creatures. They have been hunted in various localities, but are now on the protected list.

The white-faced glossy ibis breeds from Oregon and Utah south to Texas and southern Mexico and is found locally also in Louisiana. It winters from California and Louisiana southward. It occurs also as a nesting species in South America, south of the Amazon Valley.

A related species, the glossy ibis (*Plegadis falcinellus falcinellus*), rare in the United States, differs mainly in not having white at the base of the bill. For several years a few pairs nested regularly every spring in the alder bushes on Bird Island, in Orange Lake, Florida.

The breeding glossy ibises of southeastern Louisiana are of this species, which ranges southward to Cuba and Haiti. This species is common in many parts of Europe, with related forms in Asia and Australia. In 1925 I visited a large colony nesting in the tall rushes of Kis Balaton, in southwest Hungary. They were associated here with white spoonbills and purple herons.

Scarlet Ibis

(Guara rubra)

Average Length, Twenty-three Inches

Although the adult scarlet ibis possesses such an amazing red plumage, the young for a time are grayish brown. The pink and then the reddish feathers develop through a series of molting seasons over two or three years.

Our knowledge of the habits of this species is limited and fragmentary. Travelers in South America have written of visiting breeding colonies of scarlet ibises, but the accounts of their observations do not always agree. Thus Schomburgk, in 1848, says that they use the nests several seasons in succession, while Lloyd (1897) states that this ibis never builds a nest of any kind, but instead takes forcible possession of the nests of the snowy egret. There is agreement, however, in the statements that in the nesting season they colonize in enormous numbers.

Two eggs ordinarily constitute a set, with sometimes three and rarely four. The ground color varies from grayish or greenish to yellowish white, marked with shades of brown.

The scarlet ibis inhabits the coastal areas of northern and eastern South America from Venezuela and Trinidad to Brazil. There are various records of its occurrence in the United States, but many of these are vague and not well substantiated. The reports of specimens found in Texas are perhaps the most convincing. One account from Corpus Christi tells of a bird evidently blown there from the south by the storm of August, 1916.

White Ibis

(Guara alba)

Average Length, Twenty-five Inches

John James Audubon, writing a hundred years ago, said that sometimes white ibises will drop pieces of mud down a crayfish hole, wait patiently until the little crustacean comes up pushing the mud before it, and then seize it.

White ibises accumulate in large colonies to breed, sometimes thousands occupying the trees of some small island. The nests are of sticks and are crowded closely together, often many in a single tree, at times nearly touching each other. Egg-laying often begins before the nest has been finished. Four or five greenish or bluish-white eggs, spotted with various shades of brown, are deposited. They are two and a quarter inches long and one and a half inches wide.

The bare skin about the head, as well as part of the long, curved bill and the legs, is yellowish, turning to light red in the breeding season. As Major Brooks has shown in the color plate, the gular sac beneath the base of the bill becomes distended at this time. The immature bird is grayish brown, with the rump and underparts white and with the white of the head and neck streaked with grayish brown. In this plumage it is known in some regions as the "Spanish curlew." An adult specimen has an expanse of wings of about three and a third feet.

The white ibis breeds from southern Baja California, central Mexico, Texas, Florida, and South Carolina, south to Haiti and northern South America, wintering from Florida, Louisiana, and Mexico southward. Casual occurrences have been reported from Colorado, South Dakota, New York, and elsewhere.

LONG-LEGGED MARSH LOVERS DON'T WORRY ABOUT HAVING WET FEET

Most widely distributed of our ibises is the **White-faced Glossy Ibis** (upper), an inhabitant of open marshes in the Southwest. Occasionally blown by protracted gales as far north as the southern United States, the **Scarlet Ibis** colonizes in northern South America in enormous numbers during the breeding season. Audubon, a hundred years ago, reported that the **White Ibis** would stop up crayfish holes with mud and seize the occupants when they came up to remove the plugs. One of the fairest winter sights in Florida is the return to roost of successive flocks of this graceful bird, each flock numbering many hundreds (see page 67).

Great White Heron

(Ardea occidentalis)

Average Length, Fifty Inches

Florida Bay and the immediately adjoining regions are the home of the great white heron, from which it never regularly migrates. No other large bird of North America occupies such a restricted range. It lives about the waters just off the southern tip of the mainland and principally in a region less than 30 by 50 miles in extent. Here the sea is very shallow and the bottom is covered with mud. At low tide vast reaches of this slimy marl are exposed.

When the tide comes in and flows over the flats, the great white herons collect in small, scattering groups to feed. One may see them at a distance of one or two miles, standing as immovable as statues. They feed largely upon fish, which they procure by simply waiting for them to come along.

As the bird feels the rising tide touching its body, it lifts in the air and departs with slow, measured wing beats. The neck is drawn in until the head appears to be attached directly to the body and the long legs are extended straight out behind.

Scattered about in this extraordinary sea are numerous small, mangrove-covered keys, to one of which the bird repairs to rest and to digest the ample meal so recently consumed.

Audubon, who studied the habits of these little-known birds in 1840, records that their appetite was astonishing. For example, he says that two young birds "swallowed a gallon of these fishes." Apparently they would consume almost any animal food they could capture, for he tells that they killed and swallowed young Louisiana herons and reddish egrets, although they were being fed bountifully on green turtle flesh at the time. Audubon found that he could not make friends with these birds as with young great blue herons.

The islands of their haunts are usually small and are covered with either the red mangrove or both the red and black mangrove. To these the great white herons resort in small colonies to raise their young. Egg-laying may be at any time of year from October to the succeeding July, although December, January, and February are the months when most of them engage in nest construction. The nests are heavy structures of sticks and twigs. Three or four pale bluish-green eggs are laid.

In 1858 the ornithologist Baird described the Würdemann's heron, which inhabits the south Florida region, as a distinct species. The latest studies of Ernest G. Holt and others, however, revealed the fact that *Ardea würdemanni* is a hybrid of the great white heron and the Ward's heron.

The great white heron is confined to the southern tip of Florida, mainly in Florida Bay, and near Cape Sable and Cape Romano, ranging to Cuba and Jamaica.

Great Blue Heron

(Ardea herodias)

Average Length, Forty-six Inches

The stately form of the great blue heron decorates the shallows, ponds, streams, lakesides, and estuaries from Alaska and Canada to the West Indies and the Galápagos. As is usual with large birds, individuals vary considerably in size. Some have a six-foot wing spread and weigh six to eight pounds.

The rise of the water when Makepeace Reservoir, in Atlantic County, New Jersey, was created killed a grove of white cedar trees. Visiting the lake on June 1, 1919, I found 66 great blue heron nests in the dead trees, all apparently of recent construction and placed at heights varying from 12 to 40 feet above the water. Twigs and small limbs had been employed as building materials and the nests were substantial, some a yard wide.

In addition to consuming fish and frogs, this bird preys upon snakes of considerable size, as well as young muskrats, grasshoppers, dragon flies, lizards, meadow mice, pocket gophers, and young rats. It has even been known to eat young birds. However, fish is its principal diet. The food taken to its young is carried in its stomach and delivered by regurgitation.

When fishing, it regularly employs two methods. One is to stand motionless and patiently await the coming of the prey. The other is to stalk carefully along until a fish is seen; whereupon the head darts forward with lightninglike rapidity. The fish is first stabbed and disabled, or, if it be a small one, it is tossed upward and swallowed head first.

A much rarer method of the bird is to fish in deep water. Only once have I seen this. On the Cape Fear River, in North Carolina, I discovered seven herons fishing in this way. One at a time they would spring from the top of some old pilings and land squarely in the water. As the current carried them downstream they would strike repeatedly, as if floating amid a school of fish.

The great blue heron nests from Nova Scotia, Quebec, and southeastern British Columbia to Nebraska, Iowa, and South Carolina, wintering south from Massachusetts and New York.

The form known as Ward's heron (*A. h. wardi*), distinguished from the typical great blue by its larger size, is found from South Carolina, Florida, the Gulf coast, Indiana, and Oklahoma southward. Other subspecies are: Treganza's heron (*A. h. treganzai*), found from Wyoming to Baja California and Sonora; northwestern coast heron (*A. h. fannini*), breeding from Cook Inlet, Alaska, to Washington; California heron (*A. h. hyperonca*), Oregon to northern Baja California; and Espíritu Santo heron (*A. h. sancti-lucae*), inhabiting southern Baja California. Also, there are other forms of the great blue heron in the West Indies, Mexico, and the Galápagos.

HERONS' LONG BILLS SERVE AS DEADLY FISH SPEARS

Occupying the most restricted range of all large North American birds, the **Great White Heron** (left) is a permanent resident of Florida Bay and the adjoining regions. On the vast tidal flats, hundreds of these herons may be seen, waiting for fish to come in with the tide. The **Great Blue Heron** (adult above a young bird) is a familiar sight beside stream or lake throughout most of North America. Preëminent as a fisherman, this heron also preys upon frogs, snakes, rodents, and grasshoppers.

American Egret

(Casmerodius albus egretta)

Average Length, Forty-one Inches

Because of its large size, its snowy whiteness, and the remarkable grace it exhibits in flight or when at rest, the American egret arrests the attention of every observer. In the breeding plumage the bird is adorned with about 50 aigrettes, which grow from the back between the wings and extend well beyond the tail. These exquisite, filmy feathers attain a length of 21 inches. As the nesting season advances, these are gradually shed.

Of the three species of egrets in the United States, this is the largest. The slender, dagger-shaped bill is nearly five inches long and is a dangerous weapon when driven vigorously by the bird's long and flexible neck. The yellow color of the bill easily distinguishes this species from the snowy egret when larger size is not evident.

The birds apparently eat almost any small animal life encountered. Among the various articles they have been known to consume are fish, small snakes, frogs, dragon flies, crickets, grasshoppers, and moths.

The American egret occupies the tropical and subtropical sections of America, breeding from Maryland, Arkansas, and Oregon (rarely) southward to Patagonia. Allied forms are found in the Old World.

Snowy Egret

(Egretta thula)

Average Length, Twenty-four Inches

The snowy egret is a handsome bird; its plumage is of snowy whiteness, and in the spring and summer its back is decorated with numerous recurved aigrette plumes. It is smaller than the egret and has the bill and legs black and the toes yellow. Formerly this bird was shot for the millinery trade in such immense numbers that by the beginning of the present century it was regarded as one of the rare and fast-disappearing birds within the United States. The passage of the Audubon laws to prohibit killing it and to make the sale of its plumes illegal, followed by years of intensive public education and the guarding of its breeding colonies, has been one of the most successful efforts in the protection of any single species of North American bird. It has regained its numbers, and to-day exists by tens of thousands.

The birds frequent shallow ponds, quiet salt-water lagoons, and flooded rice fields, where they seek minnows, frogs, and other small life.

They are the most animated members of the heron family of which I have personal knowledge. In feeding they dart about most vigorously in the shallow water, and in their nesting colonies they are pugnacious and resentful of the approach of other birds. They breed usually in company with other herons and lay from three to five bluish-green eggs.

Like the American egret, this species wanders north in late summer to Kansas, Maryland, and casually to southern Canada.

The nesting range of this egret extends from North Carolina southward in the coast country to Florida and Texas, and on through tropical America to Argentina and Chile.

The extensive Bear River marshes adjoining Great Salt Lake on the northeast are one of this country's most famous resorts for water birds of many species and are a well-known feeding and nesting ground for the form of this heron known as Brewster's egret. Here, in the tule marshes, they gather in numbers to construct their nests and raise their young.

Brewster's egret (E. t. brewsteri) breeds from Utah and California southward to Baja California.

Reddish Egret

(Dichromanassa rufescens)

Average Length, Twenty-nine Inches

The general habits of the reddish egret are similar to those of other herons. It feeds in shallow water, builds nests of sticks and twigs, lays bluish-green eggs, and, if successful, rears three or four young in a season. However, it appears mainly to frequent only salt and brackish water areas. Its food consists chiefly of small fish. When animated, the long feathers of the back of the head and upper breast and the aigrettes of the back are erected in such a manner as wholly to change the form and appearance of the bird.

This species occurs in two very distinct phases of plumage. The dark one is of a bluish slate color except the head and neck, which are rich chestnut. Specimens of the white phase show no color in their plumage, except that in some cases there are faint markings of gray at the tips of the long wing primaries. In both phases the end of the bill is dark. This egret superficially resembles a little blue heron, but is larger.

Like all other wild birds, reddish egrets have their natural enemies. On Green Island, Texas, where is situated their largest breeding colony in the United States, the chief foe appears to be the great-tailed grackle, which is a great destroyer of eggs. Like the fish crows in the heronries of the South Atlantic States, they are ever on the watch to seize the unguarded eggs of the herons and egrets.

The reddish egret (Dichromanassa rufescens rufescens) breeds from the Gulf coast of the United States south to Jamaica, Haiti, and Guatemala. Formerly it was common in southern Florida, but is nearly extinct there. Now, however, the few remaining are protected.

Dickey's egret (Dichromanassa rufescens dickeyi), found in Baja California, differs in being darker on the head and neck.

NO LONGER ARE THEY HUNTED FOR THEIR PLUMES

Until protective laws were passed, the demand for aigrettes to decorate milady's hats seriously threat-ened egrets with extinction. Graceful alike in flight or at rest, the large **American Egret** (left) sports about 50 long, filmy aigrettes during the breeding season. Individuals migrate northward after the nesting season, a strange habit shared by the **Snowy Egret** (lower right), one of the most active and pugnacious of the herons. The **Reddish Egret** (above, dark and white phases), like the little blue heron, has two distinct plumages. In the United States it breeds along the Gulf coast, its general habits closely resembling those of the other species.

© James E. Stanley

AT EVENING, LITTLE BLUE HERONS FLY HOME FROM THE FEEDING GROUNDS TO THEIR FAVORITE ROOSTING PLACE

These handsome birds, sometimes called blue egrets, are abundant in the South. Graceful in flight, and usually silent when not alarmed, a flock on the wing is a magnificent spectacle. The young birds are white, often being mistaken for snowy egrets, and do not assume the full adult plumage until they are two years old (see Color Plate). While still clothed in the feathers of youth, they may mate and raise young.

EGRETS, LITTLE BLUE HERONS, AND LOUISIANA HERONS WADE FLORIDA'S SHALLOW PONDS FOR FOOD

These species are congenial companions, frequently found together. Egrets usually nest in colonies in the cypress and mangrove swamps or in the cover of ponds grown up with buttonbushes. Frequently their nests are interspersed with those of the little blue heron and the Louisiana heron, whose pale-blue eggs are not distinguishable from the snowy egret's.

SOCIABLE COUSINS GATHER FOR A MORNING'S FISHING

The young **Little Blue Heron** (white bird behind slaty-blue adult, lower right) is often mistaken for a snowy egret, although distinguished from that bird by greenish, instead of black, legs and bill. Commonly the most numerous species in a southern heronry is the slender, graceful **Louisiana Heron** (upper), also one of the most affectionate and "domestic" of the herons. The **Green Heron** (lower left), less of a colonizing species than most, is known in many sections of the East as the "fly-up-the-creek."

Little Blue Heron

(Florida caerulea caerulea)

Average Length, Twenty-two Inches

This handsome species breeds in colonies in swamps, where usually it is associated with other herons. The eggs, four or five in number, are dull blue in color, and are laid in nests of twigs built in trees or stout bushes. The down of the young little blue heron is white and the feathers that follow also are white. It is not until well along in the summer of the next year that the slaty-blue plumage of the adult is acquired. In the white plumage it is often mistaken for the snowy egret by beginners, but may be distinguished by the dull greenish, instead of black, legs and bill.

In a cluster of young cypress trees growing in an arm of Orton Pond, in Brunswick County, North Carolina, many little blue herons have their nests every spring. The young, like those of other herons, are fed by regurgitation. The power of expelling food is also well developed in the young. While sitting in a boat at the edge of this colony one May morning, I noted with what frequency the young were disgorging their recent repasts. This is not an unusual performance when the herons are old enough to stand on the nests or clamber awkwardly about on the near-by branches.

As each lot of minnows fell, there was a swirl in the water. Wondering what was happening beneath the surface, I pushed my boat beneath a small tree containing several young birds and was quickly presented with a dozen minnows by one of them. Using these as bait and dropping the line overboard, I discovered that the water was swarming with yellow perch and black bass, drawn to the colony by the food which was continually falling like manna from above.

The little blue heron is found during the nesting season from Delaware and Arkansas southward to the Gulf coast and Central America. In late summer many individuals migrate northward and remain for some weeks. At this season they come at times to New England, Iowa, Colorado, and Nova Scotia and other points near the Canadian border. An allied form is found in the West Indies and northern South America.

Louisiana Heron

(Hydranassa tricolor ruficollis)

Average Length, Twenty-six Inches

A southern heron colony is a very busy and fascinating place. From the vantage of some elevated limb one looks out over the tops of the bushes below, where various kinds of herons are carrying sticks, incubating eggs, shading newly hatched young, fighting intruding neighbors, and engaging in many pretty love antics. Black vultures are usually perched here and there; they eat young herons. Fish crows are skulking about in quest of eggs. Sunlight reveals the great variety of colors in the plumage of the several species inhabiting one of these cities of the long-legs.

Among these is the Louisiana heron, generally the most numerous, sometimes several thousand being gathered in a single breeding colony. It is an exceedingly slender, graceful bird. "Lady-of-the-waters," Audubon called it.

When one meets its mate, there is always some expression of interest and tenderness. They bow, they elevate their crests and aigrettes, touch each other with their necks, and gently pick each other's plumage. The male brings many sticks for the nest, and his mate places them to her liking. He helps her in incubating and guards the four or five pale-blue eggs while she goes away for food.

In feeding, the Louisiana heron advances through the shallow water with stealthy tread until suddenly, with amazing swiftness, the head darts forward and the bill seizes a luckless minnow, insect, or frog.

This bird inhabits both fresh and salt water, feeding in shallows where small fish abound. It usually avoids places where tall grass or rushes interfere with a view of its surroundings.

It breeds from Cape Lookout, North Carolina, and the Gulf south coast to the West Indies and Central America, and on the Pacific side from central Baja California south into Mexico. An allied form is found in northern South America.

Green Heron

(Butorides virescens)

Average Length, Seventeen Inches

Most farm boys in eastern North America know the green heron, although they may not recognize it by this name. Perhaps they call it "shite-poke," "fly-up-the-creek," or "Indian hen." While found commonly about large swamps and marshlands, it may be startled from the shore of almost any creek. With a sharp, lusty squawk it will take sudden flight, perhaps disappearing around a bend in the stream or perching on a limb to watch the intruder.

The herons' custom of nesting in colonies applies to this species less than to most of the others. The slight nest, made of small dry twigs, is often not more than ten feet from the ground and frequently much lower. Four or five eggs are usually in a nest of this heron, but as many as nine have been found.

The eastern green heron *B. v. virescens* breeds from Nova Scotia and North Dakota to northern Honduras and westward to New Mexico. It winters from Florida and Texas southward to Central America and Colombia. Besides the eastern green heron, there is Frazar's green heron *(B. v. frazari)* of Baja California, and Anthony's green heron *(B. v. anthonyi)*, found from Oregon south to Sonora and northern Baja California. Other forms are found in the West Indies and Central America.

YOUNG NIGHT HERONS BEAR SLIGHT RESEMBLANCE TO THEIR PARENTS

In dense hardwood thickets, on a bulky, deeply hollowed nest, the **Yellow-crowned Night Heron** (lower, striped young and adult) lays its bluish-green eggs. In its habit of hunting its diet of small fish, crawfish, crabs, snails, and snakes both by day and by night it is like the **Black-crowned Night Heron** (upper pair, young at left). Although it nests frequently very high in trees above dry ground, the black-crown also inhabits swamps, mud flats, and salt-water marshes.

Yellow-crowned Night Heron

(Nyctanassa violacea)

Average Length, Twenty-three Inches

In a heavy hardwood forest near Levy Lake, Alachua County, Florida, is a little pond not more than 100 feet across in any direction. It is closely surrounded by tall trees and large buttonwood bushes. Here, deep in the shade, a small colony of yellow-crowned night herons came for many years, during April, to lay their four or five bluish-green eggs. No others nested with them except now and then a green heron. They built heavy nests, so deeply hollowed at the top that it was practically impossible for eggs to roll out and be lost. I first discovered this rookery in 1896.

There is a large swamp, known as The Burn, in West Feliciana Parish, Louisiana, where both of the white egrets and other herons have a nesting place. In May, 1920, I found that eight pairs of yellow-crowns had constructed their nests a little to one side of the main nesting area. The largest known breeding colony of this species is in Gros-bec Lake, Louisiana. One thousand birds nest there.

These are typical of various locations where I have found these birds engaged in nesting operations. They like deep shade for their nests and seem rarely to colonize in any great numbers. Quite different are their nesting habits on some of the almost barren islands of the Bahamas. There it is difficult to find shade, and they have become accustomed to brooding in the light.

These birds feed both by day and by night. They eat small fish, but are partial to crawfish and a wide variety of crabs; they also feed upon snails, leeches, snakes, and small quadrupeds.

The plumage of the immature bird differs much from the adult's. This first coat of feathers, with its many rows of brown and whitish spots, is worn until the next March or April succeeding the hatching of the bird.

The common cry of this bird is the usual heron squawk. If alarmed when sitting on its nest, it creeps stealthily away through the intervening branches and then springs upward with a hoarse call.

The regular breeding range of the yellow-crowned night heron reaches from South Carolina and southern Illinois to the West Indies, Brazil, and Peru. It has nested rarely in Massachusetts and New Jersey. It seems less inclined to wander northward after the nesting season than do some others of its tribe. Yet there is from year to year a certain number of instances of this peculiar migration. Casual visitors have been found in Colorado, Iowa, Nebraska, New Hampshire, Ontario, Nova Scotia, and elsewhere.

Bancroft's night heron (*Nyctanassa violacea bancrofti*), with larger, heavier bill, is found locally in southern Baja California.

Black-crowned Night Heron

(Nycticorax nycticorax hoactli)

Average Length, Twenty-four Inches

Our best-known nesting colony of black-crowned night herons, the Barnstable rookery on Cape Cod, occupied for more than 100 years, though periodically deserted, has perhaps been visited by more bird students than any other heron colony in this country. It was often raided by gunners, and on some occasions was literally "shot out," but continued to persist. It was located on Sandy Neck, a region of sand dunes in which grow many trees. In the summer of 1920 Dr. Alfred O. Gross found that it contained 2,536 nests, 850 trees being occupied. Ninety per cent of the nests were in pitch pines, the remainder in scrub oak, maple, and a few bushes. These trees stand on dry ground, not in a swamp.

In Oregon an ornithologist visited a colony of 200 pairs in a forest of fir "in which none of the nests were less than 130 feet up." Near San Francisco Bay he found "41 nests of the great blue heron and 28 nests of the black-crowned night heron in a single giant sycamore tree 120 feet high." I have seen photographs by this same gentleman showing night herons standing beside their nests in a tule marsh in Oregon. In Texas this bird is known to nest on the ground. The pale bluish-green eggs usually number three to five in a set.

It will be seen that this heron easily adapts itself to its environment. Although the name implies that this is a night bird, it also is active during the day, especially toward evening or when the sky is overcast. It inhabits many swamps and lonely reaches of salt-water marshes. It will even come to exposed mud flats in our large cities. Not long ago I saw several standing at their nests, built on a great vine that climbs over the flying cage in the National Zoological Park, Washington, D. C. Probably they were drawn here by their sociable, colony-breeding instinct. Confined in the flying cage are several night herons whose nests are visible to their wild neighbors on the outside.

These birds feed largely on fish. Not long ago I saw a night heron in the air carrying an eel and being closely pursued by three other night herons bent on plunder.

Since herons consume so much fish, it would seem that their flesh might not be palatable. However, I know of regions where the young great blue heron is highly regarded as game, and many have been illegally taken for food. The black-crowned night heron seems to be most enjoyed as food. Great numbers of these have been shot along the Gulf coast.

The black-crowned night heron breeds from the northern United States and southern Canada to Paraguay, being locally distributed over the area. A related form is found through much of the Eastern Hemisphere.

AT THE APPROACH OF DANGER, CAMOUFLAGED "STAKE-DRIVERS" PLAY POSSUM

The **American Bittern** (right foreground) is famous for its booming springtime call from which it derives its nicknames of "stake-driver" and "thunder pumper." One foot long, the **Least Bittern** (adult male middle one of three foreground figures) is smallest of the herons. It rises into the air with weak, awkward flappings, but, in full flight, is swifter and abler than most of its kind. The bird in the rushes (upper right) tries to avoid notice by posing motionless, with compressed feathers, head erect, and bill pointing at the sky. The variation called **Cory's Least Bittern** (adult male, extreme left) is apparently extinct.

American Bittern

· *(Botaurus lentiginosus)*
Average Length, Twenty-eight Inches

Few North American birds vary so much in size as does our large bittern, individuals sometimes differing a foot in length. The total expanse of their wings varies from 2 feet 8 inches to 4 feet 2 inches.

This bird inhabits marshes, bogs, and wet meadows. When alarmed by the approach of an intruder, but still believing itself unseen, it has the peculiar habit of remaining perfectly still, with head erect and bill pointed upward at a sharp angle. At the same time the feathers of the neck and body are compressed, so that the bird assumes the appearance of a discolored limb or old root, or even a slender clump of marsh grass.

The bittern depends on its color protection to escape its enemies and often will not move until it is almost trodden upon.

Upon taking flight, the bird rises with loosely flapping wings and departs slowly. Such a slow-rising bird naturally is a tempting shot to many who wander the marshes gun in hand, and in spite of the laws, it often is shot. A wounded bittern is a very animated creature and may prove to be a dangerous one. Squatting on the ground, with arched wings and with every visible feather of back and breast elevated to the utmost, with its daggerlike beak presented, it awaits the approach of its tormentor. On such occasions there is an element of real danger in coming too close, for the bittern strikes for the face with a swift and vigorous blow.

This hermit of the fen is famous for its booming call in spring. The various notes suggest to many hearers the sounds produced by a wooden pump in action, or those made when a stake is being driven into a bog; hence such descriptive names for the bird as "stake-driver" and "thunder pumper." Its actions when producing these strange sounds have thus been described in part by Arthur J. Parker:

"First, a forward thrust of the head with opened beak, whereby air was gulped, the bill being audibly snapped upon each 'mouthful.' The swallowing motion would be repeated perhaps five or six times, and during the operation a strange swelling and contortion of the neck could be plainly seen; it was as if the bird had swallowed a frog. There was a downward movement of the enlarged part of the neck. There at once followed the explosive eruption of air, the *boom,* closely followed by the second sound, a clear syllable *ka,* like the stroke of a mallet on a stake."

The bittern nests on the ground in a marsh and lays four to six olive-brown eggs. It nests from British Columbia and Newfoundland into California, Arizona, Kansas, and New Jersey, and even farther south. In winter it migrates as far as the West Indies and Panama.

Least Bittern

(Ixobrychus exilis)
Average Length, Thirteen Inches

This is the smallest of all the members of the heron tribe. Audubon found that one passed readily between two books set one inch apart. This ability to move through narrow openings is constantly employed, as it traverses the dense reedy marshes in which its life is spent. At times the least bittern wades in shallow water in true heron fashion, but often it progresses through the reeds by grasping the stalks with its long, flexible toes.

It eats frogs, tadpoles, and fish as well as various insects and their caterpillars.

No bird of the marshland world in which the least bittern dwells is possessed of such a peculiar flight. It rises slowly and with feeble, awkward movements takes its departure.

If, however, the bird finds it desirable to make an extended flight, it soon stretches its legs straight out behind and proceeds in a more rapid and businesslike manner.

The nest of this species is built over the water in cattails, rushes, or bushes. I have found them at heights of from one to four feet, but never higher. Some have been found so low that the bottom portion of the nest, usually about six inches across, touched the water.

A variety of nesting materials is used. Bent-over reeds or marsh grass generally serve as the base upon which a collection of grasses, stems, or twigs is laid. In Florida I have often found them nesting among colonies of boat-tailed grackles in clusters of buttonwood bushes. The nests here were made chiefly of twigs. The bluish or greenish-white eggs range from four to six in number.

The young are fed by regurgitation. When a parent arrives at the nest, the hungry offspring seize its bill and shake it until the old one opens its mouth and permits the bills of the young to enter, one at a time.

The eastern least bittern (*I. e. exilis*) breeds from the southern Canadian Provinces southward, but in winter is not found north of Florida. Its range extends through the West Indies and Central America.

Recognized as a subspecies is the western least bittern (*I. e. hesperis*), which inhabits the Pacific coast country of North America from southern Oregon to central Baja California and western Guatemala.

The form that has been called Cory's least bittern (*I. neoxenus*) is known from about 30 individuals taken mainly in Florida and in Ontario. It differs from the ordinary least bittern in the richer, darker browns of its feathers, and many ornithologists now consider it merely a color phase of the least bittern, though others call it a distinct species. Its habits and life, so far as known, were like those of the ordinary bird. None has been reported recently, and it seems now to be extinct.

BRILLIANT FLAMINGOS HUNT FOR MOLLUSKS IN THE SHALLOWS

Only an accidental visitor to the shores of the United States, the striking **Flamingo** breeds on two islands of the Bahama group, on a few small islands off the north coast of Cuba, in Yucatán, and locally in South America. It lays its one or two chalky white eggs on the cup-shaped top of a mound of packed marl, scooped up in the hooked bill from surrounding mud flats. In response to a plea from the National Association of Audubon Societies, the Bahama Government has given legal protection to the flamingo colonies of Andros Island for more than 30 years.

Flamingo

(Phoenicopterus ruber)

Average Length, Forty-five Inches

For 100 years rumors have persisted that flamingos have at some time bred in Florida. John James Audubon, studying birds in the Florida Keys about 1840, tried hard to establish the fact that they nested in that region. He hunted assiduously, saw flamingos, but died without ever finding the nest.

Today we know that there are three great breeding colonies about 200 miles from the region of his search. These are on the islands of Great Abaco and Andros, in the Bahamas, and on small islands near Morón, off the north coast of Cuba. These regions are about 125 miles apart. Undoubtedly from one or more of these places flamingos come to the coast of south Florida at rare intervals, usually during the winter or early spring months.

Since Audubon's time visiting flocks ranging from 500 to 1,000 birds have been seen on several occasions in Florida Bay. Smaller numbers have been reported many other times. On May 14, 1884, C. J. Maynard discovered a colony of flamingos on Andros Island, and later published a statement of his findings.

"The rookery occupied about a half acre of land, or rather what was once land, for all, or nearly all, nests were surrounded by water, and were built on a kind of peninsula which had water on three sides of it. The nests were constructed wholly of marl piled layer upon layer, without waiting for any layer to dry, for in some cases the bottom was as soft as the top. In scooping out the marl, the birds evidently used the lower mandible of the bill, while it is spread and flattened with the feet. The clay is not gathered at random about the nest, but from a pit on either side, or often from three pits, and it is the joining of these pits that causes the nests to be surrounded with water.

"None of the nests are constructed quite to the margin of the peninsula; thus a dike nearly surrounds the rookery. I say nearly, for this was broken through on the southern end, and the creek water flowed in; thus the slight inland tide rose and fell among the nests.

"The nests were, as a rule, not over two feet apart, measuring from their base, but they were generally constructed in groups of from three to seven or eight, each one being joined to one or two of the others at the base, ofttimes for a foot or more. This rookery had evidently been used for at least one year previous to this, as we saw many nests, especially the higher ones, which had, to all appearances, been constructed on top of an old foundation.

"New nests built throughout of soft marl were, on an average, only a foot high, and were built in a certain part of the rookery.

"All the nests in the older part of the rookery contained eggs, as a rule only one being deposited, and this was placed on the slightly cup-shaped top of the truncated pyramid. Incubation had begun and in nearly all the eggs the embryos were considerably advanced."

Mr. Maynard estimated that there were 2,000 nests in this colony. In all but about fifty cases each nest contained a single egg, the others holding two and in one case three. The eggs are chalky in texture, usually dull white, though rarely tinged with pinkish.

It remained for Dr. Frank M. Chapman to give a very full and rich account of this Andros flamingo colony, or its successor, as a result of his observations on that island in 1902 and 1905. His remarkable photographs and the publication of his careful, intimate studies attracted wide attention.

Dr. Chapman estimated the colony in 1905 to contain about 2,000 adult birds. Of the habits and movements of the very young birds, he said in part:

"The young flamingo when hatched is sufficiently developed to leave the nest before it is dry, under the stimulus of an apparently instinctive fear. At my approach young birds with the plumage still wet from the eggs would crawl over the edge of the nest and fall to the ground or water below, when their strength seemed to fail them. A few hours later, when the plumage was dry, chicks could swim and run readily, and when they were a day old they invariably left the nest as I drew near. When not disturbed, the young remain in the nest three or four days. During this time they were brooded by the parents."

The food of the flamingo on Andros seemed to consist wholly of a small, spiral-shelled mollusk known as "cerithium." The old birds feed the young with the regurgitated fluid from this shell.

At one of the first meetings of the directors of the National Association of Audubon Societies after its incorporation, in 1905, Dr. Chapman presented the need of extending protection to the Andros flamingo colony. Guardianship seemed necessary, for the natives were killing and eating these birds in large numbers. A resolution, therefore, was passed asking the Bahama Government to extend legal protection to flamingos. Such action was taken shortly afterward by the Bahama Parliament, at the request of the Colonial Governor. Since that time the birds have been carefully guarded by agents of E. W. Forsyth, Commissioner of South Andros Island, who prizes the flamingos as the chief attraction of his island.

Flamingos from Andros or Cuba are occasionally imported into the United States for zoölogical parks. As a rule, they do not long survive.

The flamingo breeds locally in the Bahamas, Cuba, Haiti, Yucatán, Guiana, and Peru, wandering to some extent after the nesting season, but not going far outside these limits.

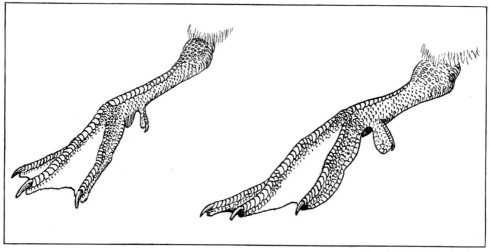

BY THEIR FEET YOU MAY KNOW THEM

The badge of membership in the group of diving ducks (canvasback, etc.) is the lobe, like a little paddle, on the hind toe, as shown in the drawing of a redhead's foot at the right. The unlobed hind toe on the mallard's foot at the left distinguishes the fresh-water, surface-feeding ducks (mallard, black duck, gadwall, baldpate, widgeon, teal, shoveller, pintail, wood duck). With the aid of the "paddle," some of the diving or bay and sea ducks (see page 122) reach considerable depths and have been caught in fishermen's nets from 80 to 100 feet below the surface.

"DUCK HEAVEN" ON AN ARKANSAS ESTATE

Many thousands of ducks gather annually under the care and protection of George S. Wilcox on his property in the White River bottoms of Arkansas County, near Stuttgart. They are mostly mallards, with a sprinkling of pintails and green-winged teal. The region is one of the foremost concentration areas in the world for mallards.

THE SWANS, DUCKS, AND GEESE

Far-Flying Wild Fowl and Their Foes Carry On A Dramatic Struggle for Existence

By Major Allan Brooks

"Dark flying rune against the western glow—
It tells the sweep and loneliness of things."

SO WROTE Pai Ta-shun (an American and not a Chinese) in the finest of all poems on wild fowl, and many others have drawn inspiration from the striking formations that especially characterize the movements of swans, geese, and ducks.

That flying wedge or undulating line etched against the sunset sky or the orderly, swift-moving formation high overhead! Here is the symbol that inspires the imagination of even the casual observer, as it has the poets who have written of flying wild fowl through the ages.

Behind this aura of glamour and mystery lies the fascinating life story of the majestic wild swans, the wily geese, the hardy and adaptable ducks, and the fish-loving mergansers, which, all together, form the family Anatidae. They are a fairly compact and homogeneous group of birds, their only relatives of undoubted connection being the screamers of South America, large, gooselike, wading birds with unwebbed toes.

Geese and ducks are found all over the world wherever water exists, except on the oceans far from land.

Common to the family are a long neck, sometimes very long; short legs, webbed toes, and a bill covered with sensitive skin and provided inside with comblike structures known as lamellae, modified in the mergansers to sharp "teeth" for holding slippery fish.

The eggs are without markings, and the young, hatched covered with down, are able to find their own food very soon after they emerge from the egg.

The graceful, snow-white swans, sometimes five feet in length, make up the first of seven subfamilies into which are divided the North American members of the suborder. The other six are the geese, treeducks, surface-feeding ducks, diving ducks, stiff-tailed ducks, and mergansers.

Much that has been written about swans has been influenced by their æsthetic appeal.

This is apt to distort the facts to their advantage, and it is just as well, because no other birds can provide the thrill that a flock of wild swans gives the nature lover.

First in order and in size, they have a form too universally known to require description. The two North American species are so similar that they can be differentiated with certainty only by the character of their internal structure and by their very distinct voices.

SWANS ARE MODELS OF BEAUTY AND FIDELITY

Swans are perfect models of conjugal conduct. They mate for life and the sexes share the domestic responsibilities.

The downy young when first hatched are not the "ugly ducklings" of popular belief, but lovely little creatures, clothed in silky, golden down and without the exaggerated neck and huge paddlelike feet of their parents. Very soon, however, these characteristics begin to appear and ungainliness replaces their natal loveliness until the grace and beauty of maturity appear.

Fortunately, there is small if any possibility of the extermination of the whistling swan, and with careful conservation it may even be possible to perpetuate the trumpeter.

The goose family is well represented in North America, especially in the West, where in some localities six species may be seen on the same ground.

Their extraordinary migrations and the mystery of their breeding grounds intensify the interest that both sportsmen and naturalists take in these fine birds. Even yet, there are a few whose summer homes are unknown, while the systematic status of some of the races and their relation to each other have still to be worked out. Much study in the field, especially at their nesting grounds, is required to establish these facts.

Geese, like swans, pair for life, and the young birds remain in the company of their parents for nearly a year after they are hatched.

Endowed with keen intelligence and extreme wariness, they can be depended on to maintain a fair degree of abundance as long as adequate wintering grounds are afforded them. But, above all, they, like swans, require freedom from molestation when they are at rest, so that a large measure of solitude and wide spaces are the chief requirements for their perpetuation.

Both groups have a lower rate of reproduction than ducks, as they require several years to attain maturity and the number of eggs laid is much smaller than with most species of ducks.

Whether by day or night, geese do a lot of calling while in flight; when migrating high overhead the clamor of their voices falling from the sky draws attention to the flock in arrowhead formation, cleaving the upper air. Species can be identified by their different voices. When feeding they are silent, only gabbling a little to each other in low tones. The first appearance of danger will bring a warning challenge from the sentinel and every head is erected while the danger is scrutinized.

GEESE AND SWANS ARE LONG LIVED

Both geese and swans are noted for their longevity, the latter being among the Methuselahs of the bird world.

There is actual record of a mute swan that lived 70 years, while rather uncertain report has attributed even a greater age to the birds.

Somewhat intermediate between ducks and geese are the tree-ducks. They have only two representatives north of the Mexico-United States boundary, and neither of these penetrates much to the north of this line. Their name is misleading in our own territory, as here we seldom see them perching in trees and their nests are on the ground.

The great group of ducks is divided into two main sections, the surface-feeding and diving ducks. While these names actually afford a general basis of distinction, it does not follow that surface-feeders never dive for their food, nor that diving ducks never feed on the surface.

To separate the groups, look at the foot. In the diving ducks, the hind toe has a lobe, so that it resembles a little paddle. In the surface-feeding group it is not particularly specialized (see page 90).

If sportsmen wish to identify the ducks they shoot in all plumages, it is essential that they recognize the distinction between the two groups.

THE "HIND-TOE" FORMULA

By the "hind-toe" formula, stiff-tailed ducks fall under the category of diving ducks, but in many features of structure, plumage, and life characters they are further removed from true ducks than are the mergansers. The sometimes pugnacious and somewhat ludicrous-appearing ruddy duck is the sole representative of the stiff-tailed ducks in the United States and Canada, although a South American species, the masked duck, has been twice recorded in the Eastern States as a straggler.

Mergansers, the last of the duck group, are ducks with a narrow, specialized bill edged with saw teeth which enable them to catch and devour good-sized fish. Their feet, though proportionately smaller, resemble those of the diving ducks in having a paddle-shaped hind toe.

Ducks, for the most part, are very different from swans and geese in their family habits. While they pair much like other birds and are not as a rule polygamous or polyandrous, the male in most species is not a constant husband, and abandons the female and all family cares as soon as incubation of the eggs is well under way. Stiff-tailed ducks are notable exceptions to this rule, and in some true ducks, like the eiders, the male is not altogether indifferent to his family obligations.

Few ducks have striking voices. They are entirely different in the sexes, that of the male being often more musical than that of the female, which varies from a quack to a croak in most of the species. Only one or two species may be called loquacious, the most notable being the old-squaw, which derives this name and many others from the syllabication of the musical call of the males, whose morning concert is one of the cheeriest sounds of the seashore.

The sexual difference in the voices has its origin in the very different patterns in the formation of the trachea. In some species this organ has a curious and elaborate sound box formed by an abrupt enlargement above the bronchial tubes in the male. There is a large variation of this character in different species.

The plumage of ducks is notable in the peculiar formation of some of their characteristic markings; many of these are repeated in several species, often in widely different genera. The white mark in front of the eye of the blue-winged teal is repeated in the harlequin and in both species of golden-eyes.

The transverse bands of black and white on the sides of the breast may be seen in the wood duck, green-winged teal, hooded merganser, and male harlequin. Indeed, the harlequin may be said to possess all the bizarre markings peculiar to the duck tribe on his own small body, including the white spot between the thighs and the base of the tail, which is found in one form or another in so many species.

A feature of these adornments is that the white feathers composing them are specialized, usually of a texture different from the surrounding plumage.

THE DUCK'S "BEAUTY SPOT"

The speculum, or beauty spot, formed by the iridescent color of the secondary feathers of the wing, is a conspicuous feature of most surface-feeding ducks, although absent from nearly all the diving ducks, except the eiders and the male harlequin, and here again the harlequin shows up!

Towards midsummer the bright plumage of the drakes is gradually shed and replaced for two months or longer by a more somber feathering resembling that of the females. This phenomenon, known as the "eclipse," in the fullest expression is peculiar to the ducks, and is generally regarded as being a measure of protection while the bird is shedding his flight feathers, all of which are lost at the same time. While thus rendered flightless, the accompanying dull-colored plumage will enable him to hide from his enemies more easily as he skulks in the rushes.

But this theory falls down when it is realized that only in the ducks of the Northern Hemisphere does this eclipse occur. In the Southern, even when climatic conditions are similar to those in the far north, no eclipse occurs in any species. The extreme example of this is the cinnamon teal, whose range is divided into a northern and southern "colony," one in North and one in South America.

In the north, a regular eclipse occurs when the male assumes a dress somewhat similar to the female's for several months.

In the southern colony, extending south to Patagonia, no change takes place, and the male has only one molt in the year instead of two.

Strangest of all, ducks from the Southern Hemisphere when brought in captivity to our northern zoos do, in some species, after the lapse of a few years, commence to evolve an eclipse similar to that of their northern brethren.

This I have witnessed myself in the case of the Australian red-breasted teal kept in the zoölogical gardens in London.

In some northern ducks there is little or no eclipse. It is absent in all the scoters and only slightly in evidence in the canvasback, while in the case of the old-squaw the eclipse takes place in May prior to the northward migration, and this summer plumage is almost as handsome as the winter dress.

The ruddy duck is distinguished from all our other ducks by possessing an ordinary sequence of spring and winter plumages similar to the plovers and sandpipers and so many small birds.

As the subfamily to which the ruddy belongs, that of the stiff-tailed ducks, is regarded as a "primitive" type, it is possible that the eclipse is evolved from a similar condition. In other words, the eclipse may be only a modification of the ordinary fall or winter dress.

A strange phenomenon of the eclipse is the thoroughness of the imitation of the female aspect in most species. Gadwalls and shovellers not only acquire a female plumage but their black bills change to the olive and orange color of the females, while the male of the American merganser, a crestless bird in full plumage, not only acquires the duller colors of the female but also the long crest of reddish feathers.

The character of the eclipse has been dealt with at some length. Comparatively few people are aware of its existence, even though the drakes of our barnyard go through it each year; also, the consequences of its action have a direct bearing. The wood duck is protected over nearly the whole of America, and the striking plumage of the male is fairly well known; yet in the open duck-shooting season, starting in September in many Provinces of Canada, no trace of the well-known plumage of the male exists, all males resembling the dull-colored female.

A great divergence in the arrival of ma-

Photograph by George Shiras, 3d

SURFACE-FEEDING DUCKS "STAND ON THEIR HEADS" FOR THEIR DINNER

To reach the succulent morsels of aquatic life on the bottom, the pintails, despite their long necks, have to "tip up," as do the mallards and black ducks feeding with them in the shallow waters of Currituck Sound, North Carolina (see page 92).

turity exists in the duck tribe. Swans are not fully mature before their fourth year; most geese probably nest in their third year, while ducks of most species usually pair and nest in the spring following their hatching, or before they are a year old. This has a direct influence on the rate of reproduction in each species and should be taken into consideration.

All the surface-feeding ducks nest before they are one year old, although this may not be universal in the case of some species, such as the pintail and the widgeon.

A similar condition exists in most diving ducks, but notable exceptions are golden-eyes, buffle-heads, harlequins, and old-squaws, in which the males do not acquire full plumage until they are nearly two years old. In the eiders and scoters the adult stage is still further delayed.

Mention should be made of the extinct Labrador duck (*Camptorhynchus labradorius*), the last verified record of which was a bird taken in 1875.

The passing of this species is a mystery which cannot be accounted for; even from the earliest days for which we have any record of the bird, it was a scarce species in the limited area of its range on the North Atlantic coast.

Frequenting the shoal water of the shallow bays, it could not have been in much demand for food and few were brought in to the markets. There is no record of its nesting, nor even, with any certainty, of its summer home. Although it was a diving duck, the peculiar shape of its bill suggests that it sifted its food in shallow water.

PROBLEMS OF CONSERVATION

Of all the questions relating to wild fowl, the problem of their perpetuation is the most important. Everyone naturally takes an interest in their conservation and wishes to see an increase in their numbers. But unfortunately there are two divergent schools at work, one that wishes to protect wild fowl from the viewpoint that they provide sport, and the opposite group that insists they be protected vigorously and that all shooting be abolished. Between the two extremes lie all shades of compromise.

For the good of the wild fowl of North America, it is essential that these different views be reconciled, and a concerted course of action that has the support of all parties is unquestionably the goal for which we must strive.

There can be no question that the total abolishment of their pursuit for sport can never be achieved. Equally certain is it that the old days of huge bags and reckless killing are gone forever. Taken as a whole, modern sportsmen are exceedingly tolerant and are obviously eager to support any sound schemes for protection.

While the dire prophecies of the total extermination of the ducks and geese of North America are obviously the product of a distorted outlook, yet action is required to cope with many of the dangers to which they are now subjected.

The basic requirement is a realization of the immense difference in conditions in the West as compared to the East. What must strike the most casual observer familiar with eastern conditions is the fact that in the West almost every puddle of water has ducks on it, and the drier the region the more certain it is that small ponds will be inhabited. Conversely, the westerner on a visit to almost any region in the East is struck by the large areas of untenanted duck marshes and lakes.

Probably the basis of this is the fact that the whole of the West has been a nesting region for ducks and, to a less extent, geese.

Draw a line from the mouth of the Mississippi River due north to the Coronation Gulf on the Arctic coast. Nine tenths of the ducks of North America breed to the west of this line, although many of them may winter entirely to the east of it. This fact should be the basis for all protective work.

While duck shooting is one of the causes for our failing duck supply, it must not be considered to constitute the major cause for remedial action. Duck shooters must realize that the restrictions for smaller bag limits and in the firearms allowed must be made permanent, but it is equally important that the conservationist who wishes to curtail their sport should recognize the value in certain cases of some of the practices he may most strenuously oppose.

The chief enemies of our ducks and geese may be classified under the following heads:

Shooting; predators and natural enemies; parasitic diseases; failure of water supply; duck disease (botulism); destruction by crude oil, chemicals, lead poisoning; destruction on their nesting grounds by climatic conditions.

Of these, shooting in all its forms and abuses has been exhaustively dealt with, and this has a tendency to minimize the danger incurred from the other factors.

Predators and natural enemies include a number of foes not usually considered as such, and the damage is mainly confined to the nesting season. The enormous increase of the crow in the West is a danger that cannot be overestimated, and this increase is a comparatively recent condition, as is the tremendous increase of range of the coyote during the present century. The last constitutes a serious menace to some of our largest and finest species, such as the trumpeter swan and whooping crane.

MANY OF THE WILD FOWL ARE BEING BRED IN CAPTIVITY

W. L. McAtee, Senior Biologist, Bureau of Biological Survey, states that nearly 50 species of the ducks, geese, and swans of North America have been bred in captivity, most of them, however, upon only a small scale. About 20 species have been bred rather frequently either in this country or abroad, and one, the common mallard duck, can be propagated as readily as, if not more readily than, the ring-necked pheasant, of the group of upland game birds.

Approximately 50,000 wild ducks and 5,000 wild geese constitute the present annual production. Some of these birds are bred by individual or organized sportsmen for their own use, some by fanciers because of their interest in the birds, and others by breeders for sale. The market for two species, the mallard duck and the Canada goose, demands birds for use in restocking, for decoys, and for food.

Species other than the mallard and the Canada goose are produced only in small numbers and are sold to propagators and collectors of ornamental birds and to zoölogical gardens. The demand for all the species exceeds the supply, and for all but the two commonly bred kinds is sure to absorb all that are likely to be produced for a long time to come.*

* See "Propagation of Aquatic Game Birds," by W. L. McAtee, Farmers Bulletin No. 1612, U. S. Department of Agriculture.

Trumpeter Swan

(Cygnus buccinator)

Average Length, Sixty-five Inches

This, one of the largest living native birds of North America, presents a problem for its perpetuation that requires all the intelligence and effort that conservationists can concentrate on it.

The trumpeter is only slightly larger than the whistling swan and the main distinction is the voice. That of the trumpeter has a hornlike quality, very low in key—it might almost be called a groan at times—but possesses an extraordinary resonance. When a flock is passing overhead, the calls do not seem to be particularly loud, but long after, from miles away, the low groaning trumpet comes back, clear and insistent. I do not think the clear whistling shout of the whistling swan will carry half the distance.

I greatly doubt the stories of the former abundance of the trumpeter. Many of these, as well as some of the records of its recent capture, are based on the old diagnosis for distinguishing the two species.

Formerly all adult swans that did not show a yellow mark on the bill were called trumpeters. Now we know that many adult whistlers have an all-black bill, and all other distinctions are more or less unreliable, except the different characters of the windpipe and sternum.

Young birds of the trumpeter also have a lot of yellow on the feet. This is never present in young whistlers.

But the notable distinction and the only infallible one in life identification is the voice, and unfortunately swans have a habit of silence when on the water.

The ranges of the two species are very different. Simply put, the whistler summers as far north as he can and winters far south, while the trumpeter breeds as far south as he can find the necessary solitude and winters precariously as far north as he can find open fresh water.

Formerly the trumpeter nested far to the south of its present breeding range wherever the necessary degree of solitude was available, but the traditions of the Indians do not tell of anything but widely scattered pairs, never of the abundance of the whistler, even in the winter months.

Outside of a few pairs in Yellowstone National Park, the main stronghold of the trumpeter now is in northern British Columbia. Possibly 500 birds are scattered through that rugged region in the summer. Concentrations of more than 200 birds have been counted recently in places where unfrozen water was available in the interior, and we know that there were several other points in the country where smaller numbers were present.

Contrary to general belief, these birds are not molested by man except in rare instances, and even in early days few were shot, although the young birds are excellent eating.

The great danger lies in their enemies on the nesting grounds. Eagles and ravens were probably their chief menace at one time, but now the increased range of the coyote, which has invaded parts of the country which formerly offered them haven as their most inviolate sanctuaries, spells nothing but complete disaster unless some remedial action can miraculously save them.

The old estimates of the great weight of a trumpeter swan are probably all exaggeration. Thirty pounds is probably a fair maximum for a large bird.

Whistling Swan

(Cygnus columbianus)

Average Length, Fifty-five Inches

Whenever I think of swans, one experience stands out. I am standing by the shore of a lake in northern Alberta on a still, dark night in late October, with the black dome overhead spangled with stars and a keen touch of frost in the air.

Suddenly comes the clear call of a whistling swan, another, and another, closer and closer, until right overhead there is, I know, a long wedge of birds cleaving their way southward. The thin, whispering whistles of the young form a background for the staccato shouts of the old birds.

Now they have passed, but already from the north I can hear the approach of another flock, and when this in turn has gone, another is heralded by the same magnificent chorus.

Flock succeeds flock. Sometimes the cries seem so near that I strain my eyes upward, expecting to see the stars blotted out, but they must be very high, for not even a whisper of the magnificent pinions is to be heard.

Half the swans of the Arctic are on the way, and I am right in their track. I realize that all the thousands of swans that I have seen feeding and at rest in the last two weeks are only a fraction of the host that is traveling overhead.

We never need to worry about the whistling swans; even if the present protection were removed, they would be well able to take care of themselves. They are a hardy, prolific species admirably equipped to survive changing conditions.

The spread of the coyote to the Arctic coast will mean a considerable destruction of their young, but they will always be able to find nesting sites and conditions that will enable them to combat this menace.

Breeding almost entirely north of the Arctic Circle, these swans winter well to the south. Chesapeake Bay and Currituck Sound on the Atlantic and the Sacramento Valley in California are especially favored winter resorts.

A VANISHING AMERICAN IS THE GREAT WHITE TRUMPETER SWAN

Over lonely lake and mountain in northern British Columbia ring the low-keyed, far-carrying calls of this majestic five-foot bird (in flight), one of the continent's largest waterfowl. A few pairs survive also in Yellowstone National Park. Not man, but the marauding coyote on the nesting grounds threatens to send the trumpeter the way of the great auk and the passenger pigeon. Slightly smaller, but far more numerous, are the **Whistling Swans** (full-grown in foreground, young in water). From Arctic to Gulf they fly. Long wedges often cleave the upper air high above the earth.

Wood Duck
(Aix sponsa)
Average Length, Eighteen and One-half Inches

No other duck has such an æsthetic appeal as the wood duck. The plumage of the male is usually described as "gorgeous," but this does not do justice to its combination of delicate vermiculations and bold slashes of white against a rich, dark background. It is essentially and wholly an American duck, with no relatives save the still more strikingly garbed mandarin duck of Asia.

It is dispersed throughout the southern Canadian Provinces and all of the United States south into Mexico wherever the combination of water, woods, and hollow trees affords it a home.

A long period of protection throughout the United States and Canada has brought about a fine recovery from its former precarious state, and it is now a common bird wherever conditions are favorable. The essential requisite is a supply of hollow trees for nests.

In the valley of the lower Fraser River, flocks of a thousand birds or more have been seen in recent years, and I shall never forget a residence during the winter months at a point in the interior of California where winding sloughs bordered by oaks and willows afforded it both shelter and food.

I knew that the wood duck was a loquacious bird for a duck, but had not expected anything like the chorus of squeals and clucks that reached me through my open window all night long! The birds were attracted by the acorns, many of them two inches long, with one end of exceeding sharpness, that were dropping into the water from the overhanging boughs. These were swallowed whole, the most indigestible food imaginable.

In this same locality, Mr. Joseph Dixon made careful investigation of how the young reached the water from their hollow-tree nests. No evidence of their being carried or assisted by the mother was observed. They simply planed down by themselves, tiny wings and feet extended, in response to the call of the mother from the nearest water. The movement was so rapid that the camera could record only a little meteor-like blur.

Wood ducks in flight look somewhat like baldpates, the size and white lower surface being similar. The distinctive marks are the dark breast, wings, and tail, the latter being large for a duck, and, above all, the downturned bill, not pointed forward as in a baldpate.

Black-bellied Tree-duck
(Dendrocygna autumnalis autumnalis)
Average Length, Twenty-two Inches

The only region within the United States where this duck may be found is the coastal strip of the Gulf of Mexico, from Corpus Christi southward. It is more common in Mexico and has occurred as a straggler in Arizona and California.

The black-bellied tree-duck is arboreal in its habits, perching freely, and its nest is always in the hollow of a tree.

There is a conspicuous white patch on the forward portion of the wing above, but the wing shows all black from below in flight.

Fulvous Tree-duck
(Dendrocygna bicolor helva)
Average Length, Twenty and One-half Inches

Tree-ducks, usually known to gunners as "fiddler ducks," are long-legged and broad-winged, with an erect carriage when standing. The flight is unducklike, and their ample wings, dark both above and below in the present species, are moved slowly while their long legs trail behind.

The fulvous tree-duck possesses the most extraordinary range of all species of bird, being found in five widely separated "colonies": India, eastern Africa, including Madagascar, southeastern South America, northern South America, and northern Mexico to California and southeastern Texas.

In the last area, it is fairly common in the San Joaquin Valley, arriving early in April. The majority leave for the south before the duck-shooting season opens, in October. Stragglers have occurred as far north as British Columbia.

A medium-sized duck with rather goose-like habits, the fulvous tree-duck is notable for the enormous numbers of eggs to be found in one of their nests—thirty or more, probably the product of several females. In California the nests are always on the ground, but in their more southern colonies the birds nest in hollow trees at times.

Tree-ducks are of a retiring disposition and very nocturnal in their feeding. Often the only evidence of their presence is the whispering whistle of their cry as they pass overhead in the darkness.

Bahama Duck
(Dafila bahamensis bahamensis)
Average Length, Eighteen Inches

Sometimes known as the "Bahama pintail," this duck owes its inclusion in our list to casual records in Florida and Wisconsin. It should occur more frequently, since it is common on the near-by islands that give it its name, as well as in most places in the West Indian region.

The sexes are similar, and it gives the impression of sleekness and elegance, a graceful mover both on land and water. The tail has not the long central feathers of the pintail, but looks as if it had been whittled to a point from a piece of soft pine.

A MASTERPIECE OF NATURE IS THE WOOD DUCK'S GORGEOUS SUMMER COAT

He clings to the dead branch just below his less showy spouse, while another pair flies above them. True to their name, they often wander into the woods, far from water, to eat insects or swallow acorns whole. Their nest is in a hollow tree, or even in a farmer's hayloft, and their numbers are increasing, thanks to protection. From the South come the long-legged and broad-winged **Black-bellied Tree-duck** (extreme right); and the **Fulvous Tree-duck** (left and flying above). The sleek and elegant **Bahama Duck** (lower center) occasionally reaches American shores.

Baldpate

(Mareca americana)

Average Length, Nineteen Inches

The baldpate, or American widgeon, breeds from northern California to the Arctic, but mainly in the West. On its winter migration it has been taken as far south as Panama.

This is one of the commonest of California ducks, and it is hard to realize that the sun-baked birds of the San Joaquin or Imperial Valleys are the same species that are found wintering under severe conditions more than a thousand miles farther north.

There is something distinctive about bald-pates—their graceful action on the water, their sitting lightly with tails held high, pivoting about as they peck daintily from the surface; their way of trotting about like pigeons on the turf, where they graze like little geese; or the splendid evolutions of their flight, when the birds are so closely bunched that there seems hardly room for the long, pointed wings to function.

Yet they wheel and turn in massed formation like sandpipers. Above all rings the sweeping challenge of the male's musical whistle. On the other hand, the female's note is one of the harshest of all duck sounds—a loud, rasping, rattling croak.

At one time, through market hunting and spring shooting, the baldpate became so reduced in numbers that its future was jeopardized. The protection extended to it and its kind by the Migratory Bird Treaty has restored its numbers, so it is again fairly numerous in most of its former haunts.

When it is disturbed in ponds near the coast it has learned to find safety on the ocean. It has become one of the wariest of ducks and, like the black duck, has, in many localities, become a night feeder, devoting the hours of daylight to safeguarding its life by incessant watchfulness.

Like most other ducks, the baldpate is fond of wild celery, but since its skill as a diver is small, it essays the role of highwayman, and when the canvasback or redhead appears on the surface with a bill full of the coveted grass, the fruit of honest toil, it snatches the booty.

European Widgeon

(Mareca penelope)

Average Length, Nineteen Inches

The Old World widgeon is easily distinguished from the baldpate, when the adult males are compared, the red head and gray body of the former being very distinctive.

Young birds and females are more alike, those of the European species being redder and with the axillars, the long, pointed feathers beneath the wing at its base, strongly freckled with gray and not white, or only slightly marked, as in the American species. The European widgeon is turning up more and more frequently, especially on the Atlantic coast, where at some points it is more common than the baldpate.

It breeds in Greenland, Iceland, and Scotland east to Kamchatka Peninsula, and winters in the regions south to southern Asia and northern Africa.

Gadwall

(Chaulelasmus streperus)

Average Length, Nineteen and One-half Inches

The gadwall has probably the widest range of all species of duck, being absent only from South America and Australasia. It is curiously irregular in its distribution, being entirely absent from some localities and abundant in others.

Because of its subdued coloration, it is often overlooked where it is scarce, or is confused with other species. It can be told by its yellow feet, this and the wood duck being the only medium or large-sized surface-feeding ducks with this characteristic.

On the wing, gadwalls look much like mallards, showing the same white underwing, but in adult birds the under surface of the body shows white like that of a baldpate.

Their nesting range is rather southerly, few going farther north than the southern portion of the Canadian Provinces. This brings them under the domination of the predatory crow, so that at times a very small proportion of their eggs produce flying birds.

Once I saw a gadwall which had lost her first nest select a strange site for her second effort. The eggs were laid in an old crow's nest in a small tree, where they shared the same fate as the preceding ones.

Though seemingly as well fitted for the struggle for existence as any of its fellows, the gadwall apparently was never very abundant in any part of its range. Formerly it was not uncommon in New England and in the middle and eastern States, but it is now practically unknown to the sportsmen of the Atlantic seacoast, though still found in considerable numbers in Texas, and other western States. The gadwall is seldom seen in large flocks, but usually singly or by twos or threes in company with ducks of other species.

It is a denizen of fresh water and is fond of shallow lakes and ponds, where its habits somewhat resemble those of the mallard. It is a good diver when the need arises, but usually finds little occasion for the exercise of its skill, since it frequents the shallow margins of ponds and lakes in company with mallards and other species.

The gadwall may be seen often standing on its head in shallow water grubbing for food on the muddy bottom, when only its feet and the tip of its tail stick out. Its bill of fare includes aquatic grasses, seeds, nuts, insects, mollusks—in short, almost any edible substance it can obtain.

WITH ITS "POLICE WHISTLE" THE BALDPATE OFTEN GIVES THE ALARM

Stealing food brought up by better divers is another trait of the **Baldpate,** or American widgeon, mainly found in the West (foreground, male, female; upper left flying). The **European Widgeon** (in water) frequently visits the New World's eastern shore. Above, a swift-winged mother **Gadwall** is about to land just ahead of her spouse and a daughter (upper right).

American Pintail

(Dafila acuta tzitzihoa)

Average Length, Male, Twenty-eight Inches;
Female, Twenty-two Inches

The pintail, or "sprig," as it is known in California, is a far more common duck in western than in eastern North America. In the West it may be found nesting from Nebraska and California to the Arctic. In winter it migrates as far south as the West Indies and Central America.

The return of spring on the northern prairies is heralded by the musical whistle of the pintail as soon as the first sign of open water appears. The long flying lines of these graceful ducks, the snowy necks and breasts of the drakes, clear-cut against the blue sky—what a thrill this brings after the long months of the white silence of winter!

On the wing the pintail looks like a large duck—as large as a mallard; this fact is due to the long neck and wings. Actually it will weigh but little more than a baldpate or gadwall in good condition, about two and a half pounds.

It is swift of wing, and an old pintail coming downwind will tax the nerve and skill of the most experienced sportsman. In California an observer once witnessed a life and death race between an adult male pintail and a prairie falcon. The duck covered a half mile at its topmost speed, but notwithstanding its swiftness, the falcon outmatched it, and would have dined on duck that October day had not the fowl, apparently realizing the extremity of its danger, swerved in a half circle toward the interested spectator, when the falcon, too distrustful of man to follow, gave up the chase in disgust.

Nelson states that in Alaska in August the pintail fattens on berries and becomes the most delicious waterfowl of the region.

The pintail is one of the few ducks that brave the long 2,000-mile trip from the Aleutians to the Hawaiian group to winter.

Green-winged Teal

(Nettion carolinense)

Average Length, Fourteen and One-half Inches

This, the smallest of our ducks, may be found in summer from about the limit of trees in the Arctic south to New Mexico and California at higher elevations. On the coast of British Columbia it may be found throughout the winter, but in the interior the rigor of the winter usually sends it south before January. The southern limit of its winter migration is in southern Mexico and the West Indies.

Green-wings are usually rated as the last word in gastronomic delicacies, but this is not the case where they have access to the salmon-filled rivers of the Northwest. It is an extraordinary sight to see these lovely little birds in such surroundings. They scuttle over the rocks and gravel, shoveling up the masses of maggots in the rotting fish or working the shallow riffles for salmon eggs.

It is well to know what ducks may be classed as safe to eat when the salmon are running.

I have never found any of the following species indulging in this accessible but disgusting source of supply: pintail, baldpate, blue-winged and cinnamon teal, shoveller, and wood duck. All other ducks should be avoided under such conditions, but the taint can usually be easily detected in birds that have been indulging in this diet. Ruffle the breast feathers and the putrid smell is evident.

The green-wing has managed to hold its numbers remarkably well considering the ease with which it may be decoyed. The green-wing does not frequent large lakes and open water, but shows a marked preference for fresh-water marshes and grass-fringed ditches. It is remarkable in how small a waterway a flock will hide and if undisturbed feed contentedly for hours.

Few ducks decoy better, and when a number of the flock are stretched on the water, the survivors will once and again return to their comrades as if totally unable to grasp the situation or to realize the necessity of saving their own lives by flight. This teal is not much of a diver, for it usually feeds in shallows.

Of all ducks the newly hatched young of the green-wing are the most beautiful. The tiny balls of silky, olive-brown fluff marked with golden yellow are a delight to the eye, and the little mother with her brood of perhaps ten midgets, tightly massed and swimming close to her tail, is never to be forgotten.

The nest also is a pretty thing, usually at some distance from the water, tucked away at the base of a small bush or bunch of flowers, the olive-cream eggs concealed by a blanket of dusky down.

The spring note of the male is very like that of the pintail, but in a higher key—a soft, broken little whistle often repeated.

European Teal

(Nettion crecca)

Average Length, Fourteen and One-half Inches

This, the Old World representative of our green-wing, has occurred casually and frequently along the Atlantic coast from Greenland to North Carolina.

No doubt it occurs on the Pacific, since it breeds on the Aleutian Islands, but it may be easily overlooked because of its close resemblance to the related species. The females are indistinguishable from those of the green-wing. In the male the white crescent in front of the wing is replaced by a longitudinal line of white bordered by black on each side of the back.

MANY A SPORTSMAN FIRES IN VAIN AT THE "GREYHOUNDS OF WATERFOWL"

A brace of the long-necked, stream-lined **Pintails** racing downwind makes but a fleeting target (female and male at right and flying). The bantam resting on one leg, with his mate about to alight, is a **Green-winged Teal,** smallest of North American ducks and remarkably quick at leaping into the air. The **European Teal,** swimming, nests in the Aleutian Islands.

WILD GEESE LOOK AROUND FOR DANGER BETWEEN BITES AND EVEN POST REGULAR SENTINELS

Biggest is the handsome **Canada Goose** (second from the right) whose honking, V-shaped columns etch the sky in spring and fall. Vest-pocket editions abundant in the West are the two **Cackling Geese** (at the left) and the **Lesser Canada Goose** (center). The small **Hutchins's Goose** (extreme right) comes from the eastern Arctic (page 107).

Canada Goose

(Branta canadensis canadensis)

Average Length, Thirty-nine Inches

"Honker" in the West, "gray goose" in the North, and "outarde" in Quebec are only a few of the names by which this, the largest of our geese, is known.

Breeding from the Yukon across the continent to Labrador and south to Quebec and the northern tier of the Prairie States east of the Rocky Mountains, it extends its breeding range south in the mountains to northern California and Utah.

It may winter as far south as Florida and Mexico, but also as far north as the interior of British Columbia.

The wedge-shaped flocks of wild geese that, spring and fall, with melodious honking, wing their way respectively to their breeding and wintering grounds, are a very familiar sight, and advertise in a most spectacular way that wonderful phenomenon—bird migration. The bird observer of speculative mind may find interest in answering the question—Why do geese usually fly in wedge formation? Is it because the powerful wings of the leader make easier the passage of those behind him, or, as suggested by Forbush, does the wedge formation enable each individual member of the flock to see better?

The "honker" is still far from extinct, and owes its numbers to its wariness and to the fact that it nests chiefly in the unfrequented territory of the far north, where its only enemies are the wild beast and the roving Indian.

Everywhere a very wary bird, except sometimes on its breeding grounds, the honker is well able to take care of itself under the existing laws for its protection.

It is notable among our geese for the variety of its nesting sites. In certain regions it may be found nesting in high cliffs and even trees, although the ordinary sites, such as muskrat houses and islands, may be available.

I have several times seen it nesting in the high tree nests of the osprey, laying its eggs before the return of the ospreys from their winter homes.

When these hawks return, there is a battle royal. It usually ends in a victory for the ospreys, which lay their own eggs alongside those of the geese and proceed to incubate. What happens if the young geese are hatched out first? Unfortunately, no observer has made any record of this. Possibly it has never occurred, but the mixed sets of eggs may be seen in several museums.

I have never talked with old goose shooters without stories of 20-pound geese coming up, but 14 pounds is my own maximum record.

On the northwest coast from Vancouver Island north to Prince William Sound, in Alaska, a dark form of the Canada goose is resident. This, the white-cheeked goose *(Branta canadensis occidentalis)*, has been taken in winter as far south as northern California, but it is always confined to the coastal strip and islands.

It is only very slightly smaller than the typical Canada goose, being merely a dark race induced by the heavy rainfall.

Cackling Goose

(Branta canadensis minima)

Average Length, Twenty-four Inches

The *"canadensis"* in the scientific name should be left out. In my opinion this is a full species, nesting along the coast of northwestern Alaska with its larger relative, the lesser Canada goose. Its winter quarters are the Sacramento and San Joaquin Valleys of California, and it has never been taken away from the Pacific coastal strip.

A small goose, only slightly larger than Hutchins's goose (pages 104, 107), it weighs from three to five pounds when in good condition. It is darker in color than the other members of the Canada goose group. Its note is shriller than that of the lesser Canada goose and in its winter quarters, where it is known as "little brant," it is recognized by its loquacity and its short-necked, long-winged appearance, as well as by its erratic flight.

In spite of its limited range it is an abundant species, though less so some years than others. This is probably due to inclement weather during the nesting season, the penalty incurred by all birds that nest in the Arctic.

Lesser Canada Goose

(Branta canadensis leucopareia)

Average Length, Thirty-five Inches

This goose occupies an enormous range in western North America. Nesting only north of the range of the Canada goose or along the Arctic rim of the continent north of the tree line, it passes far south in the fall, even well into Mexico.

It is a medium-sized goose weighing from four to eight pounds, and ranging from very dark birds to very light, the latter grading into the typical Canada goose, some individuals being hard to place. The dark, short-necked birds with small bills probably come from the western portion of the breeding range, and are known to the Sacramento Valley gunners as "big brant."

Throughout the interior valley of California, it is the most abundant goose, wintering in numbers that seem almost incredible to sportsmen from any other region.

Here it associates with the other geese of the same approximate size, white-fronted, snow, and cackling geese. A "V," or line of geese, may be seen with all four of these mixed up, yet each conforming to the regular formation.

BRANT, SMALLEST OF WILD GEESE, RIDE THE WATER GRACEFULLY LIKE RACING YACHTS

A full-grown **American Brant,** common along the Atlantic coast, swims with one of its young at the right, while others wheel overhead. A **Black Brant,** more abundant in the Pacific, wades ashore. In the Middle Ages men believed geese were hatched from barnacles; hence the name bestowed on the **Barnacle Goose** (poised on one foot), a straggler from the Old World. The **Emperor Goose** (left) lives mainly in the region around the Yukon's mouth.

American Brant
(Branta bernicla hrota)
Average Length, Twenty-six Inches

True brant (or brent in the British Isles) are sea geese and their occurrence away from salt water can be only by accident.

Breeding only in the northern part of the Arctic regions, mainly on the northernmost islands, brant extend on their migrations down both coasts as far as Florida and Baja California. On the Pacific side the American, or white-bellied, brant is scarce, being outnumbered by the black brant. Both birds are small, short-necked, long-winged geese, but slightly larger than a mallard, and the habits of the two are identical.

The recent disappearance of the eelgrass, *Zostera*, on the Atlantic coasts may spell disaster to the brant, since this is their staple diet and their choice of a wintering ground is governed by the supply of this succulent food. Feeding on it, they become extraordinarily fat.

In some winters the brant, like the cackling goose, is notably scarce. Observation will show that the usual family parties of five or six young birds with their parents are absent, and that the flocks are composed of adult birds mainly or entirely. This is the result of a bad nesting season when a continued stretch of rigorous weather in the Arctic has destroyed their nests or possibly even the newly hatched young.

No other ducks or geese can compare with brant in sheer beauty of movement. On the water they sit as lightly as gulls, the tail upraised and the neat little head poised on the graceful neck. Seeking their food, they pick daintily at the water and pivot swiftly to do so. On the wing they are at their best.

Black Brant
(Branta nigricans)
Average Length, Twenty-five and One-half Inches

The black brant breeds on the Arctic coasts of eastern Siberia and of western America, migrating in winter down both coasts of the Pacific to Baja California and Japan.

Except for its darker coloration and the uninterrupted white collar in front, it is a replica of the Atlantic species. Since the white on the tail and flanks is the same, the bird looks almost as white on the water as its eastern confreres. Its voice, habits, and food are identical, and so far it is not menaced by any failure in the supply of eelgrass, although this staple food is certainly not so abundant and luxuriant on the coast of British Columbia as it was 25 years ago.

Nowadays the brant of this region have exhausted the eelgrass supply by the end of January and are forced to a diet of seaweed. They then rapidly lose not only their fine condition but also the delicate flavor of their flesh.

Their method of stowing away the long ribbons of eelgrass is peculiar. It is neatly folded in zigzag fashion as it is swallowed, and an enormous quantity can be packed away by a hungry bird.

Barnacle Goose
(Branta leucopsis)
Average Length, Twenty-six Inches

The barnacle may be called a glorified brant, but in habits it is more nearly akin to other geese, since it comes ashore and grazes on the short grass of coastal pastures instead of seeking its food afloat.

It nests sparingly in northeastern Greenland and more commonly on the larger Arctic islands and coasts of the Old World, occurring only as a straggler on the Atlantic coastline of America.

The barnacle owes its name to the ancient Norse belief that these geese were produced from the marine shellfish of that name.

Emperor Goose
(Philacte canagica)
Average Length, Twenty-six Inches

The emperor goose has a very restricted range—the region of Bering Sea and the Arctic coasts of Alaska and Siberia for a short distance east and west. Stragglers are frequently found on the western coast of America as far south as California and even in Hawaii.

It is essentially a marine goose, feeding for the most part on shellfish exposed at low tide, but resorts to the estuaries of rivers to nest on the swampy tundra of their shores. On account of its diet, the flesh is rank and strong-flavored, but this makes no difference to the Eskimo and other natives, who kill these geese in large numbers and freeze the carcasses for winter food. Their numbers are greatly reduced at present, according to the records of their abundance made fifty years ago by Dr. E. W. Nelson and L. M. Turner.

Hutchins's Goose
(Branta canadensis hutchinsi)
Average Length, Thirty Inches

This diminutive goose, originally described by Sir John Richardson more than a century ago, has been overlooked by more recent ornithologists and only recently reëstablished.

It is only slightly larger than a mallard, and a full-sized bird will weigh but four pounds.

Except for its proportionately smaller bill, it is almost an exact replica of the big Canada goose, but less than half the size (page 104).

It breeds on the Melville Peninsula and some of the Arctic islands to the eastward, and apparently occupies the same ground as its larger relative, the lesser Canada goose. This does not conform to its present rank as a subspecies. Its migration route is imperfectly known, but it has been taken when migrating at the Gulf of St. Lawrence and west regularly to Manitoba and the Mississippi Valley, wintering in northeastern Mexico.

HUNTERS PRIZE THE WHITE-FRONTED GEESE, DROPPING DOWN FROM A CLOUDY SKY

The old bird, descending with one of its offspring, wears a speckled vest and utters a laughing cry. They are closely related to domestic geese. Left to right stand **Ross's Goose**, a little westerner; the **Blue Goose**, which winters in Gulf coast marshes; and the West's **Lesser Snow Goose** (young and adult), perhaps the continent's most abundant goose.

White-fronted Goose
(Anser albifrons albifrons)
Average Length, Twenty-eight and One-half
Inches

Also known as "gray goose," "speckle-belly," and in the Mississippi Valley as "brant," this goose has the widest distribution of all geese, breeding in most of the Arctic and sub-arctic belt of both the Old and New Worlds.

Its southward movement starts very early, taking it to southern British Columbia by the first week in September, long before the arrival of other Arctic-breeding geese. The main wintering grounds are to the west of the mouth of the Mississippi and the interior valley of California. Many also winter in northern Mexico. In the Old World the white-front reaches its southern limit in northern India.

At certain points in the Sacramento Valley in California, a large edition of the white-front occurs in the winter months. This is the tule goose (Anser albifrons gambeli), almost as large as a "honker," but with a darker colora-tion, distinct voice, and rather different habits.

The tule goose when full-grown is not much smaller than a Canada goose and weighs as much as nine pounds, with proportionately larger bill and feet than the white-front.

The mystery of its summer home is as yet unsolved, but the capture of a migrating in-dividual in central British Columbia in the fall of 1933 may afford some clue.

Ross's Goose
(Chen rossi)
Average Length, Twenty-three Inches

The breeding grounds of this tiny goose still remain a mystery. The "warty-nosed wavey," as it is known in the fur countries, arrives at Lake Athabaska from the north in the first week in September, the earliest of the geese. From this general region the flocks all pass through the mountains west of Great Falls, Montana, and fly southward to the west of the Rocky Mountains. They winter entirely in the Sacramento and San Joaquin Valleys of California, where they are known to gunners by the name of "China geese" and now enjoy absolute protection under the game laws.

Blue Goose
(Chen caerulescens)
Average Length, Twenty-eight Inches

The status of the blue goose is almost ex-actly parallel to that of the greater snow goose. Only in recent years have the nesting grounds of their vast hordes been found on Baffin Island. Their southward migration takes them to the Valley of the Mississippi, and they winter in a small area west of its mouth.

Some systematists regard the blue goose as a color phase of the lesser snow goose because its extraordinarily variable plumage is often dappled with varying amounts of white.

Lesser Snow Goose
(Chen hyperborea hyperborea)
Average Length, Twenty-five and One-half Inches

Snow geese are seldom known by that name by the men who hunt them. "Wavey" is the name in the Hudson Bay region and on Cana-dian prairies, and in western and southwestern States they are called "white brant."

This numerous species nests from Point Bar-row, Alaska, east to Baffin Island along the rim of the Arctic coast and adjacent islands. There must also be some nesting ground on the Siberian coast, for large numbers cross Bering Strait in summer to the Asiatic side.

There are three important wintering grounds: the coast of Texas, the northern interior of Mexico, and the Sacramento and San Joaquin Valleys in California. Not that they are confined to these regions; large num-bers can be found all winter at the mouth of the Fraser River in British Columbia and pos-sibly even farther north.

The lesser snow goose probably represents the most abundant goose in North America and the poorest of all gastronomically, the scarce emperor goose excluded.

"They are not bad, made up as sausages," an old hunter of vast experience once said of them, and under special feed conditions they may be excellent; but, as a rule, their flesh is dark and coarse.

Enormous numbers of snow geese are killed each year for food, especially around Hudson Bay, where, preserved for winter consumption, they mean the very existence of some of the tribes.

In California dire predictions of their com-ing extermination have been made for many years past. While unquestionably their num-bers in that State are much reduced from those of early days, it must be remembered that present-day conditions tend to attract geese in enormous flocks to certain areas, and so cause a seeming scarcity in others.

My own experience in this region goes back only to 1911, when I saw thousands of geese between Sacramento and the Bay. Never have I seen a greater concentration of snow geese than I saw in the rice fields near Wil-lows in February, 1933.

Completely restricted in its range to the Atlantic coast is the greater snow goose, Chen hyperborea atlantica. This is merely a large, heavy-billed edition of the smaller bird. Its numbers may be said to be confined to one flock of thousands which appears at Cap Tour-mente, on the St. Lawrence, each year, in Oc-tober, remaining there until weather condi-tions compel withdrawal to more temperate regions along the coasts of Virginia and North Carolina.

Summer homes of this horde are a mystery, only isolated pairs having been seen from east Greenland to Ellesmere Island.

THE GREEN-HEADED, HANDSOME MALLARD IS AT HOME IN MARSHY WILDS

From this glossy-feathered, quacking citizen of the world and his drably dressed womenfolk (left and "single" flying) many varieties of domestic ducks have sprung. Wilder and harder to domesticate is the East's **Black Duck** (extreme right pair, and flying). The **Florida Duck** (third from right) is a bit lighter colored. The **New Mexican Duck** (center, male), of limited range, has only recently been discovered.

Common Mallard

(Anas platyrhynchos platyrhynchos)

Average Length, Twenty-three Inches

Best known of all ducks and the origin of nearly all our domestic breeds, the mallard is found over the greater portion of the world's surface except South America, Australasia, and parts of Africa.

It breeds from the middle row of States south to southern California and north to the Arctic Circle; also over the greater part of northern Asia and Europe. In southern Greenland a slightly differentiated form is resident.

One fine June day I came suddenly on a mallard with her day-old brood in a recently flooded pool of crystal-clear water. At the warning quack of the mother, every little duck dived, and as the surface became still I could see the youngsters dotted over the short turf that formed the bottom of the pool. They were not stretched out, but were sitting on the bottom with heads up, their wide-open, beady eyes regarding me through the limpid water.

After watching them for what seemed to me two minutes, I waded in and touched each little form in turn. Instantly they rose buoyantly to the surface and pattered away to join the anxious mother, making no further effort at concealment. Now, by what magic were they able to remain under two feet of water without effort of any sort?

This fine duck is monopolized by no one country nor even continent, but includes in its range both hemispheres. Its size, abundance, and excellent flavor make it perhaps the most important of its family, and its value to mankind is still further enhanced by the fact that it lends itself so readily to domestication that many of our domestic varieties are derived from it.

Before the settlement of the West the ponds and sloughs swarmed with mallards, which nested there by thousands, and in fall and winter, as migrants and winter residents, covered the watercourses to the south. Today there is a very different story to tell. Many of the mallard's old breeding grounds are now farms, and the bird is represented by a few hundreds where once there were myriads.

The mallard is a most omnivorous duck, and nothing in the way of mast, grain, or small animal life comes amiss. In the Far West it has the habit, shared to the same extent by no other duck, of resorting to the stubble for waste grain.

Black Duck

(Anas rubripes)

Average Length, Twenty-two Inches

This splendid duck, which replaces or outnumbers the mallard over a considerable portion of eastern Canada and the Northeastern States, is confined to eastern North America. It has been divided into two geographical forms, the northern, true *rubripes*, and the southern, *tristis*. It is fortunate that duck shooters maintain that they are able to distinguish the two; naturalists as a rule cannot. The northern subspecies is called the red-legged black duck. But personally I have yet to see a black duck, even the young birds of the southern form, that did not have red legs.

In spite of the somberness of its plumage, the black duck is a magnificent game duck, the peer of the mallard in everything but color, and excelling the mallard in intelligence and wariness.

Probably it is also larger, since black ducks of four pounds and even a trifle more are on record.

Florida Duck

(Anas fulvigula fulvigula)

Average Length, Twenty Inches

This might be called a light-colored black duck, and like that species there is little difference in the sexes. It is confined to the marshes of the Florida peninsula, where it is known to the residents as "native mallard," as distinguished from the true mallard, which leaves the region in summer.

The mottled duck *(Anas fulvigula maculosa)* is a slightly darker form of the Florida duck, with a more spotted head. It has a wider range along the coasts of Louisiana and Texas and south into Mexico.

New Mexican Duck

(Anas diazi novimexicana)

Average Length, Twenty-two Inches

This is a fairly recent discovery among the ducks of the United States, and has been described as a link between the mallard and the mottled ducks.

It can be described as a dark-colored female mallard, both sexes being similar.

Unlike the ducks of the black and Florida group, it has the speculum of the wing bordered on both sides by white, as in the mallard.

Many individuals show decided mallard characters, suggesting interbreeding, but at several points in New Mexico, where I found it not uncommon during the spring and summer months, I never saw the two species associating.

Its range in the United States is confined to an area from southwestern Texas, across New Mexico to southern Arizona. Most of the birds pass south into Mexico before the opening of the shooting season in October and therefore are not actually important as American game birds.

MOTHER EIDER DUCK LINES HER NEST WITH DOWN PLUCKED FROM HER OWN BREAST

In Iceland and parts of Europe man provides nesting sites and in return takes some of the eider down for quilts and coverlets. In the right foreground is a pair of the **American Eider** of the North Atlantic coast with another drake flying above them. Near the North Pole dwells the **King Eider** (left pair in foreground). Garrulous **Old-squaw** ducks dressed for winter swim beyond; three others in summer garb fly above.

American Eider

(Somateria mollissima dresseri)

Average Length, Twenty-three Inches

The American eider, a subspecies of the eider of the Old World, nests from the southern portion of Hudson Bay and Labrador south to the coast of Maine. In winter it is found but little south of its summer range, rarely as far south as Virginia.

Like all other eiders, this is very much of a sea duck and, like the harlequin, it frequents the outer reefs and rocky stretches of storm-beaten coast. The food is almost entirely shellfish and the flesh of all eiders is strong and rank in consequence. They are now protected at all times in the United States and Canada, except on the Arctic coasts.

Eiders are among the best known of ducks, because of the quality and commercialization of their down. On parts of the Canadian coast this is affording a considerable revenue and eventually the "farming" of the birds will be as carefully systematized as it is in Iceland. There the protection of centuries has produced a semi-domesticated condition where the ducks have nesting places made for them, sometimes even inside the homes of the people, who take the first layings and the down.

The spring notes of the male are a musical cooing, but without the resonance of voice that is found in the old-squaw.

One of the largest of ducks, the American eider will weigh five to five and a half pounds.

In Greenland, northern Labrador, and west to the northern Arctic islands, a closely allied subspecies occurs—the northern eider, *Somateria mollissima borealis,* differing mainly in bill characters. This form is found associated with the resident American eiders in winter as far south as Connecticut.

King Eider

(Somateria spectabilis)

Average Length, Twenty-three Inches

Eiders are specialized sea ducks with peculiarities of coloration common to all the species that compose the group. The drakes have black or dark underparts with the back mostly white, and all have more or less "eider green" on the head. The females are handsomely marked and suggest the coloration of some of the larger species of grouse. Both sexes have the tertials, the basal flight feathers of the wing, strongly sickle-shaped. Except for one species, they are all large.

The king eider is of circumpolar distribution, nesting along the Arctic coasts of both hemispheres and wintering for the most part along our northern shores. Of all the eiders it is the one that is most likely to be taken south of its natural range as a straggler, and has turned up as far south as California, Georgia, and some of the Central States, as well as frequently on the Great Lakes.

The keel-like erection on the forehead at the base of the bill in the male is a seasonal adornment, shrinking materially at the close of the breeding season when the drakes go into eclipse, and assuming its fullest expansion only as the nuptial season returns.

This eider is a very large duck, although considerably smaller than the Pacific and American species.

Old-squaw

(Clangula hyemalis)

Average Length, Male, Twenty-one Inches; Female, Sixteen Inches

The old-squaw, or long-tailed duck, is a circumpolar species, being found without variation in the northern portions of both hemispheres. In America it breeds on all the Arctic tundras from Atlantic to Pacific and south along the mountain ranges into extreme northern British Columbia. In winter it can be found at times as far south as California and Florida on the seacoasts and many winter on the Great Lakes.

Here they are caught at times in nets set in deep water for cisco, a species of herring. In 1917 Mr. W. E. Saunders, investigating reports of large numbers being caught and utilized for fertilizer, found at one factory 12 tons of these ducks, estimated at 1,500 birds to the ton.

On the Pacific coast the old-squaw is decreasing each year. Not more than 10 per cent of its former numbers can be found on the waters around Vancouver Island, and no cause, such as the catastrophe of the Great Lakes, is apparent. Since it is never hunted in there by man, the loss must occur at the nesting grounds.

The old-squaw is a vivacious duck, both when swimming and in flight. On the water it carries the tail low; when feeding, often dragging on the surface; but when courting and displaying, holds it almost erect. The male then presents a beautiful appearance. Sitting lightly on the water, with head held high, he utters his musical cry again and again. This cry has been syllabified in nearly all its vernacular names and, as Dr. Phillips puts it, "more ink has been devoted to describing the call of the male than is the case with any other duck."

The call must be heard to be appreciated fully. It has the sweep of a saber in its final inflection and the emphasis on the second syllable is the keynote. Probably its New England name gives the best idea of this—"South-south-southerly." The call is repeated again and again on the wing, and in flight no duck can surpass the old-squaw.

The short neck and long, pointed wings, dark above and below, are the field marks that distinguish it. In flight the bird is impetuous and as erratic as a sandpiper or plover.

ESKIMOS KILL EIDERS WITH CLUBS AND MAKE THE SKINS INTO CAPS

A favorite victim is the **Spectacled Eider** (left pair and "single" flying) when in summer it is molting and cannot fly. The **Pacific Eider**, lazily floating in center, is the largest of North American ducks. In contrast, **Steller's Eider** (right pair) is small, trim, and swift on the wing. All three kinds live in the freezing waters off Alaska and Siberia.

Spectacled Eider
(Arctonetta fischeri)
Average Length, Twenty-one Inches

No bird or mammal better deserves its common name than the spectacled eider, the eyes in the male being surrounded by short, velvety feathers with a black rim around the outer edges of these circular patches. Even in the female these "spectacles" are defined in light-colored patches around the eyes.

A duck with a very restricted range, the spectacled eider breeds along the Arctic coast from Point Barrow westward and down the coast of Bering Sea to the mouth of the Kuskokwim River. Even in winter it is not found much to the south of this region. In Siberia it is found west to the Lena River.

Nelson's observations show this species to be strictly limited to the salt marshes bordering the east coast of Bering Sea, and thus favoring the shallow, muddy coast waters, which appear so distasteful to Steller's eider. The same observer estimates that the spectacled eider does not occupy more than 400 miles of coast line in the breeding season, while the width of the breeding ground will not exceed one or two miles.

Writing as long ago as 1881, Nelson said of the struggle for existence the species was even then undergoing: "The species has to contend against thousands of shotguns in the hands of the natives. The diminution in all the species of waterfowl breeding along the coast is more and more marked each season, and while this may mean a desertion of one region for another in the case of the great majority of geese and ducks, yet for such narrowly limited species as the spectacled eider, and to a less extent the emperor goose, this diminution is but the beginning of extermination; moreover, the present scarcity of large game along the coast is having great effect in causing the natives to wage a continually increasing warfare upon the feathered game."

Pacific Eider
(Somateria v-nigra)
Average Length, Twenty-four Inches

This, the largest of North American ducks, replaces the American eider on the western Arctic coasts of America and the eastern portion of Siberia, also nesting on the Aleutian Islands and the Alaska Peninsula. On account of its range along the Arctic coast, it is very likely to occur in winter in the interior of America and has already been taken twice in Manitoba.

The principal mark of distinction from the eiders of the Atlantic is the conspicuous black V, point foremost, on the white throat of the male, from which it gets its scientific name.

In habits it does not differ from the Atlantic species, but no attempt has been made to commercialize its down product. Large numbers are shot by the Eskimos for food, even in the spring, but it still persists in vast numbers in its Arctic habitat.

A. C. Bent, in his *Life Histories of North American Wild Fowl*, writes: "By the time that we reached the Aleutian Islands, early in June, the vast horde of eiders that winter in the open waters of this region had departed, to return to their extensive breeding grounds farther north. But we found the Pacific eider well distributed, as a breeding bird, on all of the islands west of Unalaska. They were particularly abundant about Kiska Harbor in small flocks and mated pairs. They frequented the rocky beaches at the bases of the cliffs, where they sat on the loose rocks, fed in the kelp beds about them, and built their nests among the large boulders above high-water mark. Here on June 19, 1911, I examined two nests of this species; one, containing 5 fresh eggs, was concealed in a hollow under or between two tufts of tall, rank grass which grew back of a large boulder on the beach at the foot of a high grassy cliff; the other, containing 4 fresh eggs, was hidden in the long grass at the top of a steep grassy slope; both nests were well supplied with down."

I can find no record of its weight, but since it is considerably larger than the Atlantic species, this must be in the neighborhood of six pounds.

Steller's Eider
(Polysticta stelleri)
Average Length, Seventeen Inches

The smallest of the eiders, this species is of the same proportionate size to the larger species that a teal is to a mallard.

In northwestern America Steller's eider nests throughout the same restricted area as the spectacled eider, but is found much farther along the Siberian coast than that species. In winter it is found as far south as the Kurile Islands and eastward to northern Norway. It may even nest in the latter region.

Steller's eider is a trim duck with little of the heavy appearance of other eiders. The shape of the bill suggests that of the extinct Labrador duck. It is a frequenter of rocky shores and seeks its food in deep water, often in company with harlequins and old-squaws.

On the wing it is very swift, as might be guessed from its long wings which whistle like a golden-eye's.

Nelson found these ducks rather numerous in the quiet waters of bays and fiords of the Aleutian Islands the last of May, but they were very shy and he failed to secure a single individual. They winter in such of the Alaskan bays as are free from ice, and at this season the natives who depend upon them for winter food kill great numbers. This eider is a true sea duck and keeps well offshore except in boisterous weather. Its food consists of animal life gleaned from the sea and the bird is a skillful diver, reaching great depths and staying under a long time, as do eiders generally.

UNEASY ACTIONS OF AMERICAN SCOTERS SOMETIMES FORETELL A STORM

Largest of these tough, deep-diving "sea coots" is the **White-winged Scoter** (right pair, and young drake taking off). The **Surf Scoter** (left, female, male, and alighting on water in distance) thrives on shellfish, swallowed whole. In the near background a pair of **American Scoters** swims in characteristic "chin-up" fashion, the lady first; others flash silvery under-wing feathers in flight.

White-winged Scoter

(Melanitta deglandi)

Average Length, Twenty-two Inches

Scoters are sea ducks of large size and dark coloration, the males black and the females dark brown. They are not confined to salt water but require large bodies of deep water for their inland homes. Five species are found throughout the Northern Hemisphere, of which three are North American.

The white-winged scoter is represented in eastern Asia by a closely allied subspecies, the Asiatic velvet scoter, and in Europe by the European velvet scoter *(Melanitta fusca)*; the latter has occurred in Greenland. The white-winged scoter is the commonest of the three American species. It nests from Alaska to Ungava Bay, south to North Dakota and the Gulf of St. Lawrence. In winter it is found in large numbers along both coasts south to South Carolina and Baja California, on the Great Lakes and many inland bodies of water.

On the Atlantic coast the "white-winged coot" is hunted to some extent, but on the Pacific it is rightly regarded as unfit for food.

I have frequently seen these birds in the line of their flight from the Puget Sound region to the valley of the Mackenzie River. Often they will rest at some deep water lake en route, flock after flock pouring in from high in the air until thousands are bedded down, every bird with its bill buried in the feathers of the back and actually fast asleep. They never feed under such conditions, but continue their flight a day or two later.

Flocks get up separately, usually just after sunset, and pass and repass in all directions until at last, having acquired the requisite altitude, they all move off to the northeast in wavering lines high over the mountain tops.

The males return by the same route in small flocks often as early as the first week in July, the females and young following about three months later.

White-wings are the largest of the scoters. A big male will weigh as much as four and three-quarters pounds, the females a pound less.

Surf Scoter

(Melanitta perspicillata)

Average Length, Twenty Inches

The surf scoter is somewhat smaller than preceding species. Its range is almost exactly the same as that of the white-winged scoter, the nesting range not quite so far south—extreme northern British Columbia, the northern section of the Prairie Provinces to James Bay and the Gulf of St. Lawrence.

It is outnumbered by its larger congener in all its winter resorts and is rather scarce in the interior lakes.

In actions and habits it is little different from the white-wing. Its most striking char-acteristic is the deep whistling of the wings, which is made only when the bird is rising and again for a few strokes before it alights.

Surf scoters of all ages can be distinguished from all other ducks in life by their action when alighting. As the bird touches the water, the wings are extended upward and held so, as the body plows through the water to a standstill.

The eclipse present in nearly all northern ducks is absent in all the scoters. In the surf scoter the white patch on the nape of the neck is deciduous and falls out, leaving a smooth, black-feathered surface during the late summer months.

The surf scoter can be called a large duck, males weighing as much as three pounds. Females, however, weigh only about two pounds.

American Scoter

(Oidemia americana)

Average Length, Nineteen Inches

The range of this scoter is very northern in the breeding season, when it is found from eastern Siberia along the Arctic coast of America to Newfoundland. In winter it is found on both coasts and the Great Lakes.

My own experience with the American scoter is limited to the Pacific portion of its range, where I have found it to be absolutely and exclusively maritime, all the so-called records of the species from inland localities proving to be merely reports of all-black specimens of the surf scoter.

In life the American scoter is an utterly different duck from the other two species. Like the harlequin, it loves the exposed rocky points and beaches, rarely seeking shelter even in exceptional weather. Also, like the harlequin, it is an active, restless duck, much given to rambling flights. In fine weather the males, often four or five to each female, pursue and surround the latter like a bodyguard. These flights are more common in fine, calm weather, when numbers of little parties may be seen turning and twisting in the air, to return eventually to the starting point. The call of the male is musical, with a mournful and haunting cadence.

Much has been written as to how to distinguish the scoters in life by the character of the white markings, but to anyone who knows the American scoter it stands out from the others by the carriage of the head when on the water. This is held high, as a rule, the bill always either horizontal or tipped up, never deflected downward, as in the surf and white-winged scoters. On the wing the American scoter has a much finer flight, the underside of the flight feathers showing silvery in both sexes.

The American scoter is a large, heavy duck, males weighing three pounds or even more, the female about two and a half.

THE MERGANSER'S BILL IS EDGED WITH SAWTEETH SO THE BIG ONES WON'T GET AWAY

Even during a New England winter "sawbills" may be seen, swimming and diving for fish in the cold open stretches of a rapid stream. Rivers and other inland waters are frequented by the **American Merganser** (left foreground, drake and hen). The beautiful **Hooded Merganser**, on the dead limb with his mate, likes small ponds. Both seacoasts and inland waters are visited by **Red-breasted Mergansers**, pair swimming and drake in swift flight.

American Merganser

(Mergus merganser americanus)
Average Length, Twenty-five Inches

This is the largest of the mergansers, or "sawbills," and it has a wide distribution in North America, from Alaska to Newfoundland in summer, and south in the mountains to California and New Mexico in winter, whenever open water and suitable food conditions are to be found.

A line of these handsome birds resting at the water's edge along some gravel bar is a beautiful sight. The sun reflected from the water on the deep cream of their breasts makes them glow like gold, showing off the coral red of their feet.

Just how much damage they may do to game fish is dependent on local conditions; where coarse fish abound, they do not bother trout much, and where bullheads are plentiful on the spawning beds of trout and salmon, the merganser is a positive benefit. But where trout and small salmon are the principal fish inhabiting a stream, the presence of sawbills is disastrous, their voracity meaning the destruction of many fry and larger fish.

The American merganser usually nests in hollow trees, but where these are not available the nest may be under rocks or in cliffs. A pretty sight that I once saw was the spectacle of two females sitting on nests in clefts on opposite sides of a cave, their white chins showing above a mass of white down. The following season they were absent, for one of the clefts was occupied by a horned owl with one large youngster.

The American merganser is a very large-sized duck. The male will weigh four pounds, the female about half a pound less.

Hooded Merganser

(Lophodytes cucullatus)
Average Length, Seventeen and One-half Inches

This is another duck peculiar to North America, although, like some others, it has occurred as a straggler in Europe. The hooded merganser's range is rather southerly, and it nests in nearly all the States that provide it with the necessary hollow trees, north to northern British Columbia and the wooded portions of the Prairie Provinces, while in the East it does not nest north of southern Ontario and New Brunswick. In winter it may be found as far south as Mexico and north to southern British Columbia.

Its range and requirements very closely parallel those of the wood duck, and, like that species, it loves the wooded ponds and winding, slow-running streams in preference to large bodies of water. Its safety must suffer from such an environment and its numbers certainly do show a decrease, but how much this is due to the clearing away of the timber along the streams it loves and to the decrease in nesting facilities it is hard to say. Certainly it is able to take care of itself under the most dangerous conditions, and very few adult birds, especially males, are shot.

The nest is in a hollow tree, usually very close to water, and the eggs are unique among those of American ducks, being very round, of an ivory-white color, with the shell very thick. The downy young are unique.

The beautiful flattened crest of the male hooded merganser is rarely displayed in all its beauty. When the bird is feeding it is folded down, and in flight there is never the slightest indication of it, the head being held straight out like a slender stick, while the small wings move with great rapidity, giving an appearance of speed even in excess of the really rapid rate achieved.

There is little difference in the size of the sexes. The weight is about one pound.

Red-breasted Merganser

(Mergus serrator)
Average Length, Twenty-two Inches

The red-breasted merganser has a more northern range than the other two sawbills, and it may be called an Arctic species, in summer breeding along the northern rim of both the Old and New Worlds and south in America to Michigan and Maine. I have never seen it nesting in southern British Columbia, many of the so-called "records" being the result of misidentification, but on the Queen Charlotte Islands and northward along the coast it gradually replaces the American merganser. In winter it reaches the southernmost States and Mexico.

The red-breasted merganser is much more maritime than the larger species and at the proper season attends the spawning of the herring schools as its chief object in life. As soon as the wireless of the sea fowl tells of the spawning in some bay, all the mergansers are headed for that locality until thousands are congested above the doomed fish. To see the turmoil of sea birds on such occasions is to wonder that any of the herring or their eggs survive after the first onslaught.

Gulls generally are the first to locate the feast. Mergansers are soon on the spot, followed by murres, guillemots, and three species of loons; grebes (Holboell's and western) and cormorants of several species are the last to arrive. To see the large loons arriving, flying straight and swift, and hurling themselves into the melee, causes one to wonder that birds as well as herring are not killed.

Females of the American and red-breasted mergansers are very much alike, but in the flesh are easily distinguished by their build and weight. The red-breasted merganser is a much smaller bird, being slender in shape. Males will weigh a little less than three pounds, females about two and a half pounds.

Shoveller

(Spatula clypeata)

Average Length, Twenty Inches

The shoveller, more commonly known as the "spoonbill" or "spooney," has, like the gadwall, an almost world-wide range. In the New World it reaches in summer to the sub-arctic regions, but the main nesting ground is on the prairies of the Canadian Provinces and the northern tier of States. In winter it reaches Central America and even the Hawaiian Islands.

Aside from the tremendous bill, the shoveller is full of character. When feeding it is a dabbler, sifting the mud through its specialized bill with a lateral motion, rarely tipping up as other surface-feeding ducks do. It rises from the water with a jump, and the rattle of its wings as it does so can be picked out above the noise of other rising ducks. When it is settling, this rattle is once more in evidence, and the bird alights almost vertically with hardly a splash.

The old historians, such as Alexander Wilson, rated it high as a table bird. "An old hunter will never pass up a spoonbill even when after canvasback." But anyhow, in the West it is not ranked so highly, and it is seldom shot where better ducks are available.

When first hatched, the young have a bill shaped as in other surface-feeding ducks, without any evidence of the spatulation that characterizes the older birds.

In size the shoveller is small medium, a fat bird weighing one pound twelve ounces.

Cinnamon Teal

(Querquedula cyanoptera)

Average Length, Sixteen Inches

This is a western duck, only stragglers of which have been found on the Atlantic coast, and it has a more southern breeding range than the blue-wing.

The center of its abundance is in the interior valleys of California, although it is fairly common in summer north to about latitude 52°. East of the mountains, it becomes scarcer and it is a rare bird in Montana or Saskatchewan.

Cinnamon teal in the summer are confiding little birds, and it is a pretty sight to see the handsome red male with his inconspicuous spouse sunning themselves among the bright-green grasses at the margin of some small pool. They allow a very close approach before the female jumps into the air, closely followed by her handsome mate, and usually they will settle again within 40 yards, or else return to their starting point.

The females and young of the cinnamon and blue-winged teal are practically indistinguishable. Although works of reference point to differences in the size and shape of the bill and color of the breast, these distinctions are not infallible. In spite of this similarity among the females, hybrids are of exceptional occurrence, even when the two species are kept in confinement together.

I have twice seen fights between males of these two ducks. In each case the cinnamon was the winner.

Although classed as a teal, this duck, as well as the blue-wing, is more closely related to the shovellers, both in structure and coloration, as well as in feeding habits. This affinity is very apparent when the species of shoveller inhabiting South America and Australia are compared. The South American shoveller is colored like a cinnamon teal, and the Australian has the markings of a blue-wing.

Blue-winged Teal

(Querquedula discors)

Average Length, Sixteen Inches

The blue-wing is essentially a more southern species than the green-wing and its northern breeding limit is much farther south. It has been found nesting in almost every State in the Union and Canada. Its normal western limit is through the central portion of the western Provinces, although it is occasionally found farther north. It extends its winter migration farther south than any other North American duck—as far as central Chile and Brazil.

Its decrease in recent years on the Atlantic coast is marked by an increase on the Pacific. During the last few years this increase has been especially notable in British Columbia, where its gain is at least 500 per cent over the numbers of 20 years ago.

Much has been written regarding the great speed of the flight of the blue-wing. In this respect it should not be classed as swift as the green-wing, and most of the estimates of the speed of both species should be cut in half. Several times when traveling on a train going about 35 miles an hour, I have seen blue-wings flying parallel make several efforts to pass in front of the engine before they were able to do so.

The white patch in front of the eye and another in front of the tail, together with the dark coloration, make the drake blue-wing a conspicuous bird in summer, but all these characters are lost by mid-July, and the males are practically the same color as the females. The old drakes leave for the south before August, and I have never seen one among the bags of teal at the commencement of the shooting season. The full plumage is not acquired until after December, later than in any other duck.

In weight they will average two ounces heavier than a green-wing, or about one pound as a maximum.

THE SHOVELLER USES ITS LUDICROUS BILL AS A GOLD MINER DOES HIS PAN

"Nuggets" sifted out of the mud are worms, tadpoles, shellfish, and seeds. Some **Shovellers,** or "spoonbills" (left pair and alighting in distance) fly more than 2,000 miles over the Pacific Ocean from Alaska to their winter home in Hawaii. Small relatives are the West's **Cinnamon Teal** (pair in center) and the **Blue-winged Teal** (pair at right and trio flying at top), which sometimes migrate to central Chile and Brazil, farther south than any other North American duck.

Canvasback

(Nyroca valisineria)
Average Length, Twenty-one Inches

With the canvasback we start the series of diving ducks. With its huge paddles of feet, heavy body, and rather small wings, it forms a typical representative of this group.

This fine duck, so often called the "lordly" canvasback, is distinctly an American bird and has never been recorded outside of its North American range. It breeds from Alaska and Great Slave Lake to northern New Mexico and in winter reaches well into Mexico.

Epicures first made the canvasback's reputation, and along the Atlantic States where it can get a plentiful supply of its favorite food, the wild celery (*Vallisneria*), which grows so abundantly in the brackish water of Chesapeake Bay and other similar inlets, it is certainly an outstanding bird. But where this water weed does not grow, the canvasback is not superior to the redhead or many species of surface-feeding ducks. On the bays of the Pacific coast, where shellfish form its principal diet, it becomes almost inedible.

Aside from its reputation as a table delicacy, there is something regal and outstanding about the canvasback. All its actions are full of character. The big white body that seems to sit so high on the water, surmounted by the slender-shaped head on the long, thick neck, forms a striking picture.

But when a flock is in full flight the big birds are seen at their best. Such power is expressed in the speed and directness of their driving flight, usually made in line formation, that the "cans" seem superducks.

On its nesting grounds it is an early breeder. A full month before its congeners, the scaups and redheads, have started to lay, you can find the female seated on top of a huge pile of rushes, often anchored in water two feet deep and some distance from the shore, with very little attempt at concealment.

Redhead

(Nyroca americana)
Average Length, Nineteen Inches

The redhead has a decidedly more southern breeding range than the canvasback, ranging from the center of the Prairie Provinces and British Columbia to southern California. In winter it reaches no farther south than Mexico.

The redhead is one of the least maritime of all diving ducks. On the Atlantic it may be found on the brackish inlets, like Chesapeake Bay and Pamlico Sound, in large numbers, but on the Pacific it is practically unknown on salt water. This fact makes it one of the best of all diving birds for the table.

It is a beautiful sight in southern British Columbia to see the return of the redheads at the first sign of spring to the large lakes of the interior. The first break of the winter conditions used to bring them pouring in (I say used, for they no longer do so) until many hundreds were bedded together out in deep water. These were at first nearly all males in high condition, and as darkness fell, they filled the air with their mewing spring call.

I know of no lake in the Province where this early movement occurs nowadays, and the birds have quite changed their habits, being found on the small upland ponds where they never used to occur. To nest they resort to lakes with a heavy growth of rushes.

One year the nests on a lake close to my home were badly drowned out by the damming of this lake for irrigation supply, and the ducks laid their eggs in any kind of nest that survived. Some extraordinary combinations of mixed eggs were to be seen.

A little pied-billed grebe whose floating nest had survived was having a hard time, for, in addition to her own eggs, three coots' and two redheads' had been imposed upon her. The little mother was furiously engaged in trying to eject the latter, three times the size of her own, and I saw her at last succeed in rolling one of the huge eggs into the water.

Even under ordinary conditions some ducks have this cuckoolike habit and the redhead is particularly casual in this respect.

Redheads may be called large ducks, but even fat birds weigh under three pounds.

When feeding in deep water—and they can bring up their duck-weed food from a depth of 40 feet or more—redheads are commonly attended by baldpates and coots. Both of these watch the redhead's return to the surface, its bill full of weed, and this is deftly tweaked away, without any protest from the much-enduring redhead, which at once proceeds to dive for a fresh mouthful.

Ring-necked Duck

(Nyroca collaris)
Average Length, Sixteen and One-half Inches

"Ring-bill" is a commoner and much more appropriate name than ring-neck for this little duck. The ring on the neck is an obscure character confined to the old males, but in life the two bands of brilliant white on the bill are a conspicuous character in both sexes.

The range of the ring-neck is much the same as that of the redhead, even more southerly, and it is rare or absent from the New England States and along the northeastern coast of Canada.

Ring-necks are very fast flyers; few other ducks can equal them when going at full speed.

Of late years the species has shown a decided decrease throughout its range. That may be only temporary, for it has always been a duck which showed wide fluctuations between abundance and scarcity.

Ring-necks are usually exceptionally fat and will weigh a pound and a half or more.

LORDLY BEARING STAMPS THE CANVASBACK A KING AMONG WATERFOWL

Hardy and strong, splendid flyers and divers, "cans" often stay in the north until the lakes are covered with ice (right pair and "single" flying). From breeding grounds in the far north and west many head for Chesapeake Bay regions, where they feed on "wild celery." Often flights of thousands parade across the sky. Close relatives are the **Redhead** (pair in left foreground and group flying) and the **Ring-necked Duck** (beyond), most widely and aptly called "ring-bill."

Ruddy Duck

(Erismatura jamaicensis rubida)
Average Length, Fifteen Inches

The ruddy is a duck of southern distribution, nesting from southern Canada through all the States into Mexico. It is notable among ducks for many characteristics. Chief of these is the faithfulness of the male in his parental duties. As soon as the young are hatched—and these are huge compared to other downy ducks—the male escorts them in all their forays for food. Not that he interrupts the continuance of the bobbings and gulpings that constitute his display during the breeding season, but he ever keeps watch for danger, ready to fight any bird or mammal, regardless of size, that threatens his charges.

This courage, not to say irascibility, is common to both sexes. I once found a small female being tumbled about in the surf of the Pacific. Slammed down on the sand by each breaker, she pulled herself together and met the towering descent of the next with wide-open beak and stretched to her full height. I managed to capture her and carried her across the sand dunes to a spot where I had my canoe on a protected lagoon.

Placed on the floor of the canoe, she kept up a determined attack on my feet until I released her at a suitable haven, where she sat on the water scowling at her deliverer. A final wave of the paddle toward her was regarded as an insulting climax and she hurled herself forward, seized the paddle in her bill, and hung on like a bulldog.

There is a marked discrepancy in size between the sexes of the ruddy duck. The male might be called small medium, slightly smaller than a little blue-bill, about a pound and a half. The female is decidedly small.

The wonderful color of the bill in the male must be seen to be appreciated. During the nuptial season it is a vivid turquoise blue, and this with his bull neck, striking colors, and tail held cocked over his back like a wren's, make him notable in any company. In the fall and winter the plumage changes and the bill is dark gray.

No other bird has a greater assortment of vernacular names than this curious little duck. A full list of these may be found in Dr. J. C. Phillips's *A Natural History of the Ducks*.

Lesser Scaup Duck

(Nyroca affinis)
Average Length, Sixteen and One-half Inches

Lesser scaups are much smaller-sized birds than the preceding species, but even at that the weights will overlap. To distinguish them, one must place reliance on the much smaller bill, the purple instead of green reflections on the head, and the smaller extent of white on the wing in the smaller species. The last-named character is the most reliable, the inner primaries, or long flight feathers, having their outer webs white in the greater scaup and pale brown in the lesser.

The breeding range of the lesser scaup is well to the south of that of the greater. It extends well up into Alaska and northern Canada, south to the northern Prairie States and southern British Columbia. Throughout this range it is one of the commonest ducks, nesting both in small ponds and larger lakes, wherever plenty of cover is available. The bird is a marsh breeder and the nest is always close to water and usually has a waterway, such as a muskrat's passage, leading to it. It is a late nester and young broods are sometimes unable to fly when the first ice of the early northern fall is forming.

The "little blue-bill," the commonest name of this duck, is the common and confiding duck seen in winter along the Indian River in Florida, on the bayous of Louisiana, or on the sloughs of California, and it is seldom molested where better ducks are available. Under such conditions it often becomes so tame that it will take bread from the hand.

At its nesting grounds it is equally confiding and I have often stroked the sitting birds as they sat on their nests.

Lesser scaups may be classed as of small medium size, or exactly the same as the ring-neck in weight.

Greater Scaup Duck

(Nyroca marila)
Average Length, Eighteen Inches

Scaups, more generally known as "blue-bills," "blackheads," and "raft ducks," are divided into two species, the similarity of which causes much confusion, especially in the delimitation of their nesting ranges.

The greater scaup is an Arctic-nesting species, breeding along the northern rim of the continent north of the tree limit. It winters as far south as California and the Gulf of Mexico, where it is much scarcer than the lesser scaup. It is also found over the whole northern portion of the Old World.

Scaups are hardy birds and the most maritime of the "pochard" group of ducks, which includes the canvasbacks, redheads, and ring-necks in America.

In the stormy waters of our northern coastline they can be seen holding their own with the typical sea ducks—eiders, scoters, and old-squaws—diving just outside of the line of tumbling breakers for the shellfish which constitute the food supply of all these birds. At such times they are "fishy" and practically uneatable, but inland their food is like the redhead's and their flesh is excellent.

Greater scaups may be called large medium ducks, weighing in good condition about two pounds, with two and a half as a maximum.

THE RUDDY DUCK IS KNOWN BY 61 DIFFERENT NAMES

With fanlike tail, bull neck, and pugnaciously uptilted bill, a **Ruddy Duck,** alias "fool duck," "sleepy duck," "blatherskite," and so on, proudly escorts his lady. Near the shore, fat male ruddies in winter plumage struggle to rise from the water. Two **Lesser Scaup Ducks,** sometimes called "black-heads" and often seen in huge rafts on the bays and inlets of the Atlantic coast, swim toward the left, leading a pair of **Greater Scaups,** also portrayed above in flight.

Harlequin Duck

(Histrionicus histrionicus)

Average Length, Seventeen Inches

The harlequin has been divided into an eastern and a western subspecies, but the distinction is barely recognizable. Harlequins are maritime ducks, frequenting the outer reefs. Here they feed in the surf and climb nimbly out to the topmost rocks to rest.

When the spring is well advanced, harlequins appear on the mountain lakes of the interior, from Alaska to California, and ascend the rivers until these become foaming torrents of glacial water. Here is their summer home, and they find the turmoil of these cascades as easy to negotiate as the breakers of the storm-beaten coast. The nest is made in a cliff, steep bank, or log jam.

As soon as the eggs are laid the males desert the females and reappear on the seacoast, often hundreds of miles from their nesting quarters. Here they molt their striking plumage to one that resembles the female dress, becoming flightless as the wing feathers are shed. Flocks of these "flappers" give rise to the stories of young broods on salt water.

Females and young follow in the early fall as soon as the young can fly, and at only a few points can the harlequin be seen throughout the winter anywhere in the interior.

The harlequin weighs about a pound and a half in good condition.

American Golden-eye

(Glaucionetta clangula americana)

Average Length, Twenty Inches

More commonly known as "whistler" or "whistle-wing," the golden-eye belongs to a group of ducks characterized by striking pied plumage in the males and a tree-nesting habit.

The American golden-eye's breeding range follows the tree limit of the subarctic forest and extends south to southern British Columbia and east through the northern tier of States to Maine. Its winter range is governed by the ability to find ice-free water, but on the Pacific coast it extends to Baja California.

Golden-eyes of both species are notable for the chiming music of their flight; this whistling is peculiar to the old birds, especially the males. Younger birds fly with no more noise than other ducks.

They nest in hollow trees and very often they have to go far from the nearest water to find a suitable hole. This entails a long tramp for the newly hatched brood, often over rough ground, and these journeys are fraught with danger from bird and mammal predators.

As in all the members of this group, the male golden-eye is very much larger than the female and weighs as much as two and a half pounds in good condition. Females may be called small medium in size, with a weight of one and a half pounds.

Barrow's Golden-eye

(Glaucionetta islandica)

Average Length, Twenty-two Inches

Barrow's golden-eye and the harlequin duck are alike in possessing an extraordinary range. Both breed in Iceland and southern Greenland, and also in the Rocky Mountains and the region from these mountains west to the Pacific. But their summer homes are almost or entirely deserted in winter, the ducks of the Iceland colony being found along the northern American coast from Newfoundland to New England, and those of the mountains wintering on the Pacific coast.

In the regions between these two colonies neither species is often seen.

In the interior of British Columbia Barrow's golden-eye is a common bird. Every pond in the rolling foothills has a pair or more, as soon as it is free from ice in the spring. By early June the handsome drakes have returned to the seacoast from whence they came, and, soon after, the females and their broods may be seen. The latter are pitifully few, as a rule; for from some hollow tree, far back in the wooded hills, they have run a gauntlet of enemies.

Even when the lakelet is reached, their troubles are not over. Crows and magpies watch for every chance to get a duckling separated from the mother, and the latter as well as the young may fall victim to the red-tailed hawks nesting in the neighborhood.

These hunt the ducks just as the bald eagle gets crippled birds in winter—they hover over the course of the diving birds and pick them up deftly as they come to the surface.

"Broods" of one are common and once I saw a single young one attended by two mothers, one a golden-eye and the other a buffle-head.

Buffle-head

(Charitonetta albeola)

Average Length, Fourteen and Three-quarters Inches

The buffle-head, or "butterball," is another duck that is peculiar to North America and of a unique type. Its breeding range extends from the Hudson Bay region through the northern Canadian Provinces to Alaska and south in the mountains to northern California. In winter it reaches Florida and Mexico; also, as a straggler, Bering Island, Hawaii, and the British Isles.

At their nesting grounds they are more than usually engaging; even while the males are still displaying to attract the females, the latter are apt to fly off in search of a nesting hole. These, I have found, are invariably the three-inch nest holes of the flicker.

The female is much smaller than the male. The latter can be classed as small, weighing about a pound and a quarter, but the tiny female weighs less than a pound.

NATURE DAUBED THESE DUCKS WITH BOLD, WHIMSICAL STROKES

Fantastic is the **Harlequin Duck,** perched on the rock with his mate, while others fly overhead. The pair in the right foreground and the "single" above are the **American Golden-eye,** nicknamed "whistlers" from the sound of their wings. At the left is a cousin, **Barrow's Golden-eye.** Just in front of the rock and flying low over the water are small kinsmen, the **Buffle-head.** The male, with broad white bonnet, has a "swelled head" when he erects his feathers.

© Captain C. W. R. Knight

MR. OSPREY BRINGS A FISH HOME TO HIS WIFE

Captain C. W. R. Knight made motion pictures of many of the birds on Gardiner's Island off Montauk Point, Long Island. He also carried five young birds from the island and liberated them on the Scottish estates of the Duke of Sutherland and Lord Cameron. For twenty years this species of "sea hawk" has been almost extinct in Great Britain.

THE EAGLES, HAWKS, AND VULTURES

Raptors, Once Regarded as Enemies of Man, Are Now Recognized as Friends

By Alexander Wetmore

Assistant Secretary, Smithsonian Institution

THE eagle, symbol of bold strength and courageous character, has been used so widely as an emblem of power that, by name and by effigy, birds of the group to which it belongs are known familiarly to many who have little experience or conception of them in life.

Eagles and their many relatives among the hawks and vultures are distributed throughout the world, except over the open seas, the barren Antarctic Continent, and the smallest and most isolated of oceanic islands. Wherever found, they appeal even to the novice in knowledge of things outdoors because of their manner of life and predatory habits. Robust of form and strong in flight, they are remarked at every appearance.

The emblem of the Sumerian city of Lagash, in the third millennium before the Christian Era, was an eagle, which was engraved on the tablets and seals of the leaders and was carried as a military standard by the army. An eagle also appeared on the seal of the King of Ur, and continued in double-headed form in Hittite art, on certain coins of the Mohammedans, on the flags of Turkoman princes, and so on into modern times.

The eagle symbol is probably derived from forms similar to our golden eagle or closely allied to that species, as several species of that type are found in the regions mentioned.

To early Greeks the eagle was the messenger of Zeus and the only bird that dwelt in heaven—a fancy based, perhaps, on the high-flying powers of these birds. A silver eagle standing on a spear was placed on the military standards of the legions of Rome, and this emblem has been used widely as a conventional badge of military power. Today it is a common decoration on flagstaffs in many countries.

An American species of this group, the bald eagle, is found in the design of the coat of arms of the United States, which appears on the Great Seal. A representation of it is blazoned on many of our coins and decorations. It also appears on the President's flag, and on the President's seal in the bronze plate on the floor of the vestibule of the White House.

The fierce harpy eagle (*Harpia harpyja*), a bird of dauntless courage, was called by the Aztecs "the winged wolf," because of its savage attack on monkeys of good size. It is distinguishable from our species by its prominently crested head and by its large size.

CONDOR APPEARS ON COATS OF ARMS

The great condor of South America figures in the coats of arms of Colombia, Bolivia, Ecuador, and Chile.

The eagles and their kin form the group of birds of the Order Falconiformes, which includes about 288 distinct species, with many additional geographic forms, so that in all there are recognized somewhat more than 700 living forms. The order is divided into four principal families.

The eagles, hawks, kites, and their relatives, forming the family Accipitridae, include the largest number of forms. They are mainly birds of medium to large size, with broad wings, strong legs, feet armed with sharp claws, and strongly hooked bills. Many possess light-colored eyes, which, with their active interest in any movement that might indicate possible prey, give them a fierce and aggressive appearance.

Although many have rapid flight, others are slower and more sluggish in habit. Most of them delight in soaring in great circles high above the earth, where they are conspicuous and are visible for long distances. Some of the species of this family are among the largest of flying birds.

FALCONS CAPABLE OF SWIFT FLIGHT

The falcons, with their relatives the caracaras, the family Falconidae, in general are smaller in size than the members of the

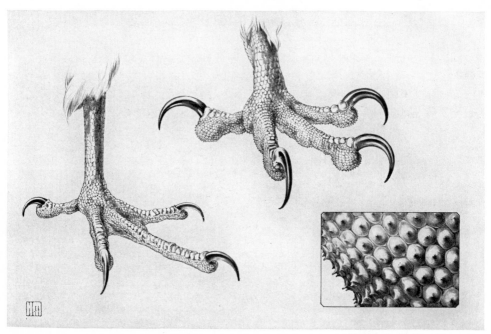

Drawing by Hashime Murayama

TWO TYPES OF FEET FOUND IN THE HAWKLIKE BIRDS

The foot of the osprey, at right, illustrates the development for grasping and holding, characteristic of the predatory forms of falcons and hawks. The foot of the turkey vulture, at left, is a
weaker type, fitted for walking and perching and not for seizing living prey. The inset shows an
enlarged view, magnified four times, of the spines of the foot pads of the osprey, which enable it to
hold slippery fish, an arrangement found only in this species.

other group of hawks, and have longer,
more pointed wings, which give them swifter
flight that may be maintained at high speed
for long distances.

Though some, such as the chimangos, or
carrion hawks, and the caracaras, may be in
part carrion feeders, the majority, the true
falcons, are fiercely predatory hunters,
whose appearance strikes terror among
other birds. The bill of the falcons, sharply
pointed at the tip, has a projecting tooth on
the margin that assists in tearing their food.

The New World vultures, family Ca-
thartidae, although hawklike in form of
body and spread of wings, have relatively
weak legs and feet which are not used to
seize or carry prey. Their beaks, though
strong, are not prominently hooked, and
except for their flying muscles these birds
are far less powerful than their relatives.

These are the scavengers among birds, for
whom no food is too repulsive, that spend
their days in scanning the surface of the
earth for dead creatures on which they may
feast. They are confined to the Americas,
the carrion-eating vultures of other lands
belonging to the Accipitridae.

The secretary bird, the only living species
in the fourth family, Sagittariidae, one of
the most remarkable birds of the entire
order, stands nearly four feet high, having
long, slender legs like those of a heron.
Though it has strong wings, it ordinarily
runs on the ground, traveling at need with
great swiftness. It is found only in Africa,
from the Anglo-Egyptian Sudan and Sene-
gambia to Cape of Good Hope Province.
It feeds on snakes, lizards, and various other
animals, often killing them by stamping on
them with its feet.

The most aberrant types in the entire
order are the American vultures, which are
far removed from the hawks and eagles and
in some ways have peculiarities that set
them off from most other birds.

Aside from the peculiar types just mentioned, the various species of this order are
fairly uniform in build and form, differing
principally in length of legs, grasping power
of claws, and size and degree of robustness
of bill. Thus, the bill of the eagle is strong
and heavy, but that of the everglade kite is
extremely slender and elongated.

The bateleur eagle (*Terathopius ecau-*

Photograph by William L. Finley

A FULL-GROWN CALIFORNIA CONDOR ENJOYS A SUN BATH

He differs from the South American members in dress, but not appreciably in size. His head and neck are much more colorful and there is no caruncle. The tremendous wing spread here shown gives this bird marvelous powers of flight.

datus) has the tail so short that it does not project beyond the wings—an anomaly in a group that as a whole has long, strong tail feathers. In spite of this peculiarity, the bateleur sails with ease, using its wings as planes, though it is said to have difficulty in keeping aloft when there are no wind or air currents to assist it.

One of the striking phenomena of some of our American hawks has been the fall migrations, in which hundreds, or even thousands, move together in southward flight. Years ago, in eastern Kansas, in the pleasant weather of October, it was usual to encounter flights of red-tailed and American rough-legged hawks, in which these splendid birds drifted steadily across the sky for hours in never-ending procession. Occasionally, attracted by rising currents of air over some hill slope, they paused to wheel in enormous spirals.

MIGRATION OF SOME HAWKS SPECTACULAR

Often I lay on soft grass, in the warm sun, watching several hundred of these hawks turning slowly through the sky, some at such an elevation that they looked no larger than swallows. On occasion I have seen similar flights of the Swainson's hawk of the western plains, these birds traveling in bands on migrations that carry them far into South America.

The migration flights of the sharp-shinned and Cooper's hawks in the East are better known, though they are seen only in favored localities. Point Pelee, which projects as a long peninsula from the Canadian shore of Lake Erie, for many years has been famous for its hawk flights. In October, 1931, in the course of a few hours, I saw there several hundred sharp-shins drifting down with the north wind, alternately flapping their wings and sailing with pinions outstretched, passing without pause out over the waters of the lake toward the distant American shore.

While there were never many in sight at one time, they passed at intervals of two or three minutes in a steadily moving stream. Elsewhere in the fall I have observed Cooper's and sharp-shinned hawks scattered over the entire sky, moving steadily toward the south. These flights of hawks are most marked in fall, for in spring the birds seem to travel northward over wider areas.

At a number of places it is regular prac-

Photograph by George Shiras, 3d

A DUCK HAWK FINDS HIS PREY A WOODEN DECOY: SANDUSKY BAY, OHIO

The hunting method usually pursued by these birds is to rise in spirals until directly above the victim, then to drop swiftly upon it. However, they are fast flyers and are capable of catching other birds in direct chase.

tice to shoot these birds for sport, and many thousands have been killed in this manner. Occasionally, as near Cape May, New Jersey, they are used for food.

The different species of the hawk group vary widely in the extent of their migrations. Some, such as Swainson's hawk, make journeys that carry them from the western plains south into Argentina, while others, such as the sparrow hawk, may be quite sedentary except in the northern sections of their range.

In general, birds of this group withdraw at least in part from the extreme northern areas that they inhabit, probably because food becomes scarce and difficult to obtain. The gyrfalcons, however, are typically northern, never coming far south, and rough-legged and allied hawks course over the northern plains in the greatest extremes of cold weather.

FLIGHT METHODS VARY

Flight in the hawklike birds varies considerably, according to the kind. Eagles, the large hawks, and the vultures, both of the New and Old Worlds, have broad wings which they flap slowly. Frequently they soar with set wings, utilizing air currents rising from the heated surface of the earth, or currents generated by winds. These birds frequently soar for hours with scarcely a wing beat, turning and wheeling in the sky, often at such altitudes that they appear as mere specks against the blue.

The turkey vulture is a well-known species that is particularly adept in this art. In fact, it finds this method of progression so adapted to its needs that frequently it remains in its roost through the day when the air is heavy and still.

THE DUCK HAWK IS A DESPOT OF THE AIR

The falcons have longer, more pointed wings, that enable them to fly with great speed, and, though they may enjoy soaring, they do not practice this so constantly as the other hawks. The larger species can capture the swiftest-flying sandpipers and ducks on the wing without the slightest difficulty.

The flight of the duck hawk, perhaps the best known of the falcons, is truly exhilarating to watch, as it is executed with a dash and vigor that mark it from that of all other birds. On the Bear River marshes, at the

Photograph by C. A. Proctor and B. B. Leavitt

STANDING GUARD NEAR HIS NEST

Duck hawks are strong and courageous, and this one, having just alighted on the nesting shelf, seems to be challenging anyone or anything to try conclusions with him. The duck hawks are the nearest American relatives of the peregrine falcons, famous hunters of the Old World.

northern end of Great Salt Lake, in Utah, I have spent many hours in observing this falcon, both in its hunting and when at play.

When at rest they perched in low willows, or on logs or bits of drift, where they had clear view of the teeming bird life about them. When hungry, they dashed across the open flats at high speed, striking ruthlessly at any birds that appeared, from small sandpipers to large ducks.

Their appearance in the air was always the signal for chattering cries of alarm from blackbirds and avocets that put all their bird neighbors on the watch. These warnings had little effect, however, as the duck hawk, killing practically at will, was truly despot of this realm.

THE DUCK HAWK A PRACTICAL JOKER

I have seen this falcon dash through closely massed flocks of flying sandpipers, striking out two or three with as many thrusts of the claws, allowing each bird to drop and then wheeling swiftly to seize the falling prey in mid-air before it reached the ground. Again, I have seen one in a stoop, swift almost as light, knock a redhead duck to the ground, where it landed with a broken wing and other injuries.

On one occasion a pair of duck hawks harried a helpless nighthawk, stooping at it playfully until one in passing gave it a quick squeeze with one foot. It then allowed the nighthawk to fall, when it was seized by the other duck hawk. Then as the pair flew away, the one with the booty at intervals dropped it, so that it could be seized in air by its mate.

When not hungry, the duck hawk, feeling its superior strength, frequently indulges in harmless play at the expense of its bird neighbors.

Often I have seen them flying along the river channels, driving ahead of them a motley flock of blackbirds, herons, avocets, and other birds, herding them in disorder like sheep, but without offering to harm them. Again, as night herons flew ahead of my launch, a duck hawk would dart at them repeatedly, forcing them down lower and lower, until finally, with protesting squawks, they struck the water. They were not allowed to rise, but had to swim into the shelter of the willows to escape.

Photograph by A. A. Allen

SWALLOW-TAILED KITES SOAR AND CIRCLE ALOFT WITH BUOYANT GRACE

So well provided with wing and tail surface are these larger prototypes of the barn swallows that they spend nearly all of their time in the air. They even feed in the air, often on small water snakes, which they deftly snatch from among the reeds and devour aloft.

One pleasant afternoon in fall I heard a great roaring of wings overhead and looked up to see a cormorant that a few minutes before had been soaring peacefully high in air, dashing down with set wings toward the river, with a duck hawk a few feet behind. Just above the water the hawk suddenly accelerated, tapped the cormorant lightly on the back, then circled easily away, while the frightened quarry took refuge unharmed in the water. Frequently falcons at play dashed at top speed through milling flocks of flying sandpipers, scattering them like leaves in the wind, but not striking any of them.

The food of birds of the hawk group is highly varied, though it is taken entirely from the animal kingdom. The larger species of falcons subsist mainly on various kinds of birds and small mammals, but the smaller kinds, such as sparrow hawks and falconets, eat lizards, grasshoppers and other insects, and mice. The common red-tailed hawks and their allies, known universally as "chicken hawks," may on occasion eat birds or even visit hen-yards for prey, but confine their attention principally to

mice and rats. Therefore, they are in the main beneficial, as they destroy large numbers of rodents that are injurious to crops and orchards.

VULTURES AS "BONE-BREAKERS"

The bearded vultures of the Old World carry turtles and large bones from the carcasses of dead animals to a great height, in order to drop them on rocks, where they break open so that the bird can eat the marrow. From this habit the Spanish call these birds *quebranta-huesos,* signifying "bone-breakers." The ancient naturalist Pliny relates that the Greek poet Æschylus (who died 456 B. C.) met untimely death when one of these vultures, mistaking his bald head for a stone, dropped a tortoise on it from the air!

Some species of hawks, particularly certain forms that range in the Tropics, eat snakes as their principal food. There is one group of species found in India and adjacent regions in which this habit is so constant that the birds are known as "serpent eagles." The osprey and some of the sea eagles confine their attention mainly to fish,

Photograph by A. A. Allen

LOOKING OUT ON THE WORLD FROM A MOSSY NEST

Mr. and Mrs. Kite, of the swallow-tailed kites, built their home in the top of a tall tree near a watercourse. Dry twigs, sticks, hay, and moss were used. The birds of this family breed over a wide range of territory and incubation may start any time from March to June.

which they capture alive by plunging after them as they approach the surface of the water.

As their name implies, the peculiar bat-eating hawks (*Machaerhamphus alcinus*) from the East Indies and Africa feed on bats. Since these hawks capture their prey on the wing, they are abroad in the evening and early morning, being at least partly nocturnal in habit. The honey buzzards of the Old World (*Pernis*) are fond of honey and of the immature stages of bees.

Swainson's hawk, a bird of large size, feeds extensively on grasshoppers, the broad-winged hawk is fond of frogs, the everglade kite subsists on large fresh-water snails, and the powerful harpy eagle feeds regularly on monkeys.

Possibly the strangest food in the group is the repulsive carrion eaten by the vultures. These birds spend the daylight hours soaring in the air, while they scan the earth below them in search of dead animals that may supply food. Small animals, dead fish, and birds are bolted entire or are torn into suitable fragments. The skin on large carcasses may resist the bills of the scavengers

until softened by putrefaction, when the birds gorge on a meal of the utmost repulsiveness.

While we may turn in physical revulsion from contemplation of this habit, we may ponder on the adaptations that seemingly give these birds absolute immunity to the poisons, generated in decaying flesh, that would destroy any creature of ordinary digestion.

The bird-eating hawks pluck most of the feathers from their prey and then tear the flesh into bits that may be swallowed. Mice are often swallowed whole, but rabbits and mammals of similar size may be partly skinned and the feet may be discarded.

The food passes down into a stomach that is thin-walled and capable of considerable distention, and in the throat there is developed a distensible crop that holds a large amount of food until the stomach is ready to receive it.

Bones, feathers, fur, and other hard elements that cannot be digested are formed into pellets and regurgitated to leave the stomach empty for another meal. These pellets accumulate beneath favored perches

Photograph by A. A. Allen

THE MALE MARSH HAWK NEVER INCUBATES AND SELDOM
COMES TO THE NEST, BUT HERE HE IS, ON GUARD

sometimes at high and sometimes at low elevations, they encounter the odor from carrion and follow this scent to its source. Others believe that in their flight the piercing eyesight of these birds brings to view possible sources of sustenance, and that vision accounts for the facility with which vultures locate their food.

In warm weather, proponents of the scent theory have concealed bodies of animals so that they could not be seen, and claim that in a short time, as the carcasses became odoriferous, turkey vultures gathered. Even though the carrion was so concealed in buildings or under other cover that the birds could not get at it, they remained on hand, attracted by the odors, in the attempt to locate this potential food supply. Experiments dealing with this matter began in the days of Audubon and have been continued by other naturalists until the present day.

and offer a valuable index to the food preferences of these birds. Hawks, falcons, and eagles carry food in their talons to their young in the nest, but vultures, which do not have powerful feet and legs, feed their young by regurgitating the contents of the stomach.

Whether the carrion-feeding vultures locate the carcasses on which they feed through sight or through the sense of smell has been a subject of much controversy among naturalists, and, in spite of many observations on these abundant birds, it is far from being a settled question.

VULTURES POSSESS KEEN SIGHT

One group of observers contends that, as these birds soar back and forth through rising currents of air or against the wind,

There is not the slightest question that the turkey vulture will find food that is concealed in such a way as to be entirely invisible to a bird overhead, even though such a bird may be only a few feet distant. However, in most alleged instances of location by scent, keen sight has probably played some part.

That the turkey vulture is an observant creature, with keen perception where food is concerned, is obvious if one watches it a little, though there may be doubt as to the extent of its intelligence in other respects. These birds regularly patrol beaches to obtain dead fish, and recently have learned to watch the modern hard-surfaced roads, where speeding automobiles are constantly killing small birds, snakes, rabbits, cats, and other animals.

Also, they seem to know that the movements of men through the country will bear scrutiny, as frequently men leave behind them food in the form of animals killed, or offal from large bodies that have been butchered.

To test this, it is necessary only to sit on the open ground while skinning a rabbit or some large bird, and if you are in a region where turkey buzzards are common, it will be only a few moments until one or two are wheeling overhead. If there is promise of food, they remain; if not, they continue their search elsewhere.

In South America yellow-headed buzzards (*Cathartes urubitinga*) have followed me into woodland where I was seated on the ground entirely concealed and engaged in examining birds that I had killed for specimens. The buzzards alighted a few feet away to watch me curiously. I have had buzzards come to eat the flesh from carcasses of their own kind which I had skinned where I had shot the birds. Possibly this was unintentional cannibalism, as there was nothing about the bodies to distinguish them from the skinned bodies of any other birds.

There can be no doubt that the buzzard has learned to watch the actions of dogs whose activities may indicate the presence of carrion concealed in caves or holes. There is also the probability that the presence of buzzing flesh flies that breed in carrion may be an indication to the buzzard of a concealed food supply. Therefore, admitting that the turkey buzzard has a well-developed olfactory nerve, and thus might be expected to have some sense

Photograph by Charles Martin

A SOUTH AMERICAN CONDOR WHOSE PERMANENT RESIDENCE IS WASHINGTON, D. C.

This monarch of the Andes is one of the prime attractions in the fine collection of birds, animals, and reptiles housed in the National Zoological Park. The bare skin of his head, neck, and caruncle is dull red, and contrasts sharply with the white "fur" collar and dark plumage.

of smell, to me present evidence indicates that it finds its food mainly, if not entirely, through its acute sense of sight.

MAN'S HAND IS AGAINST THE HAWK TRIBE

The hand of civilized man has been raised universally against the hawk tribe, and birds of this group are shot or otherwise destroyed at every opportunity. It is rare, indeed, for hawks to come within gun range of a hunter without receiving a charge of shot, and they are killed in many localities by setting steel traps on the tops of posts or poles that the birds utilize as perches.

In England it is the duty of game-keepers to kill all "vermin" that appear on the property under their charge, hawks being included in this category. On a large estate near the Thames I once saw a "keeper's larder" where, near a frequented path, the gamekeeper had hung up his kills for display. These included the drying skeletons of sparrow hawks (a species related to the American sharp-shinned hawk), kestrels (allied to the American sparrow hawk), magpies, and jays, with a few small predatory mammals.

Belief in the destructiveness of hawks is almost universal. In most minds there is no distinction between hawks that habitually prey on birds and may destroy a certain amount of game, and the sluggish, heavy-flying species that feed consistently on wild mice and other destructive rodents, and so are beneficial to man.

The game commissions of many States have offered bounties for the heads of hawks and have expended hundreds of thousands of dollars in the destruction of untold thousands of them. The result is that in the eastern half of the United States these birds have decreased to less than a tenth of their former abundance.

Since the decrease has affected the beneficial kinds even more heavily than those that are classed as injurious, there has been an increase in destructive rodents formerly held in check by hawks, with the result that these animals have done severe damage to agricultural interests.

The Cooper's hawk and the goshawk are the principal species that are destructive to game, with the marsh hawk to be added in certain localities where pheasants and other game birds that range in the open are concerned. It may be permissible to keep these hawks in check, and to include among those to be killed the occasional individual of the red-tailed hawk or other species that acquires the habit of coming to the farmyard for chickens. There is, however, no excuse whatever for the widespread slaughter of all kinds of hawks that has been the fate of these birds for years.

Sportsmen have justified the indiscriminate killing of hawks on the ground that they were conserving game; in other words, with the excuse that they were providing more game for men to kill. Nowadays, with nature lovers, who do not hunt, equaling sportsmen in numbers, some consideration may be given to the rights of those who enjoy seeing hawks alive and studying their interesting ways, aside from the value that most of these birds have from their beneficial food habits.

Action should be directed against the injurious individuals rather than toward the group as a whole, for the killing of most hawks is as foolish a policy as would be the wholesale destruction of any other element that contributes to our welfare.

The majestic bald eagle, our national bird, has also fallen under the displeasure of some farmers and has been rather relentlessly hunted.

Bird lovers have taken up the fight on behalf of this great bird of freedom, declaring that he has been misrepresented and that his occasional thefts of poultry are more than offset by services in keeping our beaches clean of dead fish.

ABILITY OF EAGLES TO CARRY WEIGHT EXAGGERATED

The carrying or lifting power of hawks and eagles has been frequently exaggerated. The largest eagles can carry off young lambs and fawns, but in these the weight is not great. In observations in Montana, Cameron found that the golden eagle could bear away jack rabbits that weighed seven pounds or more. One seized and bore aloft a small cat, but dropped it quickly when the cat realized its plight and got into action.

Larger prey may be killed, but it is eaten on the spot and not carried away. Though the strongest eagles may be able to raise a weight of 10 or 12 pounds, it is doubtful whether they could carry this for more than a few feet.

The hawk tribe consists of fierce, aggressive birds, and there is widespread belief in stories of eagles attempting to carry off children. Probably such tales are based in the main on the fierce manner in which these birds often swoop at those who intrude near their nests.

In Greek mythology we read the fanciful story of Ganymede, the beautiful Phrygian shepherd boy who was carried off by an eagle to Olympus to serve as cup-bearer to the gods. Also, in every mountainous country where there are eagles, there are current stories of the predatory attacks of these birds on children.

Possibly in primitive times, if small babies were left exposed, an eagle might have attacked them, just as it would a kid

Photograph by William L. and Irene Finley

WEIGHING FROM 20 TO 25 POUNDS, THIS CALIFORNIA CONDOR HAD TO BACK-
STROKE VIGOROUSLY IN LANDING ON THE PERCH

Photograph by A. A. Allen

DOWN BUT NOT OUT

A young sparrow hawk, not at all sure of the photographer's good intentions, assumes a characteristic defensive attitude. However, despite the belligerent pose, this species is perhaps the most
friendly and sociable of all the hawks. When fully grown, the bird will not measure a foot in length.

Photograph by William L. and Irene Finley

NEARLY EIGHT WEEKS OLD AND HARDLY HANDSOME

A young California condor still in the downy stage, whose feet seem to be growing faster than the rest of him.

or a lamb under the same circumstances; but such a happening in the present day would be quite improbable.

In the Philippine Islands the powerful monkey-eating eagle (*Pithecophaga jefferyi*), a bird weighing from 16 to 20 pounds, is believed by the natives to attack men. R. C. McGregor was told of an instance where one of these birds, in protecting its nest, killed a Negrito; but he did not place entire credence in the story, as it came to him through hearsay.

When their nests are disturbed, falcons and other hawks swoop fiercely at the heads of intruders, and on occasion may actually strike a climber and cut him with their claws. But such attacks are usually more threatening than serious, though they are executed with a vicious dash that might well frighten the timorous.

SOME HAWKS WHISTLE, CHATTER, AND LAUGH

Among the Indians of North America is a widespread belief in a "thunder bird" of huge size. The legend may be based on former wide distribution of the California condor, or possibly on the extinct condor

known as *Teratornis merriami*, a huge bird whose bones are found in Ice Age fossil deposits in California and Florida.

The voice of most hawks is a harsh sound that in many instances is as wild in tone as the fierce birds themselves. Uttered as they float on broad pinions high in air, the weird cadences of their screams seem fitting and appropriate to the spreading landscapes they survey. Some species utter piercing whistles, others chattering calls. In some the notes are quite pleasing, though none possesses what might be termed a song. The adult turkey vulture is entirely silent except for a hiss, though the young are vociferous.

The strangest notes that I have heard from birds of this group have come from the handsome laughing falcons (*Herpetotheres cachinnans*) of the American Tropics. My first experience with these birds was in the Argentine Chaco near the Pilcomayo River, at that time a wild region where ranchers were just beginning to invade the territory of the primitive Toba Indians.

On my first evening in this remote section, I was engaged at twilight in setting

Photograph by A. A. Allen

A PAIR OF DUCK HAWKS HAVE CHOSEN FOR THEIR NESTING PLACE A HIGH AND
SECLUDED LEDGE NEAR TAUGHANNOCK FALLS, NEW YORK STATE

The eggs were laid on the shelf of rock in the lower left foreground, where the young birds
may be seen. One of their parents keeps a watchful eye out to see that no danger threatens them.
The falls are 215 feet high, which is higher than Niagara Falls.

traps for little mammals at the edge of a forest. I remained on the alert for any possible dangers in a country that was new to me, as many tales had been told regarding the Indians.

Suddenly, through the trees a hundred yards away, came a loud shouting sound, repeated steadily, then varied at short intervals with a series of other calls, all uttered in curiously human tones. After a minute or two, another voice joined the first, and the two called rapidly in a strange medley that left me completely puzzled as to whether the authors were bird, beast, or human, as I crouched among the bushes, gun in hand, with my skin tingling pleasantly at the thrill of the unknown in a strange and possibly dangerous land.

It was a day or two later that I traced these weird, unearthly duets to the large white-headed, bushy-crested laughing falcons that were found in pairs everywhere through the forests.

The flight and appearance of hawks and other birds, and certain of their anatomical features, were used by the augurs of ancient Rome in their prophecies of the future.

INDIANS USE EAGLE FEATHERS AS ADORNMENT

A more practical use of these birds was found among the North American Indians, particularly of the Plains and Pueblo groups, when beautiful headdresses were made from the large feathers of the golden eagle, and other ornaments and decorations

YOUNG MARSH HAWKS LOOK LIKE "TEDDY BEARS"

Young marsh hawks photographed in a nest in Oakland County, Michigan. The nest was located
in an area of dry marsh covering perhaps five acres.

were fashioned from the smaller feathers of
this bird and from the feathers of hawks.
The downy bases of the eagle feathers sometimes were twisted in strands that were
woven into feather blankets of a peculiar
and interesting type. Hawks and eagle
claws were used to make necklaces and
other decorations.

The Pueblo Indians kept hawks in captivity, as they did turkeys and macaws,
presumably to use their feathers in their
prayers and decorations. Numbers of
bones of eagles and hawks were found in
the excavations of the National Geographic
Society at Pueblo Bonito. Certain rooms
seem to have been given up to these birds.

Occasionally hawks have been eaten for
human food, but this is not a widespread
practice. In Puerto Rico and Haiti I found
that in some sections the natives considered
the red-tailed hawk an excellent meat. The
sharp-shinned hawk is eaten occasionally
in the United States. From personal experience I can say that they have a fair
flavor.

From the earliest times of which we have
record, hawks of various kinds have been
trained by man for use in hunting.

For this purpose young hawks are taken
from the nest, or adult birds are trapped
alive. In either case, the birds are accustomed to man and his ways and are trained
to come to be fed until they are tame and
can be handled. They have the eyes covered with a soft leather hood and thongs
attached to their legs, by which they may
be tethered if desired. In hunting, trained
hawks are taken afield until game is sighted,
when the hood is removed, so that the hawk
may sight the quarry.

As it flies, the hawk ordinarily maneuvers
so as to rise and strike down at the game
from above. In the case of wily, fast-
flying birds, there is often a prolonged pursuit, in which only the most skillful hawk
may hope to be victorious.

The peregrine falcon, distributed over
most of the world, has been a favorite with
hawkers, because it is fierce and at the same
time is tractable in training. Several other
falcons have been used, but to less extent.

These birds kill their prey in swift flight
in air, striking a quick blow with the foot
that knocks the victim end over end and
frequently kills it outright. The goshawk
is also used in hunting. This species kills

in short, swift flight, bears its prey to the ground, and holds fast with its long claws until its quarry is dead.

Among native peoples of Central Asia, the golden eagle is trained to hunt small antelopes, foxes, and even wolves. These heavy birds are carried afield perched on horses or on stands swung between two horses. In some cases they rest on a heavy leathern gauntlet on the forearm of the hunter, whose arm is supported in a forked stick resting in the stirrup.

Scenes depicting hunting with hawks are found among the ancient paintings in the tombs of Egypt, and this sport was well known in India, Asia, and Europe at a very early date. Practiced originally to obtain wild game for food, it finally developed into the sport of the nobility and the wealthy. Though it fell into decadence with the development of gunpowder and guns, it is even practiced to-day in a limited way, both abroad and in our own country.

The smallest of the hawk group are the little falconets of the Indian region and Africa. They are not much larger than bluebirds, but are as fierce as the largest falcons. They eat many insects and also kill small birds and mammals. They have been known to kill birds four times their own weight, and are so aggressive that in captivity they often dominate other hawks much larger and stronger.

The largest members of the group are the larger vultures of the Old World and the condors of America, which reach a length of 40 to 50 inches, with a spread of wings that is broad in proportion.

The nests and eggs of hawks vary widely in location and appearance. The majority build nests of sticks and branches in trees, where they are often located at a considerable height from the ground. Some of the larger eagles and vultures nest on cliffs and rock ledges, where the sites may be reached only by the boldest of climbers.

Marsh hawks nest on the ground in prairie or marsh regions; sparrow hawks occupy holes in trees. Falcons lay their eggs in cavities in the face of cliffs, or occupy the abandoned nests of other hawks or of rooks and similar birds.

In some species the same nesting site is used for many years in succession. Since new material is added annually to the nest, in many cases it may grow to huge proportions. This is especially true with birds like the ospreys and eagles.

The eggs of this group are moderate in size relative to the bulk of the parent. They have strong, heavy shells, usually with roughly granular surface.

© Press Cliche

TRIBESMEN OF RUSSIAN CENTRAL ASIA SET OFF FOR A DAY'S SPORT WITH THEIR HUNTING EAGLES

California Condor

(Gymnogyps californianus)

Average Length, Fifty Inches

The California condor shares with the condor of South America the honor of being the largest living hawklike bird found in the New World, exceeding in size the largest of the eagles, and being much larger than its relatives, the turkey and black vultures.

Formerly quite abundant, according to the most recent estimates (in 1936), possibly twenty individuals still exist in California. Little is known of them in Baja California, save that they have been killed for their quills which are used as containers for gold dust. On their last stronghold in this region in the San Pedro Mártir mountains a single bird was the only one observed in 1935. Few remain, and the species is one that may easily become extinct.

In days past, the California condor ranged into open valleys and other regions where it was easily accessible, but, to see it now, it is usually necessary to penetrate the wildest and most difficult mountain sections.

By those who penetrate its haunts, the condor is confused with no other bird. Straining eyes may examine distant eagles and turkey buzzards, but when a condor is sighted there is no mistaking it for its smaller relatives. Its enormous size and the broad sweep of its wings distinguish it almost at a glance when it is far distant. When nearer at hand it is marked by prominent white patches on the under side of the wings.

The condor uses soaring flight as consistently as does the turkey vulture, but is more a master of the air and can travel at higher speed. The birds range widely over the mountains, but seem to have certain limits within which they may be found at all seasons of the year. Several may occur together, except during the nesting season, when they separate into pairs and resent intrusion of others.

Although not ordinarily quarrelsome, it is said that, when provoked, the condor can drive the golden eagle from its haunts.

The food of the condor is composed of the flesh of dead animals, either fresh or in a state of decay. The feet are not adapted for seizing, but the birds hold down their food while they tear it apart with their strong bills. A diet of carrion would seem to be taken partly because the birds have no other choice. In captivity they are fed on fresh meat, and individuals, when accustomed to this ration, have refused to take flesh that was at all tainted.

The size of the California condor is indicated by its wing spread, which ranges by actual measurement from 8 feet 4 inches to 9 feet 9 inches. There are numerous reports of birds with a breadth of wing in excess of the maximum given, but these seem to be based on estimate and have not been substantiated.

Though many statements that attribute larger size to the South American condor have been made, authentic measurements indicate that it and the California condor are similar in size.

The California condor places its single egg on the bare surface in a recess, cave, or pothole on a rocky cliff, often in a cavern formed by leaning slabs of stone, and formerly was reported nesting in hollow tree trunks and hollow logs. The egg, found from January to March, is white with a bluish or greenish tinge, and measures about 4½ by 2½ inches, or about the size of the egg of the domestic goose.

The young when hatched are covered with white down, except for the head, which is bare. With growth the down changes in color to gray and is finally replaced by the full covering of feathers. From captive individuals it appears that these birds are not adult until they are more than three years old. Young birds utter curious hissing, growling calls, but adults are silent.

The nestlings grow slowly and are under parental care for about six months before they are able to fly. They seem to have greater longevity than most birds, since three living in captivity in the National Zoological Park in Washington, D. C., are now thirty-five years or more old.

The slowness in growth in the young, and the single egg produced each season give these birds a rate of reproduction that does not allow them to cope with any unusual loss of life in their ranks. It seems probable also that adults may not nest every year under these circumstances. With settlement of the country the condor has decreased steadily and only careful protection can maintain it in its present restricted haunts. As it is given that encouragement at the present time the species may persist for years to come, but with its numbers at such low ebb any unusual circumstance may serve to exterminate it.

Its onetime abundance is attested by the many condor bones that have been taken from tar pits of Pleistocene origin in California where the birds were trapped when they came to feast on the bodies of other victims of these sticky pitch deposits. Though common during the period of settlement in California, early travelers have little to say about them.

The California condor in historic times ranged from the Columbia River south along the western slopes of the Sierra Nevada, and from Humboldt County, in the same State, through the Coast Ranges into northern Baja California, extending casually into Oregon, Washington, and southeastern California.

It is now confined to the Coast Ranges in northern Ventura County, southwestern Kern County, and southeastern Santa Barbara County, ranging casually outside this area when attracted by carrion, and to the San Pedro Mártir Range of northern Baja California. Its bones are found in ancient caves in Texas, Nevada, and New Mexico, and in Ice Age deposits in California and Florida.

THE MAJESTIC CALIFORNIA CONDOR SURVEYS ITS MOUNTAINOUS DOMAIN

Only a few individuals remain of the once quite abundant **California Condor** (perched bird and one flying close above, adults; upper and lower flying figures, immature). Some observers have called the South American condor larger, but accurate measurements prove these "largest living hawklike birds found in the New World" to be of similar size. Formerly, this giant flyer frequently soared over villages and cultivated valleys, but now it must be sought in the wildest mountain areas. In flight, the species is readily identified by large white patches on the under sides of the wings.

Black Vulture

(Coragyps atratus atratus)
Average Length, Twenty-four Inches

The black vulture is distinguished from the turkey buzzard, even at a distance, by its short, square-ended tail, and by the peculiar method of flight in which the wings are flapped rapidly, followed by a short sail with stiffly extended pinions. Large light patches across the ends of the wings form another prominent mark for field identification.

The black vulture subsists on carrion, and often gathers in greedy hordes that soon pick clean the bones of large carcasses. It is active and aggressive, and at its feasts will drive away the meeker-spirited turkey vulture. It kills young chickens, young pigs, and lambs when opportunity offers, so at times it may be quite destructive.

Occasionally it utters a low, guttural note, quickly repeated, that is barely audible a hundred yards away.

Because of their scavenger services, these birds are seldom molested and often become so tame as to be almost domestic, coming into towns to feed familiarly with dogs on refuse in the streets and barely moving aside to avoid passing animals or men.

They often frequent heron and pelican rookeries, where they pick up dead fish beneath the nests, and also swallow young birds left unprotected.

Black vultures roost in colonies and when common may be highly gregarious so that a thousand individuals come at nightfall to one roost. They are common in the southern United States and in tropical America are abundant, scores of them frequenting towns and country houses. On clear days they rise by dozens to circle high overhead, often remaining for hours suspended in the air, with motionless wings. In rainy weather they are usually inactive, like the turkey vulture.

The nest is placed on the ground, usually under dense bushes, but occasionally in hollow trees, logs, or recesses beneath bowlders. The eggs rest on leaves or on the bare ground. Where abundant, the birds often breed in colonies. Two eggs constitute the usual set, with one or three found occasionally. The color is light green, spotted rather sparingly with brown and lavender.

The young when hatched are covered with buff-colored down quite different from the white found in the turkey vulture. The nestlings are fed entirely by regurgitation.

These birds are not known to carry food or any other object in the feet or in the bill.

The black vulture is found from western Texas, southern Illinois, and southern Maryland south into Mexico and Central America, being recorded casually north of its regular range. An allied form is known in South America.

Turkey Vulture

(Cathartes aura septentrionalis)
Average Length, Thirty Inches

A master of the art of soaring, the turkey vulture or turkey buzzard wheels in the sky by the hour, turning in lazy circles and spirals, seldom moving the wings except to adjust them to the air currents through which it moves to maintain its elevation. Although graceful on the wing, when at rest all attractiveness of appearance is lost.

With broad wings folded against its relatively slender body, its bare head and its awkward attitude, the buzzard seems uncouth or even repulsive.

Like other members of the family, it subsists on the bodies of dead creatures, eaten fresh or in advanced stages of decomposition. I have had them come to tear the flesh from the body of a dead bird that I had just skinned, and have found them feasting on putrid flesh.

For many years turkey vultures were protected all through the Southern States for their services in clearing away carrion, but recently there has been a growing belief that they have been responsible for the spread of anthrax and hog cholera by feeding on bodies of animals dead from these diseases, and then carrying the germs to uninfected pastures. In some sections they have been subjected to persecution and bounties have even been paid for their destruction. Reports of their spreading disease seem without foundation, and the birds should not be molested.

Turkey vultures by day cover wide areas in search of food, and at night gather to sleep in some tract of woodland, several hundred often congregating in one roost. In early morning they sit with wings expanded to catch the warmth of the sun, and on dull, cloudy days, when the air is still, may remain in their roosts throughout the day, as without moving currents of air they find flying difficult.

The turkey vulture places its nest in some recess beneath large bowlders, in a hollow log or tree, or in sheltered situations beneath shrubs. The handsome eggs, usually two in number, rarely one or three, are creamy white, spotted with brown and lavender. Occasionally one is found without markings.

The young bird when disturbed utters a curious growling, hissing call, like some angry cat, turning its back the while and striking the ground sharply with the tips of its spread wings in a manner that is truly startling. The adult is silent except for a hiss made by expelling its breath from the windpipe.

The turkey vulture ranges from southern British Columbia, Wisconsin, and central New York south into northern Mexico. Closely allied forms extend through Cuba and Central and South America to the Falkland Islands. The bird has been introduced into Puerto Rico.

MASTERS OF SOARING ARE CARRION-EATING VULTURES

More popularly known as buzzards, these big, repulsive birds are widely protected because of their services as scavengers. A short, square-ended tail and a peculiar flapping flight identify the aggressive **Black Vulture** (upper), which apparently cannot carry food or anything else in its feet or bill. Hour after hour the familiar **Turkey Vulture** (lower) wheels lazily through the sky, rarely moving its wings except to meet new air currents. Finding it difficult to fly on windless days, large numbers are often temporarily grounded.

Swallow-tailed Kite

(Elanoïdes forficatus forficatus)
Average Length, Twenty-four Inches

The swallow-tailed kite, delighting in its aerial powers, spends hours on the wing wheeling and turning without apparent effort. The deeply forked tail, the white plumage, and black wings and tail form unmistakable marks for field identification.

This species feeds extensively on snakes and also eats lizards and large insects. All food is seized expertly in the feet, and the birds customarily eat while flying, tearing their prey apart with their bills. They are believed to be entirely beneficial.

In early days these handsome birds were common and in the summer season often associated in flocks of ten or twelve that circled over or through the trees. In hunting for food they quarter back and forth near the ground like marsh hawks, but when soaring may rise so high in the air that they are seen with difficulty.

Their grace in flight is especially shown about the nest as they pause in air to hover over their eggs, lowering the body gradually to cover them. When alarmed they rise directly from the nest instead of gliding off over the edge.

The nest of the swallow-tailed kite is built in trees, often from 60 to 125 feet from the ground, and is composed of twigs and moss, the nesting material being seized while flying. Two eggs generally constitute a set, although from one to four may be found. These vary in ground color from dull white to a delicate cream, and are spotted and blotched with brown. The call is shrill and high-pitched, being heard mainly during the nesting season.

Formerly this beautiful hawk was common throughout the eastern United States, but in the last 30 years its numbers have lessened steadily, and now it is found mainly in the southern section.

The species breeds locally from Minnesota, Indiana, and North Carolina south into Florida and eastern Mexico, wintering south of the United States. An allied form is found in Central and South America.

Mississippi Kite

(Ictinia misisippiensis)
Average Length, Fourteen Inches

The Mississippi kite is another species that spends hours in the air in tireless movement.

The food of this bird consists principally of insects, with occasional reptiles and frogs. Near Lawrence, Kansas, one September I encountered a band of a dozen coursing over a range of low hills, and at intervals darting down to seize a cicada. Held in the hawk's foot, the insect buzzed protestingly until, without a pause in the bird's flight, it was swal-lowed. During several days' observation I did not once see these birds resting on a perch while feeding.

The Mississippi kite builds a small nest composed of twigs, in part with leaves still attached, placed in trees from 25 to 60 feet from the ground. The birds breed in May and June, later in the season than most species of this family.

The eggs number two or three and are pale bluish white, without markings, though often stained by the decaying green leaves of the nest lining. One brood is reared each season. The immature bird in the first fall is whitish below, streaked with dark brown and buffy.

The illustration shows the adult bird, the immature in fall being whitish below streaked with dark brown and buffy.

This kite nests from northeastern Kansas, southern Illinois, and South Carolina south to Texas and Florida. In winter it is found from Florida and Texas to Guatemala. It has been noted casually from Colorado to Pennsylvania and New Jersey.

White-tailed Kite

(Elanus leucurus majusculus)
Average Length, Fifteen and One-half Inches

Like related kites, this species is master of the air and flies with extreme ease and skill. It delights in high winds, breasting them like a gull without the slightest difficulty. In fact its light color combined with its graceful flight gives it definite resemblance to a gull, especially at a distance.

It is found over tree-dotted prairies and savannas, marshes, and semi-open valleys. Though fifty years ago it was common, it has decreased steadily until now it is to be classed among our unusual birds. Despite the fact that it has been afforded protection in recent years, the species does not seem able to increase.

The white-tailed kite, in feeding, frequently hovers with rapidly beating wings over one spot for several minutes, watching the vegetation beneath closely, ready to pounce down whenever prey appears. It lives on small snakes, lizards, frogs, and large insects, and seems to be entirely beneficial.

The note of this kite is said to be somewhat like that of the osprey, but terminating in a guttural or grating sound.

The nest, built of twigs and lined with soft materials, is placed from 25 to 50 feet from the ground.

The white-tailed kite is found in California from the upper Sacramento Valley and Humboldt County, south to northern Baja California, and from Texas, Oklahoma, and Florida to Guatemala.

An allied form ranges in South America, and similar species are found in the other inhabited continents.

STREAMLINED KITES DISPLAY SWALLOWLIKE GRACE IN FLIGHT

Formerly common throughout the eastern United States, the spirited **Swallow-tailed Kite** (above) is now found mainly in the South. Like other kites, it seizes its food in its claws and usually eats on the wing, using its bill as knife, fork, and spoon. A tireless aerial performer is the **Mississippi Kite** (lower plate, figure at right and flying bird). The **White-tailed Kite** (lower plate, at left) breasts high winds with the gusto of a gull. Common fifty years ago, it is now rarely observed.

Everglade Kite

(Rostrhamus sociabilis plumbeus)
Average Length, Eighteen Inches

This resident of fresh-water marshes is suggestive in form, white rump, and method of flight of the much larger, longer-tailed marsh hawk. It enjoys soaring, frequently ascending to considerable altitudes, but does not have the graceful, accomplished flight of our other kites. The everglade kite is sociable, and, where plentiful, a hundred may be observed together. In Florida, however, it has been so reduced that flocks are unusual.

The birds utter a rasping, chattering call of little volume, and are especially noisy during the mating and nesting season.

For food this kite depends on the large fresh-water snails belonging to the genus formerly called *Ampullaria*, known now as *Pomacea*. The kite seizes them in its long claws and bears them away to some low limb or mound, where, with the slender, sharply hooked bill, it draws the snail from its shell. Occasionally the kite extracts its food as it flies, dropping the shell when empty. I have seen accumulations of dozens of the shells gathered beneath favored perches. So far as known, this kite eats no other food. Such extreme specialization in diet is unusual among birds. The slender form of the bill and the claws, developed for this peculiar habit, is remarkable.

The everglade kite in Florida nests from January to May, the season varying locally. The nest is made of small twigs placed in a myrtle or other bush, in the top of a clump of saw grass, or, rarely, in a tree, being usually at only a few feet elevation and ordinarily above water.

The eggs number two to five or rarely six, two or three making the usual set. The ground color is pale greenish white spotted with rusty brown, the spots in most cases being so numerous as almost to conceal the lighter base. The young of the everglade kite are fed on the same large snails relished by the adult, the parent usually bringing food in the crop and feeding its family by regurgitation.

In the United States the everglade kite is found only in Florida. To the south it ranges in Cuba, eastern Mexico, and Central America, and a closely allied race occurs in South America as far as Argentina.

Marsh Hawk

(Circus hudsonius)
Average Length, Male, Nineteen Inches; Female,
Twenty-two Inches

The marsh hawk, an inhabitant of open country, ranging over prairie regions, grasslands, and cultivated fields, is marked by its slender form, long tail, and a prominent white spot on the rump. Except during migration or in mating season, this bird seldom flies far above the ground for any great length of time.

It is entirely predatory, feeding on mice, ground squirrels, and other small mammals, as well as snakes, lizards, frogs, and insects. In addition, it captures a good many ground-inhabiting birds, especially in summer and fall, when young birds are about. At times it kills game birds and in some localities, particularly where pheasants are stocked, the marsh hawk has proved a pest. In general, however, it is beneficial, and should not be destroyed except where it is found to be actually injurious to game.

The contention that it is universally injurious to quail has been found untrue, and no action leading to the destruction of the marsh hawk should be taken without definite evidence against it.

In the mating season these birds rise in curious aerial evolutions in which the males especially wheel and tumble in the air. At this season they utter shrill, screaming calls, but during the rest of the year they are silent.

The flight is easy and graceful and birds seem tireless on the wing. Hour after hour they quarter and turn over meadow, field, or prairie with head bent down to watch the ground beneath. At any movement in the grass the bird pauses instantly to hover and then drops down with long, slender legs extended to seize its prey. Its food is eaten on the ground, and the earth is usually its resting place when it is not on the wing. It is a species adapted entirely to life in the open, unlike most of the family to which it belongs.

As a peculiar feature, the face in this species is surrounded by short, stiffened feathers forming a ruff like that found in owls, a feature that is present in no other group of hawks.

The marsh hawk places its nest on the ground, usually in a marsh or on a prairie, ordinarily at the foot of a bush or a clump of grass, and in marshy ground on a tussock. It is composed mainly of dried weed stems and grass, sometimes with a foundation of twigs, lined with fine grasses and feathers.

From four to six eggs constitute a set. These are pale greenish or bluish white in color, usually without markings, though at times blotched and spotted with brown. The male is attentive to the female during incubation, bringing her food, which she often rises to seize in the air as he drops it.

As is often the case with ground-nesting birds, the young wander about on foot near the nest before they are able to fly.

The marsh hawk breeds from northwestern Alaska, central Quebec, and Newfoundland south to northern Baja California, southern Texas, and southeastern Virginia. In winter it is found from British Columbia and the northern United States south to the Bahamas, Cuba, Haiti, Puerto Rico, and Colombia.

A KITE THAT EATS SNAILS AND A HAWK THAT WEARS A RUFF

Fresh-water marshes in Florida afford feeding grounds and nesting sites to the sociable **Everglade Kite** (upper, adult perched and immature flying). It apparently eats no other food than a certain kind of fresh-water snail which the bird draws from its shell with a slender, hooked bill. The **Marsh Hawk** (lower, female with young, male flying) is adorned with an owllike ruff of short stiff feathers around the face. Entirely predatory, feeding on small mammals, snakes, frogs, and insects, it is, on the whole, a beneficial species.

DREADED OGRES OF THE BIRD WORLD ARE TWO RUTHLESS COUSINS

While all hawks are rapacious predators, most of them help man by eating animals and insects that injure his crops, livestock, or poultry. But by destroying beneficial birds the widely distributed **Sharp-shinned Hawk** (upper, adult female) makes an enemy of man. **Cooper's Hawk** (lower, adult male) is distinguished from the sharp-shin by its larger size and round-ended tail. Prince of bird assassins, it fairly deserves the title of "chicken hawk," a name unjustly applied to many of its larger relatives.

Sharp-shinned Hawk
(*Accipiter velox velox*)

Average Length, Male, Eleven and One-quarter
Inches; Female, Thirteen and One-half Inches

This small hawk, one of the most widely
distributed of the group in North America,
is an inhabitant of thickets and woodland.
It may be readily identified by its short wings
and long tail, the square end of the latter
distinguishing it from the larger Cooper's
hawk. Though fiercely predatory, flying
swiftly in pursuit of prey, this bird spends
long periods resting quietly in trees or bushes.
As it usually perches among limbs or leaves,
it is often overlooked until it flies.

The sharp-shin feeds almost entirely on
birds and is highly destructive. Although it
preys mainly on small species, such as sparrows and warblers, it does not hesitate to attack birds as large as itself, regularly killing
quail, mourning doves, and flickers.

In hunting the sharp-shin darts suddenly
through or over trees and thickets to the open
borders of fields or pastures where small birds
are congregated, to seize one of their number
before all can gain safe cover. Should all
escape, the hawk often perches quietly, watching until some movement betrays its quarry,
then stoops swiftly to the attack.

Its prey is seized in its long, sharp claws,
which grip closely and penetrate the body.
The hawk then remains on the ground, or rises
to a perch to eat. The larger feathers are
plucked carefully from its catch and then the
meat is torn in bits that are small enough to be
swallowed. This hawk is destructive to young
poultry, as well as to wild birds, and is one of
the hawks that should be kept in check.

In southward migration in fall, these hawks
often follow definite lines of flight, so that
thousands may pass leisurely by certain points
in the course of a few days. Sometimes during
these flights stuffed owls are used as decoys to
attract the hawks, so that they may be shot.

The sharp-shinned hawk makes a bulky nest
of twigs, sometimes without an inner lining,
but often with a slight padding of soft bark
or a few feathers. The nest is frequently
placed in pines or spruces against the trunk
of a projecting limb from 20 to 50 or more
feet from the ground. Three to five eggs usually make a set. The sharp-shin is bold in
defense of its nest and I have had one strike
fiercely at me, returning with chattering calls
to the attack time after time.

The immature sharp-shin has the underparts longitudinally streaked with dusky. The
female is much larger than the male.

This species breeds throughout most of the
United States and Canada from the northern
limit of trees south to Florida, Texas, and
south-central California. In winter it is found
from British Columbia and the northern United
States south to Panama.

Cooper's Hawk
(*Accipiter cooperi*)

Average Length, Male, Fifteen and One-half
Inches; Female, Nineteen Inches

This hawk, in appearance and habits, is
a large edition of the sharp-shin. Since the
sexes differ markedly in size, the female being
much larger, a small male Cooper's hawk is
about the size of a large female sharp-shin,
the rounded instead of the square-ended tail
offering the most evident character for distinguishing between the two.

The Cooper's hawk is the ogre in the world
of our birds. Fierce and ruthless, it attacks
grouse or other species as large as itself, and
destroys smaller birds without the slightest
difficulty. It darts through thickets with such
ease that it is difficult for its victims to
find cover for safe sanctuary. Rabbits and
other small mammals and reptiles are often
seized.

Like the sharp-shin, this hawk lives in
wooded country, finding partly forested sections especially to its liking. In hunting it
frequently rests quietly in a tree near the edge
of a clearing and when birds appear pounces
on them before they can escape.

In its flight it alternates between flapping
its rounded wings, and sailing. Usually it
travels at high speed only when in pursuit of a
fleeing bird.

The bird is bold and fearless in pursuit
of its quarry, and has been known to return
several times to attack a chicken, even when
people were present and threatening it. It
is one of the hawks that merit the name of
"chicken hawk" and must be considered entirely destructive. Indeed, it is responsible
for much of the damage in the hen-yard for
which its larger relatives that live more in the
open get the blame. It is also a consistent
enemy of ruffed grouse and quail.

This species often follows the lines of fall
migration frequented by the sharp-shin, but
is less abundant; so that it is killed by hunters
along these flyways in smaller numbers.

Cooper's hawks may appropriate the last
year's nest of crows or other hawks, or may
build a new structure. In either case the nests
are composed of coarse twigs lined with finer
material of the same kind, the whole frequently mixed with fragments of bark.

The eggs range from three to five in number,
with the ground bluish white or greenish white,
sometimes plain, but more often spotted with
brown. In the nesting season the Cooper's
hawk is quite noisy, uttering loud, harsh notes
that are rapidly repeated. The immature bird
is streaked underneath with dusky.

The Cooper's hawk nests from southern
British Columbia, southern Quebec and Nova
Scotia south through the United States into
northern Mexico. In winter it is found south
into Costa Rica.

THE FIERCE GOSHAWK KILLS GAME BIRDS AND POULTRY

When its hunting instincts are aroused, the destructive **Goshawk** (above) will return to a chicken
yard even after being stung with shot. Inhabiting the forests of the North and of the high mountains,
it invades the Central States when food fails and then becomes the foremost enemy of the ruffed grouse.
The Southwest's **Harris's Hawk** (below), although graceful and accomplished in flight, is more sedentary
than most hawks, being content to sit for hours surveying the countryside from a favorite perch.

Goshawk

(Astur atricapillus)

Average Length, Male, Twenty-two Inches;
Female, Twenty-four Inches

The goshawk, one of the fiercest and most destructive of our birds of prey, exceeding some of the falcons in this respect, inhabits the forests of the north and of the western mountains. It comes south sporadically from the far north during winters when there is a failure of its food supply, but at other times seldom is seen except along our northern border. Its flight is swift and powerful, and I have seen it easily overtake grouse and other fast-flying birds on the wing.

In the north the goshawk eats Arctic hares, lemmings, and ptarmigan. In its southern invasions it is the foremost enemy of the ruffed grouse, so that in the year following a goshawk flight there always is noted a decrease in these game birds.

It kills with the greatest ferocity, so that any creature marked as its prey may escape only with difficulty. While it ranges the country on the wing when hunting, it also has the habit of watching quietly from a perch until prey appears, when it dashes out to pounce upon it. It is relentless in its pursuit and when its quarry takes to heavy cover the goshawk often enters the thickets and hunts on foot.

With these propensities, naturally this hawk is highly destructive to poultry, seizing chickens and boldly carrying them away. When its hunting instincts are aroused, it seems to lose all sense of fear, so that it will return for chickens even after having been stung with shot. It does not hesitate to attack other predatory birds and will fight with large owls until both combatants are killed.

This is one of the hawks trained by falconers that have been used extensively in hunting.

In its periodic invasions from the North it spreads in hundreds through the Northern and Central States. At such times many are killed by hunters.

The goshawk builds bulky nests of sticks in either conifers or deciduous trees, but usually in heavy forest. The bird is fierce in defense of its home and will not hesitate to attack a human intruder.

The eggs vary from two to five, with three or four as the usual number. They are pale bluish white, often unmarked, but sometimes with a few spots of brown. The call is a shrill note sharply repeated, being heard principally in the breeding season. The young in the first fall have the under surface streaked like the immature Cooper's hawk.

Two forms are recognized. The eastern goshawk, *Astur atricapillus atricapillus*, paler in color, breeds from Alaska, Quebec, and Nova Scotia south into British Columbia and the northern United States, extending south as far as western Maryland. In its sporadic southern flights it comes into the Central States and irregularly into the Southwest. The western goshawk, *Astur atricapillus striatulus*, nests in the Pacific coast region from Alaska south to California and northern Mexico.

Harris's Hawk

(Parabuteo unicinctus harrisi)

Average Length, Male, Nineteen Inches; Female, Twenty-two Inches

This is a handsomely colored hawk, common only in a restricted area in the United States. From present information it is most abundant in the lowland regions of southern Texas and in southeastern California. It is in these sections that most naturalists have made their observations on its habits.

In migration Harris's hawks travel at times in flocks, as bands containing several hundred have been reported. Ordinarily they are solitary, as is the case in most of their family.

Although accomplished in flight, so that it delights in turning in huge circles high in air, it often rests for hours on open perches from which it may survey the land.

In southern Texas it is remarked frequently on telephone poles along the highways. In this region it is fairly tame and unsuspicious, often allowing automobiles to pass without taking flight, but in other areas it has been reported as wary.

The call is a harsh scream, and the birds are quite noisy in the vicinity of their nests.

Though in South America a closely related form has been reported consorting with vultures and caracaras and feeding on carrion, such is far from the case here.

In Texas, Harris's hawk has been observed dashing quickly through mesquite thickets, searching for wood rats and ground squirrels, and in southeastern California Dr. Loye Miller found parts of a green-winged teal in the stomach of one, and other bird remains, including a gilded flicker, in another. They are said also to eat lizards, and seem, on the whole, to be beneficial in their habits.

The nests are composed of sticks, small branches, and weeds, lined with rootlets and grasses. They are placed in trees or sometimes on the tops of the Spanish bayonet or the giant cactus.

From two to four eggs are deposited, these being dull white or with a faint greenish tinge, some without markings and some spotted irregularly with brown or lavender. The birds ordinarily offer no objection when their nests are approached, beyond uttering their usual calls and circling in the air overhead.

Harris's hawk is found in southeastern California, southern Arizona and New Mexico and the lowlands of south Texas, extending to Louisiana and Mississippi, and ranging south into Baja California and Central America as far as Panama. It has been observed casually in Kansas and Iowa.

RODENTS, FROGS, REPTILES, AND INSECTS SATISFY HAWK APPETITES

Although the conspicuous **Red-tailed Hawk** (upper, adults perched and flying above, immature bird flying at left) occasionally eats ground-dwelling birds, it deserves protection because of the good it does by destroying insect and animal pests. Forested uplands are its favorite haunts. The **Red-shouldered Hawk** (lower, adult left, immature right), like its red-tailed cousin, continues to decrease in numbers year by year. In flight, it may be identified by narrow barring on the under wing surfaces.

Red-tailed Hawk
(Buteo borealis)
Average Length, Male, Twenty Inches; Female,
Twenty-three Inches

This fine bird, under the name of "chicken hawk," is universally known, as it is conspicuous and widely distributed, although ranging by preference in hilly or mountainous regions where there are forests. It is strong and graceful on the wing and spends hours in soaring in wide circles, sometimes so high in the air as to be almost out of sight. Its flight is not particularly swift, and it often rests for long periods on limbs or the tops of dead trees, where it has a commanding view.

The red-tail is preëminently a mouse hawk, meadow mice particularly being a staple article in its diet. It also eats other mice, squirrels, gophers, rabbits, kangaroo rats, wood rats, moles and shrews, has been known to attack skunks, and also kills snakes and lizards. In summer and fall, particularly in the Western States, it consumes many grasshoppers when these appear in pestilential abundance.

The red-tail is beneficial, meriting protection except where some individual acquires the habit of eating chickens. In spite of the good that it does, it is shot on every occasion and has been so reduced in many sections of the eastern United States that it is now a rare bird.

The red-tail spends hours resting on elevated perches often at the borders of weed-grown fields, and does most of its hunting by watchful observance of the ground about. Food is taken by a quick pounce.

Crows regard the red-tail with as much aversion as they do an owl and often gather in flocks to swoop and dart at the hawk on its perch while their cawing notes arouse the countryside. Neighbor crows at these alarms come from all directions until finally the red-tail sails away in disgust at the uproar.

The nest of the red-tail is a large structure of sticks, sometimes with a slight lining of soft materials. The eggs vary from two to four, being creamy white, occasionally unmarked, but ordinarily spotted with shades of brown. In the South these birds begin to nest in February, the nesting period being governed in the North by the opening of spring.

The voice is a high-pitched scream, a stirring sound usually being given as the birds circle high in the air. The immature bird in the first fall has the tail brown, barred with blackish.

This is one of the species that formerly appeared in southward migration in abundance, but the soaring flocks of early days are now things of the past and each year the birds seem to become fewer.

In its wide range from Alaska through central Canada to Nova Scotia and south through the United States, the red-tail is divided into five geographic forms, and others are found in the West Indies and Central America.

Red-shouldered Hawk
(Buteo lineatus)
Average Length, Male, Eighteen Inches; Female,
Twenty-two Inches

This common cousin of the red-tail ranges in wooded country, and can maintain itself where groves and trees border cultivated fields. Though it delights in soaring, it seems somewhat less active than the red-tail. It may be distinguished on the wing by the narrow barring of the under wing surface.

Like the red-tail the red-shouldered hawk may rest for hours on a perch in a large tree from which it can watch for food. It frequents especially the borders of woodland where it is partly concealed and does not rest in the open as frequently as the red-tail.

In the south the red-shoulder is often an inhabitant of timbered swamps but ranges also in open pine woods. The form found in California lives in woods growing in the broad, open valleys.

The food is highly varied, including mice, rats, snakes, frogs, fish, large insects, centipedes, spiders, crayfish, earthworms, and snails. It seems to take even fewer birds than the red-tail, and only occasional individuals acquire the chicken-killing habit or attack game birds. There are numerous instances on record where these birds have nested in woods adjacent to hen-yards without attempting in any way to molest the poultry.

Frogs form a favorite food, especially in spring. It eats quantities of grasshoppers when these are abundant, and like the red-tail it destroys many field mice.

This hawk should be protected. Many are now wantonly killed by hunters, so that the species is decreasing in many localities.

The nest of the red-shoulder is made of twigs, placed in trees often at a considerable elevation, but occasionally as low as 18 or 20 feet. The number of eggs in a set varies from two to six. Eggs without markings are rare.

The calls of the red-shouldered hawk are loud, wailing screams that may be heard for some distance. They are mimicked by the bluejay so perfectly that it is often difficult to distinguish the imitation.

The northern red-shouldered hawk (Buteo lineatus lineatus) ranges from southern Canada to southern Kansas and North Carolina, migrating to the Gulf coast in winter. The Florida red-shoulder (Buteo l. alleni), which is smaller, nests from Oklahoma and South Carolina to Louisiana and southeastern Florida.

The insular red-shoulder (Buteo l. extimus), still smaller and paler in color, is found in the Florida Keys.

The Texas red-shoulder (Buteo l. texanus), with richer color below, nests from southern Texas to Tamaulipas; and the red-bellied hawk (Buteo l. elegans), with more rufous below, is found in California and northwestern Baja California.

A DWELLER IN EASTERN WOODLANDS AND A LOVER OF THE OPEN PLAINS

The secretive **Broad-winged Hawk** (upper, adult perched, immature flying) hides among the leaves of forest trees in the Southeast and thus escapes the notice of the casual observer. Green leaves, sometimes replaced as fast as they wilt, are often worked into its nest. Because of its taste for insect and animal pests, the **Swainson's Hawk** (lower, adult in light phase on ground, light and dark phases flying) is regarded as a valuable ally of the western farmer.

Broad-winged Hawk

(Buteo platypterus)
Average Length, Fifteen Inches

The broad-wing, smaller than the red-shoulder and red-tail, lives in woodlands, where it is seen only by those conversant with its habits, as it perches usually under cover of the leaves. In soaring it frequently rises until it is nearly out of sight. Swampy woodlands and broken country covered with forests are favorite haunts of this species, and as the trees are cleared it decreases in abundance.

It is entirely inoffensive in its habits. Except in migration, comparatively few are shot, as most depart for the South before the season for fall hunting.

In fall the broad-wings frequently join with other migrating hawks and at times form considerable flocks. Their smaller size is sufficient to distinguish them from other species of similar outline.

This hawk hunts mainly in woodlands where the growth is open, though at times it circles over open ground. When prey is sighted it hovers briefly and then makes its kill. It may eat on the ground or may carry its food to a tree. Insects and frogs are sometimes hunted on foot on the ground.

The food is mainly mice and other small mammals, frogs, reptiles, and insects. It eats small fish occasionally, but seldom takes birds. Large caterpillars are a regular item in its diet. It is partial to grasshoppers, crickets, and large beetles, and has been known to eat centipedes. It must be considered beneficial and worthy of every protection.

The nests of the broad-wing are constructed of twigs, placed in a large tree, often at a considerable elevation. Green leaves are often found in the nest, and some birds add fresh leaves to the nest lining nearly every day. The eggs range in number from two to five, with two or three as the usual number. They are dull grayish white, or occasionally greenish, spotted more or less extensively with different shades of brown and lavender.

Occasionally these birds will dash at an intruder. I remember distinctly, as a small boy, the start that one of these hawks gave me by swooping at my head as I sat on a limb beside its nest, high above the ground, admiring the eggs and the nest construction. The ordinary call is a shrill, double-noted whistle high in pitch, which is accompanied by chattering, scolding notes.

The birds vary considerably in color and markings and occasional individuals are found that are entirely black.

The broad-winged hawk nests from central Alberta, New Brunswick, and Nova Scotia south to the Gulf coast and central Texas. It migrates south to northwestern South America, wintering mainly from southern Florida and southern Mexico southward.

Swainson's Hawk

(Buteo swainsoni)
Average Length, Twenty Inches

Swainson's hawk lives in regions where tree growth is scant. Though strong in flight and delighting in soaring, it spends hours resting on some open perch where it may watch the country. Except when it has been unduly persecuted, it is tame and unsuspicious, allowing close approach without taking alarm.

The food of this hawk is varied and includes more insects than usual in a bird of its size. It feeds extensively on grasshoppers in late summer and fall, and also eats mice, rats, lizards, snakes, frogs, and rabbits. Though on rare occasions it may attack poultry, it is considered one of the most valuable hawks in the West in its relation to agriculture.

Swainson's hawk nests in trees or on cliffs, where its bulky home, composed of sticks, is often visible at a distance. The eggs, varying from two to four, are greenish white or yellowish white, spotted with brown and lavender, occasionally being without markings.

Western kingbirds and Bullock's orioles often nest within a few feet of the large structure made by Swainson's hawk, and all live in harmony. Indeed, the home of a kingbird has been found located among the coarse sticks in the base of the hawk's nest.

In migration, both north and south, these hawks often gather in bands, from 500 to 2,000 birds having been noted in such groups.

As they continue southward, these bands appear to join, so that the greater part of the species pass through Central America in company. In Guatemala they travel south in October and return again in April, so that their flights coincide with the end and the beginning of the rainy season.

To the countryman they are known as the *azuacan* and their appearance is hailed as indication of change in season, though most do not recognize that they are species of the hawk family. Often all pass within the period of a few hours, their flights being one of the striking sights so far as birds are concerned in this area. On arrival in their winter or summer homes the flocks at once disperse and the birds then range alone or in pairs where food is available for them.

This hawk, like some of its relatives, has distinct light and dark color phases, these being illustrated in the flying birds of the opposite plate. Swainson's hawk has three of the outer primaries with the inner webs cut out or indented near the tip, and the red-tail has four. This difference will always serve to distinguish these birds in the hand.

This species breeds from British Columbia, Great Slave Lake, and Manitoba south to northern Mexico, and is found in winter in South America. Stragglers have been taken at many points in the Eastern States.

FEATHERED TO THE TOES, ROUGH-LEGGED HAWKS EASILY WITHSTAND COLD

The fierce-looking and powerful **American Rough-legged Hawk** (upper, light phase; adult on the limb, immature flying) rarely attacks other birds or poultry, but selects its victims among lemmings, mice, rabbits, and large insects. This hawk nests in the far north and migrates to the United States in the fall. The West's **Ferruginous Rough-legged Hawk** (lower, adult in light phase, left; dark phase on the wing) is so large and handsome that it is often mistaken for an eagle.

American Rough-legged Hawk

(Buteo lagopus s.johannis)

Average Length, Twenty-two Inches

From its summer home in the north, the American rough-leg comes into the United States in fall migration, often traveling in flocks. As the name indicates, the rough-legged hawks differ from our other species in having the leg feathered to the toes, a feature shared with several other birds of northern distribution that has been developed without question as a protection against cold.

Though less abundant than in former years this species still is common, as most nest in uninhabited sections of the north where they are not disturbed.

In fall they sometimes migrate south in flocks, though the bands of hundreds that I saw in the west thirty years ago are now far from common. The birds are strong and skillful in flight, and these migrant bands often spend hours in wheeling and turning in great spirals that carry them to high elevations.

In hunting the rough-leg frequents open lands, often in sections that are marshy, and is frequently seen feeding late in the evening, as it is then that mice are easily secured.

The American rough-leg is large and powerfully built, but, in spite of its strength, it feeds principally on mice, lemmings in the north and meadow mice in the south being staple foods. Rabbits are eaten where they are abundant, and large insects, such as grasshoppers, are eaten occasionally. The bird is entirely harmless, as it seldom kills other birds or poultry.

This hawk nests in the far north, ranging there in open country, seldom coming into densely forested areas. The nests are composed of sticks, the cavity lined with dry grass and feathers, and are built on ledges along bluffs or are placed in trees. The same location may be used for years, and the nest grows in bulk until it is of large size.

Eggs are two to five in number, with three or four making the usual set. One brood is reared each season.

The birds vary considerably in coloration from light to dark, but may always be distinguished by the feathered legs, or tarsi. The feather growth is heavy, particularly in fall and winter, so that the severest cold may be withstood. In the West they remain in the Northern States during the coldest weather of winter.

The note, heard mainly during the nesting reason, is a low mewing call, suggesting the sound made by a young kitten.

The American rough-leg nests from the Aleutian Islands, the Arctic coast of Alaska, and northern Quebec, south to northern Alberta and Newfoundland. In winter it is found from southern British Columbia, Colorado, and southern Ontario south to southern California, Texas, and North Carolina. Closely allied forms are found in Europe and Asia.

Ferruginous Rough-legged Hawk

(Buteo regalis)

Average Length, Twenty-three Inches

This handsome hawk, so large that it is often called an eagle, is found in regions of prairies and plains, avoiding heavy timber. It lives only in the western part of our continent, and in uninhabited sections still remains fairly common. However, when an increase in agriculture takes place in any part of its nesting ground, it is crowded out.

In much of its range it is known as "squirrel hawk," as ground squirrels and prairie dogs form a considerable part of its food. It also eats many pocket gophers. Birds, particularly meadowlarks, are captured during the summer season, and an occasional grouse may be taken, but these hawks are not known to harm poultry. They also eat large snakes. They are considered beneficial because of their destruction of harmful mammals.

Frequently hunting in pairs, they capture game that might otherwise escape. In hunting prairie dogs, the hawks rest until the animal is away from its burrow, when one gets between the prairie dog and its hole, thereby making capture an easy matter. The birds are strong and powerful and can carry rabbits to their nests with ease.

The nests are placed on cliffs, on sloping hillsides, or in trees, sometimes in localities difficult of access, sometimes where they can be approached without trouble. They are often occupied for years, and occasionally grow to large size, Taverner recording one about ten feet high. They are composed of sticks, those in the base being often of large size, with a lining of grass and other soft materials.

Years ago, in the plains country, where there was little timber, these birds were said to use old buffalo ribs from scattered skeletons to construct bases for their nests, piling them up as they did sticks in other situations.

Like related hawks this species has light and dark color phases, the former being the more common. The darkest birds appear almost black, and except for their larger bills and larger size are similar to dark birds of the American rough-leg.

On their nesting grounds these hawks utter screaming calls that have been likened to those of eagles, and the young are said to be quite vociferous. Aside from this they are silent and in fall and winter seldom make any sound.

The ferruginous rough-leg breeds from southern Alberta and Manitoba to northeastern California, New Mexico, and Kansas. It is found in winter from California and Montana to Baja California and northern Mexico, and has been observed casually in Wisconsin and Illinois.

TWO NATIVES OF MEXICO THAT MIGRATE INTO THE AMERICAN SOUTHWEST

Careless about distinguishing species, shooters charge the whole hawk family with the sins of a few of its members and destroy as "vermin" birds whose beneficial or harmless habits warrant their complete protection. The graceful **Mexican Goshawk** (upper; adult right, immature left) is one of the handsomest hawks, a swift, bold flyer, and rare enough to be a "find." Also rare is the **Mexican Black Hawk** (lower, adults perched and flying) that often reoccupies its large nest of sticks year after year.

Mexican Goshawk

(Asturina plagiata plagiata)

Average Length, Seventeen Inches

Of graceful, rapid flight, this handsome species frequents groves of cottonwoods and other trees along streams in the open valleys, or in the foothills of the mountains. It is migrant within our limits, appearing rather late in spring and moving south early in the fall. The birds are usually tame, as in the wild country they inhabit there is little to molest them.

Lizards, abundant in its haunts, make up much of its food, and it feeds extensively on large insects, including grasshoppers and large beetles, which are seized expertly on the wing. At need this bird can fly with a dash and speed which approximate those of a falcon. It eats various mice and rats, and also kills rabbits and ground squirrels.

It appears that this hawk is one of negative economic importance in the United States, and that, as an interesting species, it should not be disturbed or killed.

The nests of this goshawk are placed in trees. They are usually frail in construction, and made of twigs plucked green, so that they are still covered with leaves; this makes them difficult to see, as they match the dense green foliage in which they are placed. The nests are shallow and contain two or three eggs, the smaller number being more common. In color the eggs are pale bluish white, more or less stained from the nest lining of leaves; occasionally one is marked with spots of brown.

These birds make little demonstration when their nests are disturbed beyond circling above the tree tops and uttering their calls.

This species, although not brilliantly colored, from its contrasted markings is one of the handsomest of the hawks in our limits, its comparative rarity lending interest to the naturalist. It is an active bird, with powerful flight that enables it to dash through trees or other cover with ease, turning at need with the greatest facility. The call is a peculiar piping note that has been likened to the sound made by the long-billed curlew.

In the United States the Mexican goshawk is found in southern Arizona, southern New Mexico, and the lower Rio Grande Valley, apparently being most common in Arizona. To the south it is found through Mexico, being replaced in Central America by a smaller form of paler color.

Mexican Black Hawk

(Urubitinga anthracina anthracina)

Average Length, Twenty-one Inches

The present form is another that enters the southwestern borders of the United States in a limited section, where it is an inhabitant of dense groves of trees. Though quiet and given to resting for long periods on some partly concealed perch, it is a bird of swift and active flight and rises at times to soar in the open air, being particularly sportive in spring.

Within our limits these hawks are local in occurrence and have been seen by few naturalists. To find them common it is necessary to go to Central America where they have varied haunts, as they range from the mangroves of the coast to the forested foothills of the mountains. In Guatemala I have seen them among the forest trees that shade open coffee plantations, though they are more regularly observed among the dense growths of steep-walled wooded barrancas.

The black color with the striking white band across the tail mark the adult birds instantly, either on the wing, or as they fly near to rest upon some forest perch. Near at hand the yellow legs and the yellow markings about the bill are prominent. The brown-streaked young are quite different in appearance, so that it is a surprise to find that they belong to this handsome species.

The long, slender legs of this hawk are quite remarkable as they appear almost stiltlike when the bird is in the hand.

The nest is a large structure of sticks that is frequently occupied year after year. It is often placed in a cottonwood or in a pine tree from 15 to 60 feet from the ground. Part of the sticks used for nesting material may be gathered on the wing, the bird dropping gracefully, sometimes from high in the air, to seize a dead branch in some tree top, snap it off, and carry it away without pausing appreciably in its course. From one to two eggs are deposited, being grayish white with a slight greenish tinge, spotted with brown and lavender.

In the north the birds rear but one family each season, but in the Tropics, if one set of eggs is taken, they often continue with a second or even a third nesting.

In British Honduras, where these hawks are common and are little molested, they are very bold, sometimes perching only five or six feet away while their young are being examined.

The food of these birds, from what little has been recorded, seems somewhat varied. They eat a good many snakes and lizards, and also consume frogs and fish. Sometimes they pursue birds, and along the coast of Central America they are reported to live to a considerable extent on crabs, large land crabs being favored food. They eat rodents of various kinds and large insects.

They are too rare within our limits to have any particular economic status, but should not be destroyed wantonly, as they are interesting and peculiar, and represent a group not otherwise found in our fauna.

The species is found from southern Arizona and the lower Rio Grande Valley in Texas south into Central America, being mainly migratory in the United States. Allied forms are found in tropical America.

A MIGHTY HUNTSMAN IS THE KING OF BIRDS

The **Golden Eagle** (adult on ground, immature flying) frequents the country west of the Mississippi from Alaska to central Mexico and is usually found only in wild, uninhabited areas. Prairie dogs and rabbits are favorite foods, but this powerful avian aristocrat will kill any small mammal and also has a taste for the sharp-tailed grouse. It occasionally attacks lambs and fawns and annoys hunters by pilfering traps baited with meat.

Golden Eagle

(Aquila chrysaëtos canadensis)

Average Length, Male, Thirty-two and One-half Inches; Female, Thirty-seven and One-half Inches

The golden eagle, one of the most powerful of American birds of prey and a keen and courageous huntsman, is principally an inhabitant of wild and unfrequented areas. From its great expanse of wing it is readily identified. The bald eagle in immature dress is the only bird with which it might be confused, but as these two ordinarily range in different types of country, there is little opportunity to mistake them.

The golden eagle has feathers extending clear to the toes, but in the bald eagle the lower part of the leg is covered with hard scales. This difference serves to distinguish the two in any plumage.

This species is most common in the rough country of mountains and broken hills, extending out over the plains and in other open regions mainly in winter and during the migration period.

From its large size the golden eagle requires considerable food, and turns naturally to the most abundant supply to obtain it.

Where prairie dogs are present in large numbers, these are favored food; a pair of eagles will destroy several hundred in the course of a season. At times they turn to sharp-tailed grouse when these are abundant, proving a scourge to the flocks. Jack rabbits, cottontails, marmots, and ground squirrels are killed in large numbers. In winter, when other food is scarce, they may come to dead carcasses, but in severe weather when the meat is frozen, even with the great strength that they possess in bill and feet, they get little.

E. S. Cameron records that three golden eagles working together pulled down and killed a pronghorn antelope during severe winter weather when other food was scarce. They will kill and eat coyotes caught in traps and steal the bait when wolf traps are baited with meat.

Birds and jack rabbits usually are partly plucked before being eaten, but most small mammals are swallowed—skin, hair, and all. These eagles kill many rattlesnakes, feinting at them until they uncoil, when the reptiles may be seized without danger.

The lifting powers of this bird have been exaggerated, since it has been claimed that the golden eagle was capable of carrying prey weighing 15 or 20 pounds. Reports from reliable observers, however, indicate a weight of eight pounds as about the maximum which they can carry. When larger prey is killed, it is necessary to eat it on the ground. In the case of geese when they fall in water, the eagle tows them to land. Frequent reports that these birds have attempted to carry off children are, so far as the experience of naturalists goes, without basis. However, it is interesting to note that these stories are prevalent through the extensive range occupied by golden eagles in both the Old and New Worlds.

During most of the year golden eagles are undemonstrative, but in the nesting season they call in shrill, high-pitched tones, and the male often tumbles in the air somewhat like the male marsh hawk. This is accomplished from a high elevation by suddenly closing the wings and dropping headfirst toward the earth, checking the fall just before reaching the ground; then rising again to repeat the performance.

The nest is placed on the ledge of a cliff or is built in a tree. Often it is a large structure, as the birds may use the same site year after year and add to the nest each season. It is built of sticks and limbs, usually with a lining of some softer material, and often is decorated with twigs of green pine. Bendire describes one, from notes made by Denis Gale in Colorado, which was 7 feet high by 6 feet wide, and contained at least two cartloads of material.

When the nest is placed in a tree this is usually situated where it affords a commanding lookout, so that the eyries are often conspicuous and may be seen at a considerable distance.

The nests are large, flat platforms, often of such extent that a man climbing to them gains access to the eggs over the edge with difficulty.

Nesting begins at the end of February and continues until May or June, the latter dates referring to the far north where the season is delayed. Incubation is believed to fall mainly to the lot of the female, and to last about four weeks.

During this period the male often supplies his mate with food, and later he is attentive in feeding the young. When the young are hatched the male assists in brooding them and in shading them from the sun when the heat is intense. The young leave the nest in two months or a little more, and are soon left to their own devices in securing food.

Two, or rarely three, eggs are laid, these varying from dull white to pale cream color, with blotches and spots of brown, pearl gray, and lavender. Where there are two eggs in the set, one is usually a little larger than the other. Some believe that the two young constitute a pair, though I know of no certain proof that this holds true.

Either from its size or demeanor, the golden eagle gives an impression of intelligence distinctly above that of other birds of prey. As one of our finest forms of wild life, it is to be hoped that the huge bird may hold a place in our fauna for many years.

The golden eagle breeds from northern Alaska and Mackenzie to northern Baja California and central Mexico, and in winter is found south to northern Florida and southern Texas. It formerly nested east of the Mississippi River, and possibly may still do so in North Carolina and Tennessee. Closely allied forms occur in the Eastern Hemisphere.

THE NOBLE BALD EAGLE SYMBOLIZES OUR NATION'S FREEDOM

By act of Congress of June 20, 1782, the **Bald Eagle** (adult perched, immature flying) became our Nation's emblem. Its courage, striking appearance, great size, and dominant position in the bird world well qualify it for this rank. Never straying far from water, it feeds chiefly on fish, often seized at the end of a "power dive" from a considerable height. "Baldy" is represented in North America by distinct northern and southern species.

Bald Eagle

(Haliaeetus leucocephalus)

Average Length, Male, Thirty-five Inches; Female, Thirty-eight and One-half Inches

Our national bird, the bald eagle, chosen in the early days of the Union, is figured on many of our coins, is a favored design in matters of patriotic interest, and in general is considered symbolic of our freedom. Its enormous size and the striking markings of the adult make it a prominent species that is noted on every appearance. A bird of great strength and of swift and powerful flight, it is master in its haunts and has no potent enemies except man. Its life is led in the vicinity of water and only casually is it found far from that element.

The food of the bald eagle is mainly fish. In Alaska severe complaint has been made that it destroys salmon during their annual runs up the streams to deposit their eggs. The territorial legislature set a price upon its hoary head. For years a ruthless war was waged against our national bird in that territory, until more eagles had been destroyed—some estimates running as high as sixty or seventy thousand—than were thought to exist on the whole continent. The entire question as to the protection of the bald eagle as our national bird has been one of long argument that still is not settled.

The eagle often fishes by plunging from a height, descending at an angle on its selected prey, sometimes going beneath the surface. Sometimes it grapples prey so large that it cannot rise with it and is under necessity of towing it to shore. This eagle also robs the osprey, being fiercely predatory in such encounters.

Large birds are sometimes captured, including ducks, coots, and geese. Although the eagle is sufficiently swift to seize them in flight, it ordinarily gives chase on the water, where it is able to tire them by forcing them to dive until they become exhausted.

Although the bald eagle is said to feed on healthy birds, my own experience with it has been that it pursues only birds crippled by shooting or injured in some other way.

During the hunting season I have often seen an eagle swing over rafts of ducks, which it scatters. Then, if cripples appear, they are pursued, and if none is sighted the eagle passes on to other hunting. The taking of such injured birds can hardly be condemned. These eagles on occasion kill lambs and foxes, the latter furnishing an indication of the birds' strength.

In addition to living food, the bald eagle is prone to search for carrion, following regularly along shores for dead fish cast up on the beaches, and eating dead animals of other kinds as they offer.

There was much discussion before the bald eagle was finally adopted as our Nation's emblem by act of Congress on June 20, 1782; Benjamin Franklin in particular favored the wild turkey. However, it must be conceded that the bald eagle is a bird of fine and noble appearance and that it is a master of the air.

The nests of the bald eagle are large structures of sticks, usually placed in trees, often at a considerable height, though occasionally on cliffs, or even directly on the ground. Nests 5 to 6 feet in diameter and the same in height are not unusual, and nests 12 feet high have been recorded. Dr. Francis H. Herrick (see page 176) found that one near Vermilion, Ohio, was used continuously for thirty-five years.

Ordinarily two eggs are laid, with occasional sets of three or one. They are white, very rarely with slight markings of buffy brown. Where two eggs are laid, one is nearly always larger than the other. Incubation requires nearly a month, the duty being shared by both parents. The young remain in the nest for about two and a half months, and during that time the old birds are most solicitous for their welfare and safety.

The young bald eagles do not attain the plumage of the adult for three years, and during the first year they are actually larger than their parents.

The late John G. White, of Cleveland, gave Dr. Herrick the following account of what happened on two occasions at Jackson Hole when an eagle was caught in a trap set for bear:

"We would have released him," wrote the judge, "but the trap had scraped his leg and he would not allow us near. When we came up to the stockade he was lying down. As soon as he saw us he reared himself up on his sound leg, favoring the trapped one as much as he could, and, with head drawn back and feathers erected, defied us and struck at us fiercely when we attempted to approach. As there was no way to release him, we had to kill him.

"Like the giant of old, when beaten to the earth, he promptly arose with fighting powers renewed, for in an instant he was on his feet again, as indomitable as ever, and this continued after every blow, until at length he was killed. To the end he was fiercely defiant. . . . Such a picture as he made of indomitable courage, persistent to the last, I never saw."

The southern bald eagle *(Haliaeetus leucocephalus leucocephalus)* nests from the northern United States to Baja California, central Mexico, and Florida. The northern bald eagle *(Haliaeetus leucocephalus alascanus)* breeds from northwestern Alaska and British Columbia to the Great Lakes and Nova Scotia, coming in winter south to Washington, Montana, and Connecticut.

A related species, the gray sea eagle *(Haliaeetus albicilla)* is resident in Greenland, and is found also in Europe and northern Asia.

Osprey

(Pandion haliaëtus carolinensis)
Average Length, Twenty-three Inches

Known ordinarily as the "fish hawk," the osprey is found about large bodies of water. Being dependent on fish for food, it never strays far from water except during casual wanderings when in migration. It ranges on both fresh and salt water, but ordinarily is more common near our coasts, possibly because there it may find nesting grounds and the food that it prefers with the least difficulty.

In large size the osprey suggests the eagle, but is easily distinguished when its size and markings are known. As settlement has spread along our coasts ospreys have decreased somewhat in number, but as they can adapt themselves to the haunts of man, and are often protected rather than disturbed, they have maintained a fair abundance when most other species among the hawks have been greatly reduced.

Though the osprey occasionally may capture a water snake or a frog this is unusual, practically all of its food being composed of fish, most of which are captured alive.

In fishing, the bird flies slowly from 30 to 100 feet above the water, scanning the surface closely until a fish is sighted, when it turns and drops swiftly, sometimes even going beneath the surface. Rising with its victim held firmly in both feet, the osprey pauses for an instant, supported by broad-spread wings, to shake the water from its plumage; then flies to some perch where its meal may be enjoyed. As it rises, it adjusts its grip so that the fish is carried end on, thus affording a minimum of resistance to the air (see page 130).

Any fish of proper size that come near the surface are taken. Toadfish are as acceptable as other varieties. Such species as menhaden, which go in large schools, are favorites. In summer on Chesapeake Bay I have seen fish hawks feeding regularly on eels.

The birds have habitual perches to which they carry food, the ground beneath these being strewn with fish bones accumulated from many meals. Where fishermen sort the catch from their nets, I have seen ospreys gather in flocks to pick up discarded dead fish, seizing these from the water or picking them from the sandy beach.

Occasionally ospreys are known to strike fish too large for them to handle, and when their claws become caught the birds are pulled beneath the surface and drowned. Instances have been recorded where a drowned osprey with its claws locked in the back of a dead salmon or sturgeon has been washed up on shore, affording mute evidence of such a tragedy.

In its fishing the osprey does not always continue unmolested, as the bald eagle, also with an appetite for fish, often resorts to robbery. Watching until an osprey has made its catch, the eagle descends on the fish hawk, in an effort to make it give up its prey, continuing in relentless pursuit with broadly beating wings until the smaller bird drops the booty.

If an osprey is obstinate, the eagle finally strikes, knocking it through the air to make it release the catch. As the fish falls, the eagle descends swiftly to seize it in the air, or picks it up from the surface of the water. On rare occasions an osprey with a small fish may escape, but ordinarily the bird is so burdened that its flight is hampered to a point where it can make no definite resistance.

Where two eagles combine in this robbery, the case is hopeless, for, wherever the osprey turns, one of the eagles is soon upon it and it can find no avenue of escape.

Relieved of its catch, the osprey may strike angrily at the robber, but the larger bird easily wards off such blows with its broad wings. Occasionally, however, the tables are turned, for when ospreys gather in colonies several may band together and harry marauding eagles from the vicinity.

The nest of the osprey is a huge structure of sticks, cornstalks, weeds, and other rubbish, placed in the top of a tree, on a rock ledge, on the summit of a pinnacle rock, or occasionally on the roof of a building or chimney. It may also be placed on the ground.

Frequently grackles, night herons, and English sparrows place their nests in the base of the huge structure occupied by the osprey. The larger bird pays no attention to its smaller neighbors.

The eggs, from two to four, with three making the usual set, are creamy white, spotted and blotched with brown and lavender. With their rich colors and bold markings, they are among the handsomest eggs found in this order of birds.

The osprey is easily distinguishable at a distance from the eagle and from other hawks by its white breast and long, angular wings.

Along the eastern coast from Cape May, New Jersey, northward, farmers usually protect this bird, as the osprey drives crows and other hawks from the vicinity of its nest, thus affording a measure of protection to neighboring hen yards. Wagon wheels are frequently erected on the points of long poles to attract them, as this furnishes a broad, level surface on which the birds build their nests.

The plumage of the osprey has a peculiar oily odor that clings also to the shells of the eggs. This persists for years in specimens stored in museum cases and is so characteristic that it can be recognized at once.

The shrill whistled notes of this bird once heard are easily remembered. The birds are noisy about the nest, calling to each other and scolding at any intruder that may appear. The notes are easily imitated by whistling.

It breeds from Alaska, Hudson Bay, and Nova Scotia to Baja California and the Florida Keys, wintering from Florida and Baja California to the West Indies and South America. Allied forms are found in the Old World.

THE SHARP-EYED OSPREY IS AN IZAAK WALTON ON WINGS

Often called "fish hawk," the long-winged **Osprey,** like the bald eagles flying above, is almost always found close to suitable fishing waters. Sometimes it dives beneath the surface of the water at the end of its 100-foot plunges after finny prey. Fish bones strew the ground beneath its favorite feeding perches. Watching until an osprey catches a fish, a pursuing bald eagle will often harry the burdened bird until it drops its catch. The more powerful eagle then seizes the scaly booty.

Prairie Falcon
(Falco mexicanus)
Average Length, Male, Seventeen Inches; Female, Nineteen Inches

This pale-colored falcon has the active, graceful flight of the duck hawk. In a way, it is the arid country representative of that species, but may be distinguished from it by smaller size and paler, sandy coloration.

It frequents the plains, hills, and prairie regions of the West, often in barren lands, but also ranges at times in wooded sections. While it possesses speed and dash in flight, because of its smaller size, it is not as dangerous to other life about it as the duck hawk.

The nest is placed on a cliff, being often in a recess or small cave, where the eggs are laid on the bare surface, with only whatever rubbish may have accumulated for nesting material. Two to five constitute a complete set, three or four being the customary complement. The ground color of the eggs is creamy white, more or less overlaid with a suffusion of cinnamon, and blotches of reddish brown and chocolate. They are considerably paler than the eggs of the duck hawk.

The birds range in wild and uninhabited places, and though many nests are located on high and difficult ledges others may be placed where they are quite accessible. Through most of their nesting grounds the birds have little fear of being disturbed.

The prairie falcon feeds on birds of various kinds, blackbirds, horned larks, mourning doves, and others of similar size being favorites. It captures quail and prairie chickens on occasion, and also secures domestic pigeons where flocks of these are found within its range. I have seen them harry colonies of yellow-headed blackbirds so mercilessly that these unfortunates set up a loud outcry whenever a falcon appeared in the distance. The prairie falcon also feeds on mammals, taking gophers, ground squirrels, and various kinds of rats and mice. In addition, it takes insects, particularly grasshoppers when these are abundant.

In feeding, these hawks sometimes watch from cliffs or open perches in trees until suitable prey appears, or again fly lightly and gracefully along, traveling rather swiftly as they hunt. They have been known to harry marsh hawks and make these birds drop their prey. The falcon then seizes its booty in the air as it falls.

About their nesting cliffs these falcons are quite noisy, uttering shrill screams and cackling calls when disturbed. At other seasons they are mainly silent.

The prairie falcon nests from southern British Columbia to Baja California and southern Mexico, extending east to the eastern border of the Great Plains. It is casual in occurrence in Manitoba, Minnesota, and Illinois.

A related species, the aplomado falcon (Falco fuscocoerulescens septentrionalis), which is darker and has a blackish patch on the abdomen and lower breast, ranges from Arizona and southern Texas through Mexico.

Audubon's Caracara
(Polyborus cheriway auduboni)
Average Length, Twenty-two Inches

Although related to the falcons, this peculiar species, often called "Mexican eagle," has many of the habits and mannerisms of vultures. It is found in prairie regions where there are open groves, preferring open country to heavily forested sections. Its flight is straight and rapid, and it sometimes circles high in the air, especially on days of oppressive heat. With its long legs and contrasted color pattern it will be confused with no other species.

In Florida these birds frequently nest in cabbage palmettos (page 193); in Texas they occupy mesquites and other trees, and in Arizona giant cacti are sometimes selected. The nests are bulky masses of twigs, weeds, coarse grass, leaves, and Spanish moss, usually piled together in an untidy manner. The eggs number two or three, the ground color being creamy white when it is visible. Most eggs have the entire surface obscured by a wash of cinnamon rufous and blotches of reddish brown.

This bird eats lizards, snakes, frogs, and small turtles, and also takes small mammals. It is fond of rabbits, cotton rats and other mice, and grasshoppers and other large insects. Crabs and crayfish, too, are on its bill of fare.

The caracara is also partial to carrion of all kinds, and frequently comes to carcasses on which vultures are feeding. The caracaras make the larger birds stand aside, as they are strong and aggressive, striking with both bill and feet. On the coast of Texas caracaras have been seen in pursuit of brown pelicans to make them disgorge fish that they had swallowed.

Their long legs and short claws enable them to walk and run with ease. Their voices are peculiar rattling, creaking, screaming calls, in uttering which the birds frequently throw the head backward until it touches the back.

On Guadalupe Island, Mexico, off the western coast of Baja California, there was formerly found the Guadalupe caracara, Polyborus lutosus. The last of this species was recorded about 1905. These birds were paler and browner than Audubon's caracara, but apparently had much the same habits. In 1875 Edward Palmer recorded that they were abundant. As they were destructive to young kids, goat raising being an industry of the island, and to poultry as well, hundreds were killed.

Audubon's caracara nests from northern Baja California, southwestern Arizona, central and southern Florida, and Cuba south through Mexico and Central America. It has been recorded accidentally in Ontario.

THE PRAIRIE FALCON IS NEITHER ENTIRELY SAINT NOR ALTOGETHER SINNER

The slaughter of blackbirds, larks, quail, doves, and other species of birds must be placed on the debit side in appraising the western **Prairie Falcon** (upper; adult perched, immature flying). But to its credit should be listed its destruction of creatures harmful to the farmer's interests—grasshoppers, gophers, rats, and mice. The red-faced **Audubon's Caracara** (lower; adult right, immature left), often called "Mexican eagle," eats small mammals, snakes, and insects, but, vulturelike, also feasts on carrion. It nests from the southern United States through Mexico and Central America.

Duck Hawk

(Falco peregrinus anatum)

Average Length, Male, Sixteen Inches; Female,
Nineteen Inches

The duck hawk, finest of the falcons of our
continent, lives in regions where cliffs furnish
it eyries. Truly a master of the air, it kills at
will, and its food is composed almost entirely
of birds.

It often frequents the shores of large bodies
of water, particularly in the arid sections of
the West, as there it finds an abundance of
water-inhabiting birds that give it an easily
obtained food supply.

Resting on a commanding perch or flying
easily, the hawk, when its appetite is aroused
by some luckless bird, descends with a rush of
wings so swiftly as almost to elude sight, and
strikes its unfortunate victim like a veritable
thunderbolt. Ducks, shore birds, robins, meadowlarks, flickers, pheasants, grouse, pigeons,
and many others have been recorded as its
victims.

When it has tiny young, it obtains warblers,
sparrows, and other small birds to feed them.
No form of bird is safe from it, as it has been
known even to capture the agile chimney swift.
A duck hawk comes nearly every winter to the
old Post Office Department tower in Washington, and lives on pigeons captured as they fly
over the grounds of the Smithsonian Institution or above the near-by buildings. Mammals are seldom taken.

The duck hawk usually places its nest on a
cliff, often in a spot where it is practically inaccessible. Occasionally it resorts to large hollows in trees, or very rarely to old nests of
eagles or hawks. The only nesting material
consists of whatever rubbish may have accumulated on the chosen site, this usually including bones and other fragments from birds the
duck hawk has eaten.

Three to five eggs are laid, four being the
usual number. These are creamy or yellowish
white, irregularly blotched, streaked, or otherwise heavily marked with bright brown.

Many have the ground color completely obscured, and the eggs on the average are darker
than those of our other falcons. The duck
hawk nests from March to June, the period
depending upon the season throughout the
extended range.

The parents are noisy during the breeding
season, uttering quick, cackling calls. When
their nests are approached, they circle rapidly
about, harrying unmercifully other birds that
chance to pass, and even killing ruthlessly.

This is the species most favored by falconers,
because of its wide distribution that makes
it easily obtained, and for its intelligence.
Adult birds captured wild seem to comprehend
almost at once that they will not be harmed
and are readily trained by those expert in
such matters.

The duck hawk nests from Alaska and the
west coast of central Greenland to Baja California, Kansas, and Maryland. In winter it
ranges south to Panama. Peale's falcon, *Falco
peregrinus pealei*, a darker form, nests on the
Aleutian and Commander Islands, coming south
in winter to Oregon. Allied forms are found
in the other continents of the world.

Gyrfalcon

(Falco rusticolus)

Average Length, Twenty Inches

This hunting falcon of the north in early days
was the type most prized by the devotees of
the sport of falconry. Swift in flight and possessed of almost endless endurance, these birds
were desired above all other hunting hawks.

They range far beyond the limits of tree
growth, apparently to the limits of land. They
become so accustomed to resting on the ground
or on rocks that in captivity they actually seem
to prefer such locations to a perch.

The gyrfalcons of North America appear
to like birds better than other food, capturing
them ordinarily on the wing. In the far north
they often nest in the vicinity of colonies of
auks, great piles of whose bones accumulate beneath the gyrfalcon homes.

From Labrador to Alaska these falcons are
the scourge of the ptarmigan. They also capture gulls, guillemots, shore birds of various
kinds, and snow buntings, as well as lemmings
and Arctic hares. On St. George Island, one
of the Pribilof group in Bering Sea, Hanna records that one winter gyrfalcons came in abundance and nearly exterminated the little wren
and the rosy finches.

It is a fortunate circumstance that these
falcons seldom come into inhabited sections,
as otherwise they would prove a menace to
poultry yards.

The gyrfalcon nests on ledges on the face of
cliffs, placing its eggs on accumulations of its
own pellets, or, where there is woody vegetation, it sometimes occupies nests of sticks. The
creamy-white eggs, heavily marked with reddish brown, are among the most handsome of
their group. Nesting may come in May in the
far north, so that the nests are frequently
hung with icicles.

The forms of gyrfalcons found in North
America are in some confusion because of the
considerable variation in color among these
birds. In Greenland there is found the white
gyrfalcon, *Falco rusticolus candicans,* which
also has a dark phase in which the plumage is
mainly gray. This form may breed also in
eastern Arctic America, and is casual in winter south to British Columbia, Montana, and
Maine. A darker form, varying from gray to
nearly black, known as the black gyrfalcon,
Falco rusticolus obsoletus, nests from Point
Barrow to Labrador, and in winter ranges
south into the northern United States.

DESPITE ITS CRIMES, THE DUCK HAWK HAS MANY FRIENDS AMONG BIRD-LOVERS

The magnificent flight and overflowing energy of the **Duck Hawk** (upper; adults left, three young right) win praise even from those who know its murderous habits, for it feeds almost exclusively on birds. From the cliffs which afford it eyries, this finest of the falcons drops like a bomb on its feathered victims. Active and tireless are the **White** and **Black Gyrfalcons** (lower left and right), both types formerly prized for falconry. They range in North America far beyond the limit of trees and devour great numbers of ptarmigan, lemmings, arctic hares, auks, gulls, and various other shore birds.

Sparrow Hawk
(Falco sparverius)
Average Length, Male, Nine and One-half Inches;
Female, Eleven Inches

The handsome sparrow hawk, most familiar of American falcons, has adapted itself readily to the changes brought by our civilization, being so evidently harmless that it has escaped much of the destruction aimed universally at its larger companions. It is equally at home in the diverse environments found between the green pasture lands of the east and the arid cactus forests of Baja California.

Cultivated fields bordered by trees or telephone poles that afford lookout perches are favored resorts, as are forest lands where the trees grow in open formation. In the western plains area the sparrow hawk ranges along the lines of trees that follow watercourses or perches on the points of badlands, cliffs, or banks. Today it is the hawk most often seen in driving over our auto highways.

The sparrow hawk feeds principally on mice, large insects, lizards, and frogs. On occasion it attacks birds, and may kill quail, jays, or other birds as large and heavy as itself. About cities it destroys many English sparrows and starlings.

On the whole, however, the sparrow hawk kills comparatively few birds. In late summer grasshoppers are its favorite food and it may feed on these to the exclusion of other fare.

In hunting the sparrow hawk watches from an elevated perch until food is sighted and then flies out to seize it.

Often it hovers in the air with rapidly beating wings, intently watching the grass below until a mouse or other prey comes far enough out in the open to be caught.

The sparrow hawk nests in cavities, old nesting holes of the flicker or other large woodpeckers being favorite shelters, and has come to occupy bird boxes about houses. It frequently lives in cities, and in Washington is found about the roofs of the Smithsonian buildings. The number of eggs in a set ranges from three to seven. They vary in ground color from white to cream and cinnamon buff, spotted and blotched with brown.

The call of this hawk is a rapidly repeated *killy killy killy,* from which it is often known as "killy hawk."

The eastern sparrow hawk *(Falco sparverius sparverius)* nests from the upper Yukon, southern Quebec, and Nova Scotia to northwestern California, eastern Texas and northern Alabama.

The desert sparrow hawk *(Falco s. phalaena),* which is somewhat larger and paler, breeds from southern New Mexico and southern California south into Mexico.

The San Lucas sparrow hawk *(Falco s. peninsularis),* smaller in size, is found in southern Baja California. and the little sparrow hawk

(Falco s. paulus), darker in color, resides in Florida and the Gulf coast region.

Allied forms range through the West Indies and Central and South America.

Pigeon Hawk
(Falco columbarius)
Average Length, Male, Ten and One-half Inches;
Female, Thirteen Inches

The pigeon hawk derives its name from its curious resemblance to a pigeon in certain attitudes, or in mannerisms of flight that it may assume, though at other times it is obviously and unmistakably a falcon.

It is found in wooded areas or in semi-open country, depending upon where its search for food may take it. It is a bird of swift and graceful flight and travels at high speed with little apparent effort. It is seen often along seashores or other large bodies of water, and is more widely observed during the fall migration than at any other time.

Like related falcons, the pigeon hawk feeds extensively on birds. Its speed of flight and its strength are attested by its capture of swallows and even of the chimney swift, and its killing of meadowlarks, flickers, and small doves. Mice are taken occasionally and large insects more frequently.

When not hungry, this active little hawk delights in chasing birds merely to display its mastery, threatening but not actually harming them. When in search of a meal, it kills speedily and ruthlessly. In this the pigeon is a miniature of the duck hawk, which delights in the same sort of play. Slow-flying birds like blackbirds are favorite prey, as are sparrows and other small species that fly regularly in the open.

The pigeon hawk builds a nest of twigs and bark lined with softer materials, and places it in a tree, often only a few feet above the ground, on a rock ledge, or occasionally in a hollow tree. Four or five eggs constitute a set, being pale creamy white, with a wash of reddish brown and spots and blotches of deep brown. About the nest the birds utter piercing cries and chattering, scolding notes

The eastern pigeon hawk *(Falco columbarius columbarius)* nests from eastern Canada to Maine and Manitoba, migrating in winter to the Gulf States and northern South America.

The black pigeon hawk *(Falco c. suckleyi),* blackish brown in color, nests in western British Columbia, wintering in the coastal region south to northern California. Richardson's pigeon hawk *(Falco c. richardsoni),* lighter in color than the ordinary form, is found from Alberta and Saskatchewan to Montana and North Dakota, wintering from Colorado to northwestern Mexico.

The western pigeon hawk *(Falco c. bendirei),* darker than Richardson's, breeds from northwestern Alaska to California.

SOCIABLE SPARROW HAWKS STOP TO GOSSIP WHILE RELATIVES GUARD A KILL

Smallest of its family, the **Sparrow Hawk** (upper; male right, female in nesting hole) is also the most beneficial of the falcons and the most adaptable to civilization, often nesting in holes in orchard trees close to farmhouses. The habit of hovering over fields, scanning the ground for mice and large insects, has given it the nickname "windhover." The speedy **Pigeon Hawk** (lower; male right, immature female left) feeds extensively on birds. When not hungry, it delights in chasing jays, crows, or sandpipers just for the fun of tormenting them.

THE EAGLE IN ACTION

An Intimate Study of the Eyrie Life of America's National Bird

By Francis H. Herrick, Ph.D.

Professor Emeritus of Biology in Western Reserve University

T HE choice of a national emblem and device for a national seal could hardly have been more deliberate than in the case of the American eagle, for from the day the Declaration of Independence was signed six committees had wrestled with the question for as many years, until a device satisfactory to the Congress was finally adopted on June 20, 1782.

As it happened, the choice had fallen to a true native of America, the white-headed or "bald eagle,"* which ranges over nearly the whole of the North American Continent.

The golden eagle, the only other member of the family known to enter our borders, is a more cosmopolitan species, reaching in its wanderings nearly every part of the Northern Hemisphere.

THE EMBODIMENT OF FREEDOM AND POWER

It is in action that the eagle appears at his best, for he is then a true "king of birds"; and, whether we have seen him soaring and circling far above the confines of the earth or plunging like a meteor from the sky; whether screaming defiance at the storm or fiercely striking his prey, we know why to men of every age he has seemed the very embodiment of freedom and power; why his effigy has been emblazoned on the chariots of warriors and on the shields of knights, or, raised aloft on poles and banners, has followed the legions into battle from the days of Marius to those of Napoleon and the leaders of the latest war.

In its structure and habits the eagle is a large hawk, of close kin to the falcons, buzzards, and harriers of every clime, but the biggest, boldest, and most powerful

---

* The term "bald" was often used in the 17th and 18th centuries to signify white or streaked with white, as in a "bald-faced horse," or in "bald-pate"—the widgeon, an American duck with white on the crown. Accordingly, "bald eagle," though now in common use, is historically wrong, while "bald-headed eagle," meaning "white-headed," is strictly correct.

raptor of them all. The female, which in the American eagle is the larger sex, may attain a length of 43 inches, may spread 8 feet, and, according to Audubon, may weigh from 8 to 12 pounds, though these last figures may be greatly exceeded in captive birds. It is a stranger to fatigue, can probably lift its own weight, and has been known to carry a small lamb over a distance of five miles.

The eagle's eyrie is his castle, which he will at times defend against all comers. In it his eaglets pass the first ten weeks of their life—from mid-April until early July, upon the southern shore of Lake Erie—and it is the occasional rendezvous, lookout point, and dining table for the elder pair for the remainder of the year.

With us the eagle is nonmigratory, or a very irregular migrant, never leaving his home neighborhood for long and only when his food supplies run out. In northern Ohio he nests high, choosing the crotch of a commanding tree not far from the lake which supplies him with fish and to which he makes constant sallies, varied with occasional forays into the adjoining fields.

The first year's nest is framed with sticks, usually from two to six feet long and from one to two inches thick, and well bedded with straw, cornstalks, and stubble, the whole measuring about five feet each way. In it are laid two or, more rarely, three or four dull-white eggs, resembling somewhat those of the domestic goose, and, it is believed, at intervals of several days, beginning in this latitude in mid or late March.

YOUNG EAGLES PASS MUCH TIME PREENING

In from four to five weeks the young are hatched in white down, which contrasts sharply with their dark eyes and almost black, hooked bills. This natal covering is shortly replaced with a thick coat of close gray down, to be in turn gradually combed off, until they have acquired their full juvenal dress of dark-brown feathers by the end of May or the beginning of June.

Early in the latter month the eaglets are becoming sleeker every day through their incessant attentions to their toilet, and with their brown-dappled dress and clean yellow legs make a fine appearance. Already they are nearly as large as their parents and have a wing spread of more than six feet; yet from two to three weeks of voracious feeding and ardent exercise are still required before they will have gained sufficient courage and the proper coordination of muscles and nerves to leave the eyrie under their own power.

After freedom has been attained, several months are passed in company with their parents, who still continue to bring them food, and with them they make frequent visits to their old home; but the day eventually arrives when parental guidance and protection cease and the young go forth to seek, far from their native heath, their substance and their fortune, and in due course to found homes of their own.

Photograph by Francis H. Herrick

THE EAGLE'S HOME IS A CUMULATIVE STRUCTURE

This great eyrie, in a shellbark hickory at Vermilion, Ohio, measured 12 feet in height, 8½ feet across the top, and was occupied for 35 years. When this picture was taken, one eaglet had left the nest; the other was standing on the nest perch and departed early on the following day.

The young bald eagle, in its dark-brown dress, has often been mistaken for the golden eagle, which it resembles in color and size, but the one unerring mark of distinction is the shank, which in our national bird is nearly bare, but in the golden eagle is feathered to the toes. It is not until the third year, or after, that the full adult marks—white head, neck, and tail and yellow iris and bill—are fully attained.

When each successive nesting season comes around, the mated pair, if satisfied with the location, resort to their old eyrie and build upon its top what is virtually a new nest or set in place a new layer of sticks and stubble; so that in the course of time the eagles' eyrie grows in height and breadth in accordance with the spread of its main supports. Nests which have been occupied for a number of years have been abandoned and again reclaimed, whether by the same pair or not it would be impossible to say.

What was probably one of the most remarkable eyries of the American eagle in the entire country stood, until the fatal ides of March, 1925, in the dead top of a shellbark hickory, in the town of Vermilion,

ARRIVING AT EXPRESS-TRAIN SPEED—

The female is putting on the brakes as she lands a fish, which is held in the right talon. Both eaglets are squealing, one with the wings raised, an unusual attitude. Time of exposure, 1/435th of a second.

Photograph by Francis H. Herrick

THE MOTHER EAGLE RESTS

The female, having brought in a fish, has retired to the nest perch. The eaglet on the left has spread over the quarry, claiming it as his own, while the other, not venturing to approach, patiently awaits his turn.

Photograph by Francis H. Herrick

MOTHER BRINGS HOME THE EVENING MEAL

Ohio, at a point 38 miles due west from Cleveland and a mile from the shore of Lake Erie. These Vermilion eagles had grown up with the country, and have a history which can be traced back for nearly a century, during which time six nests are known to have been occupied in that immediate neighborhood, the fourth and greatest having been begun not later than 1890.

Since the eagle is mated for life and if bereft always finds a new mate, the same pair or their successors in this partnership are known to have occupied the same nest without a break for 35 years—a record seldom matched elsewhere in the annals of natural history. This great nest, in the form of a solid inverted cone, when measured in July, 1922, was 12 feet high and 8½ feet across its flattened top; it stood 81 feet from the ground, and, according to the

estimates of a number of experienced observers, made after its fall, its weight was not far from two tons.

This historic eyrie at Vermilion offered such an unusual opportunity for an intimate study of the domestic life of the eagle that we decided to approach it by means of a specially constructed observatory. Making use of a large elm, which rose to a height of one hundred feet on the southerly side of the eagles' tree and had a girth of twelve feet not far from the ground, as a central pillar of support, we began the work of construction in the winter of 1922 under the auspices of Western Reserve University.

To the first platform, which was occupied for a month during that year, was added a second in the spring of 1923, this bringing the observer's eye one hundred

Photograph by C. M. Shipman

THE MASTER OF THE EYRIE LOOKS THE FALCON THAT HE IS

Arriving at home a few minutes after the mother bird (see illustration on opposite page), the male parent assumes his share of the responsibility for feeding the eaglets.

feet from the ground and enabling him to overlook the nest as well as the entire region for miles in every direction. The platforms were ten feet square and were reached by means of a steel ladder. When in use the upper platform was capped by a khaki-colored tent of generous proportions and protected by a rail screened with the same material.

OUR OBSERVATIONS CAUSE LITTLE ALARM

Having found that the eagle's day, at least during the late phase of nest life, began at dawn and ended at dusk, the observers divided theirs into shifts of three hours each, beginning at 5 o'clock in the morning and ending at 7 at night.

To study the eagles in action, we will ascend to the observatory, assured that from the concealment of our tent, with which they have become familiar, we can watch at leisure the unfolding scenes of the aquiline drama. By the aid of a wooden ladder we ascend to one of steel, beginning at a point seventeen feet up.

Carefully watching our steps, we rise vertically twenty feet, cross on a diagonal through a network of studs and joists, amid the great spreading branches of the tree, to the northeast side. Ascending vertically again and heeding only the business in hand, we pass through two traps, and, careful to close the last, finally stand on the upper platform and gaze for a moment upon the remarkable scene spread out to our view.

THE EAGLE OBSERVATORY OF WESTERN RESERVE UNIVERSITY, NEAR VERMILION, OHIO, OCCUPIED TEN WEEKS, APRIL-JULY, 1928

The steel tower rose 91 feet and brought the observer's eye and camera 38 feet from the front of the big nest, which is in a living ash, more than seven feet in diameter.   The female eagle is standing guard on her favorite perch, at the left.

Photographs by C. M. Shipman

WHEN THE FATHER EAGLE DISAPPEARED, THE MOTHER ASSUMED THE FAMILY BURDEN ALONE

The mother eagle has just deposited a load of straw on the eyrie, but hears a disturbing sound and comes to attention.

The mother eagle is interrupted while feeding her surviving eaglet. Suspicious, she erects her headdress and looks straight at the camera.

The dominating object is the great eyrie itself, with its feathered occupants, which fixes our gaze, fascinates us, as we see it for the first time, not raised against the sky, but projected upon the brown tapestry of the fields below. We look directly down upon its top, as upon the stage of a theater, and the eye wanders quickly to the scenes beyond, from the tree tops of the grove to the well-ordered fields of growing corn and waving grain; thence to the shore, a mile away, and the blue waters of Lake Erie, blended with the sky at the horizon and stretching from the Point and city of Lorain on the east to near the town of Vermilion on the west.

The whole countryside is intersected with railroads and highways of pleasure or commerce, where at times the eagle's scream is strangely mingled with the voice of the steam siren, the locomotive's whistle, or the hum of a passing airplane.

We shall now enter the tent, knowing that once under its cover, provided that no suspicious objects are moving on the ground below, the confidence of the eagles will be restored and we shall soon have action in plenty. The sides of the tent are pierced with V-shaped peekholes, and the front with larger "windows" for the cameras.

A few minutes only are required to set in place the camera, which is provided with a telephoto lens of good depth and speed; then, with an eye at a peephole and with notebook and binoculars at hand, we are ready for eventualities.

THE BABIES ARE WELL CARED FOR

The time is April 23, 5:45 p. m. The female eagle has been brooding her callow young, which are now in white down and about two weeks old. She deliberately rises, walks over to the carcass of a large fish, stands on it and begins tearing off small pieces of the flesh and passing them to the three eaglets, which line up before her.

Twenty minutes later the male drops on the eyrie and immediately joins his mate in the work of satisfying the appetites of their hungry brood. The old eagles bend to their task and pass up bits of food at the rate of about five to the minute. At least the passes are at this rate, but the proffered food is not always taken. It may indeed go the rounds, to be eaten finally by one of the old birds.

The feeding over, the female eagle digs a depression in the floor of the eyrie with her bill and prepares to brood, while the male takes his stand for guard duty on one of their habitual perches. When her eaglets have crawled beneath her breast and wings, she carefully draws the earth and stubble about her body and, after shaking out any troublesome particles that may have lodged in her mouth, settles snugly over her brood.

For many days we had the old eagles before our eyes for hours at a time; and we saw their young advance, through their long term of infancy, from strength to strength, until, prepared by their later persistent exercises and their play, with instincts sharpened and habits formed, they were ready for independent flight.

As we approached the grove in going our usual rounds, the old birds, if stationed on one of their customary perches, were likely to leave in silence and take a stand farther away. Never did we hear, at such intrusions, their protesting scream and but rarely the loud *kak-kak-kak* alarm of the male.

At the late stage we often saw the young standing close together upon the eyrie, as motionless as statuettes and visible for half a mile; but if they were engaged in feeding or lying down, the great nest would appear to be empty. When an old eagle, at an earlier stage in nest life, was engaged in brooding, again all was quiet, but the ever-watchful male was certain to have observed us, and, as he circled above the grove, a white head rose from the center of the nest, like a jack-in-the-box, and we could see that head extended in our direction, with the mandibles opening and closing in protest. In a moment the female eagle was in the air and moved away in silence to join her mate.

When the great eyrie at Vermilion, which had endured for 35 years, crashed, in March, 1925, its solid core, consisting of a brown loamlike substance, was sprinkled with the bones of fish, mammals, and birds, the remains of innumerable eagle dinners, besides a great variety of miscellaneous objects.

Since the eagle does not regularly sweep house, but is content to refresh it from time to time with a layer of straw and stubble, its domicile, rising at the rate of about three inches a year, becomes in time a mass of vegetable decay, in which

Photograph by Francis H. Herrick

EAGLETS TWO TO THREE WEEKS OLD

This eyrie stands at a height of 86 feet, in a living ash. The rampart of sticks surrounds a large bed of fine, dry grass. The smaller bird at the right was so mistreated by its larger nestmate that it died a week after this photograph was made. A sight of eggs or newly hatched young was rarely obtained by the observer because of the care with which the old birds covered both upon leaving them.

bones, feathers, and hair may be preserved for long periods. Naturally we were anxious to examine the solid core of this structure, assured that it would give us a remarkable cross-section of the food habits of these particular birds.

When exaggerated reports of the Vermilion eagles, which were accused of stealing turkeys and lambs, were spread abroad and demands were made for their destruction by the State, the findings in the core of their great eyrie were used with convincing force for their protection.

In the whole collection of objects recovered, some sixty of which were tabulated, there was not a single bone of a turkey or a goose, or of a domestic fowl larger than a chicken, and not a bone of a mammal larger than a rabbit.

WE MOVE OUR OBSERVATORY TO A NEW NEST

Ten days after the great nest went down at Vermilion, in the storm of March 10, 1925, a new nest, the fifth known to have been built and occupied in that immediate neighborhood, was under way in another part of the same grove. Two eggs were laid and two young eagles were successfully reared in that year.

The following year, May 18, 1926, another fatal storm crashed this nest to the ground and the three eaglets were killed. At slightly over four weeks of age they had a wing spread of 43.5, 39, and 34 inches, respectively, and their corresponding weights were 8 pounds 2 ounces, 6 pounds 2 ounces, and 6 pounds.

FEMALES LARGER AND HEAVIER THAN MALES

Mr. A. B. Fuller, of the Cleveland Museum of Natural History, who prepared the skins of these birds, found that the two smaller were males, while the larger and heavier was a female. This is possibly a significant fact, since the adult female eagle is known to surpass the adult male very considerably, both in size and weight.

After examining the broken top of the eagles' tree, which still bore green foliage, we reached the opinion that in this case we were really defeated by the ravages of the wood-eating larvæ of a beetle, many of which, in the form of large white grubs the size of a man's thumb, were still in action. In the course of time successive broods of these insects had gnawed away and reduced to a powder the solid foundations of the castle of the kings of the air.

After the storm had wrecked the Vermilion eyrie, we picked up our 80-foot steel tower and transported it 80 miles to another nest, at Geneva, in another county, but only to meet with eventual disappointment. At this new station the tower was erected in November, 1926, in order to be ready for the eagles in the following spring. All went well there, so far as we could see, until late in April, 1927, when something got at the eggs and destroyed them.

We then moved 80 miles back to Vermilion, and set up the tower beside a nest that had been built close to the town line, in February, 1927, to replace, as we supposed, the one demolished at a point two miles farther west the previous year, but some doubt was later cast upon this point.

In company with my friend, Mr. C. M. Shipman, who had assisted me since 1926, I passed ten weeks at this station and gained further insight into the domestic life of eagles, as will now be related. Our aim had been to have one observer on duty in the tent atop the tower throughout the day, rain or shine, cold or hot, in order to obtain as full and exact records as possible of all activities of old and young eagles during the entire ten or twelve weeks of life at the eyrie. If this end was measurably attained, it was because of the generous support given me by Western Reserve University, for without this aid little could have been accomplished.

The eagles of that section have always favored the largest available trees for their nests, in any suitable grove near the lake, and in this instance had built the eyrie in a living ash, at a height of 86 feet, amid a great canopy of foliage that tended to render our task doubly difficult. The concrete foundation for the tower was laid in November, and the work was completed in five days, early in the following January, 1928. It rose to a height of 91 feet on the southerly side of the eagles' tree, and the distance between the platform and the front of the big nest was 38 feet, which was about as near as I considered it advisable to go (see illustration, page 182).

Our first task was clearing away all obstructing branches, and a large one in particular, about which the eagles had carried

their construction so completely that it seemed to rise from nearly the middle of the eyrie. This tree, on account of the treacherous nature of its bark, proved most difficult and dangerous of ascent, even by our most skillful climber, who was obliged to break away a part of the nest in order to enter it.

FURIOUS BATTLES IN THE AIR

The eagles readily accepted all of these changes, as well as our tower, but after the tent was in place troubles assailed us from a new and unexpected quarter, not from the hand of nature or of man, but from other eagles, which entered the territory of our birds and fought them with great fury. This happened in the second week of May, when the two eaglets were about two weeks old.

Two sharp battles, of which I was an anxious witness, occurred on the thirteenth and fourteenth of the former month. The birds would rush at each other at top speed, screaming all the while, and as the two came together one would try to strike with open talon, and the other to avoid the blow. The outcome seemed to be a draw until one eventually sought refuge in a tree.

Soon after the last encounter the male eagle disappeared, and though we feel certain that he kept to the neighborhood, he was never seen at the nest. The task of rearing the eaglets fell entirely to the mother bird.

What meaning should be attached to these events, which for a fourth time threatened to forestall our work or bring it to an abrupt end, cannot now be determined with any assurance. The action which I have attempted to describe was difficult to follow with accuracy because of the extreme rapidity of the movements.

Eagles, like many other birds, will defend a certain area or breeding territory, over which they strive to exercise the right of eminent domain, and will drive off all suspicious trespassers.

The fights which we chanced to witness may have been the culmination of a warfare that had long existed, or they may have dated only from a recent mating, wholly unknown to us. In the first event the birds at this nest may not have been the original Vermilion eagles at all, but invaders, which came in after the downfall in 1926, and had got a foothold before the older residents could oust them.

Be this as it may, the loss of the male partner caused a serious disturbance in the normal routine of eyrie life, for complete cooperation is the rule in aquiline domestic affairs. The mother eagle became extremely nervous when thus suddenly deprived of her guarding mate and passed less time at the nest than would otherwise have been the case. The two eaglets, still in white down, suffered in consequence, but had the season been less tempestuous both would no doubt have lived.

As it was, the older eaglet, which we had reason to believe was a female, being the more vigorous, held up most of the food and soon began to mistreat her younger and weaker nestmate. She would always strike at his head with her bill, and with such force that he was sometimes knocked over, when he would lie on his back with feet up, as if completely done for; and unfortunately we were unable to help him, either to his feet or to a square meal. When, under such conditions, the old eagle again landed a fish she would quite disregard her puny infant, then in such dire need of maternal care, and bestow her attention upon the larger and greedier bird.

So matters went on for a number of days until, on the nineteenth of May, hail and rain beat so relentlessly upon the great nest that the much-abused eaglet, with hardly enough strength to crawl beneath the mother's sheltering wings, finally succumbed, and its body was trampled into the great mass of withered grass which formed their bed.

For weeks after leaving the eyrie, in mid-July, the surviving eaglet formed the habit of using our tower for a perch; and it seemed strange indeed to see this great bird standing on the railing of the platform, close to the very spot where we had so often stood while watching her from our tent; and stranger yet to behold her leave this point, which to us seemed quite elevated enough, and, rising ever higher and higher toward the clouds, soar and circle as if in pure enjoyment of her liberty and power.

As late as the first week in September, when this young eagle was four and one-half months old and nearly eight weeks out of her nest, we found her still close to her old home. The mother bird was also there, and, to our surprise, after going to the lake and returning with a fish, she made straight for her eyrie, as in former days; and the young eagle followed her there and no doubt claimed a share of the booty.

The female eagle which was tragically bereft of her mate returned to her old eyrie the following spring accompanied by a new mate.

WHY DID THEY VANISH FROM THE EARTH?

The last Labrador duck on record was shot near Long Island, New York, 60 years ago. Today a few of these mild-looking little fellows may be seen—but stuffed and in museums.

A GOLDEN EAGLE SCREAMS AT THE MICROPHONE

Contrary to popular belief, they are shy birds and only because of their extreme wariness have they been able to persist in most parts of the Rocky Mountain region. Usually they nest on inaccessible ledges, but occasionally in the tops of tall trees. Their outcry is rather disappointing. This youngster has only recently left the nest (see page 204).

Photographs by Arthur A. Allen

A PUZZLED MOCKINGBIRD SEEKS A RIVAL IN A LOUD-SPEAKER

The bird heard his own voice, which had been previously recorded, coming out of the instrument, and, thinking it an interloper in his territory, darted at the offending case to drive it away. Round and round he fluttered, hunting for the other bird until finally, completely flabbergasted, he stood thus, with his bill open, yet not daring to sing (see page 195).

HUNTING WITH A MICROPHONE THE VOICES OF VANISHING BIRDS

By Arthur A. Allen

Professor of Ornithology, Cornell University

ALMOST within the memory of men still living, four species of North American birds have become extinct. In our museums will be found the dried skins or mounted specimens of the great auk (page 329), the Labrador duck (page 187), the passenger pigeon (page 253), and the heath hen (page 241). The Carolina parakeet (Vol. II, page 80) seems about to follow them.

Until only a few years ago, the tooting of the heath hen could be heard each spring on the island of Martha's Vineyard, but the thought of preserving its voice, in addition to its photographic image and stuffed effigy, never entered anyone's mind.

Yet there are many Nature lovers, interested in the living bird as well as in its plumage and classification, who would like to know what sounds it made when it inflated the tiny balloons on the sides of its neck and stamped its feet and flirted its tail.

They would like to know what sounds were made by the millions of passenger pigeons described by Audubon and Wilson as darkening the sky for hours at a time. They would like to listen to the call of the Labrador duck and the other species that are gone forever.

And today there are other birds, still living, which seem unable to compete with the march of civilization and which our children may know only as museum specimens. Should not their voices be preserved before it is too late?

As we were talking this over one evening when I was planning a sabbatical leave from the University, my good friend Albert R. Brand suggested that a worthwhile undertaking would be the all-time preservation of the voices of vanishing birds.

The idea grew, and soon we had a hunting expedition well in mind—an expedition which would leave guns at home and would "shoot" the birds with cameras, microphones, and binoculars; its object: specimens of bird voices preserved on film, with such photographs, motion pictures, and field observations as would elucidate the habits and appearance of the living birds and determine better methods for their conservation.

The American Museum of Natural History, of which Mr. Brand is an Associate in Ornithology, approved of the project; the National Association of Audubon Societies gave us its blessing; Mr. Duncan Read loaned us additional motion-picture cameras; and the Brand-Cornell University-American Museum of Natural History Ornithological Expedition was born.

BIRD VOCALISTS PROVE TEMPERAMENTAL

We had already had opportunity to learn something of the work we were undertaking. Not long after the first sound pictures appeared on the screen about ten years ago an attempt had been made by a well-known motion picture company to obtain a film release of singing birds as a demonstration of the quality of its sound-recording cameras.

It is one thing, however, to invite an opera singer to step before the microphone and quite another to order a wild bird to do the same thing. For nearly two weeks two of their best operators, equipped with a sound truck, struggled with the problem, but just as they got their cameras and microphones into action the singing birds flew away.

Finally, patience exhausted, they came to our Laboratory of Ornithology at Cornell for help, thinking that our knowledge of birds might supplement their knowledge of sound recording with desirable results. To make a long story short, we were able to help, and became so interested in the problem that we conceived the idea of making a permanent record of the songs of all North American birds.

ALBERT BRAND ASSISTS

This was not the province of the movie men, however, we were quickly assured. They now had enough film of singing birds for one release and that was as far as they desired to go. We could buy the truck for $30,000 and do it ourselves if we wished. But we didn't have the funds.

And so the problem rested until Albert Brand entered the picture, with a love of birds in his heart and a desire to learn their songs. He studied with us at Cornell for

Photograph from W. E. Browne

BLUE JAYS READILY LEARN CIRCUS TRICKS

W. E. Browne of Grandin, Florida, has trained many of his birds to catch fragments of peanuts tossed into the air. A Florida crane comes to his back door for cornbread.

Photograph by Arthur A. Allen

PAUL KELLOGG LOOKS DOWN UPON A CARACARA NEST

This tower, which ordinarily folded up into the box on top of the truck, could be erected in ten minutes and raise the photographer and his camera 20 feet into the air, thus saving the laborious toil of climbing (see illustration, page 192).

190

Photographs by Arthur A. Allen

A LOUISIANA HERON PRESENTS A TWIG TO HIS LADY

Nesting material is scarce in the large rookery which E. A. McIlhenny has built up for these birds on Avery Island, and the gift here offered seems to be more appreciated than would have been a gardenia or a bunch of violets.

IT FLED FROM THE MOTION-PICTURE CAMERA

This young caracara which A. R. Brand, sponsor of the expedition, is holding led the party a merry chase through the saw palmettos when they tried to catch the vulturine to return it to the nest from which it had been frightened.

Photograph by Arthur A. Allen

THE CORNELL UNIVERSITY-AMERICAN MUSEUM OF NATURAL HISTORY ORNITHOLOGICAL
EXPEDITION MAKES A ROADSIDE STOP

With the object of securing permanent records of the voices of vanishing species of birds and filming their habits, the Cornell ornithologists left Ithaca, New York, the middle of February and traveled 15,000 miles, circling much of the United States in their quest. The truck at the left, equipped for camping and photography, had a collapsible tower on its roof to bring the photographer on a level with the tree tops; the truck at the right was equipped for sound recording. The microphone was supplemented by a large parabolic reflector, shown between the trucks.

a couple of years, saw the writing on the wall, and decided his would be the problem of filming the songs of North American birds. Furthermore, he would record the songs from the films on phonograph disks so that they would be available to anyone who wanted them.

We little realized all the intricacies of the problem when we first started assembling the instruments necessary for this delicate kind of recording. But our colleagues at Cornell in the College of Engineering, Professors W. C. Ballard and True McLean, and Mr. Arthur Stallman, were very helpful.

SEEKING THE RARE IVORY-BILLED WOODPECKER

Soon, with their aid, we were embarked on a project which was to prove as fascinating as it was difficult, and as time-consuming as it was productive, and which finally took us 15,000 miles with our sound truck and cameras in 1935 in an effort to record the voices of certain birds that are threatened with extinction.

By the middle of February we were fully equipped and had started work in central Florida. Mr. Paul Kellogg, instructor in ornithology at Cornell and an expert in sound recording, had been assigned to the expedition by the Dean of the College as the sound technician. Dr. George Sutton, Curator of Birds at Cornell, was to accompany the expedition as bird artist until we should find the ivory-billed woodpecker—a rather indefinite commission. James Tanner, a graduate student in ornithology at Cornell, was to accompany the expedition as general handy man to assist in both the sound recording and the photography. Mr. Brand and the author were to plan the itinerary and take charge of the photography and the ornithological observations.

One of the first objects of the expedition

Photograph by Arthur A. Allen

JOE HOWELL EXAMINES A CARACARA'S NEST

It is a difficult climb to the top of a cabbage palm, but the investigator negotiated the smooth bark, the rough crown, and the sharp fans to get a glimpse of the young birds about ready to leave home. He discovered that they had been banded by an earlier caller. The photograph was made possible by the tower erected on the roof of one of the trucks.

was the rediscovery of the ivory-billed woodpecker, perhaps the rarest of the North American birds and at one time thought to be extinct.

In central Florida in 1924 the author and Mrs. Allen had discovered a pair that were later collected by local taxidermists, and the expedition planned to pass March in the same general region of Florida searching for another survivor. Whenever conditions were suitable, of course, we would catch the songs of other birds as well.

LEAVES NO LONGER WHISPER, THEY SHOUT

It must be realized that when the song of a bird is amplified enough to cause a recording lamp to flicker sufficiently to make a record on the film, every other sound is amplified too. Many a time records of beautifully clear songs are rendered worthless by the passing of an automobile a block away or even by the rustling of a slight breeze among the leaves. The whispering leaves of the poets are shouting leaves to the sound recorder; the babbling brooks no longer babble, they roar.

So each morning we arose at daybreak before the milk trucks, tractors, roosters, hounds, and innumerable other sounds of civilization became too frequent, and recorded the voices of such familiar Florida birds as the mockingbird, the cardinal, the Florida wren, and the ground dove.

THE LIMPKIN IS FOUND ONLY IN A FEW PLACES IN FLORIDA

This rare tropical bird is best known for its weird cry, which sounds like someone having a tooth pulled—*aow-aow*—and which may be the origin of many a superstition connected with the mysterious swamps which the species inhabits.

When conditions were inauspicious for recording, we spent long hours and covered many miles hunting for ivorybills. On some trips we obtained records or films of such unusual species as the Florida sandhill crane, the southern bald eagle, the American egret, the wood ibis, and the Audubon's caracara, which is near the northern limit of its range on the Kissimmee Prairie.

Nor were our labors ended with the setting sun, for we were always looking for ideal conditions to record the evening concerts of the barred owls, the limpkins, and the chuck-will's-widows.

One of the unusual places we visited in Florida was "Manywings," the home of W. E. Browne near Grandin. Here the familiar garden birds have grown so tame that they come to his call and nine or ten species have learned to catch from the air fragments of peanuts which he tosses to them (page 190).

The blue jays, which are particularly wary in most places, are especially adept at darting from the trees like flycatchers to snatch the titbits in mid-air. Most remarkable of all is the tameness of a Florida crane, which comes to the back door for cornbread.

While we were recording the voices of some of Mr. Browne's birds and the truck door stood open, an inquisitive Florida wren so quickly accepted us into the family that she carried nesting material into the truck. Before Mr. Kellogg realized it, she had made a good start on her nest at his elbow, as if she would induce him to remain and make his home with her. What greater show of hospitality has Florida to offer?

CHALLENGING AN UNSEEN RIVAL

Quite different was our experience in Winter Park when we were testing some of the film we had exposed. We had our projector set up inside the house with the window partly open. One after another the songs of different Florida birds poured from the

Photograph by Arthur A. Allen

NO SINGER, THE WOOD IBIS IS A SILENT GHOST OF FLORIDA MARSHLANDS

When taking this photograph, the author stood waist-deep in water among the cypress knees of a large swamp. It was obviously impossible to get the sound truck anywhere near the birds, but this made little difference because, like other storks, these, when fully grown, are virtually voiceless. Flocks of them are often seen in the Florida skies, soaring in great circles like buzzards.

loud-speaker with nothing to disturb our critical ears until the song of a mockingbird came on.

Then, as the liquid notes began to vibrate across the room, we became aware of a tapping at the window and there, fluttering against the pane, was our favorite garden mocker bristling with resentment. This house and garden were his, and he obviously objected to any other mockingbird singing in his territory.

When we placed the loud-speaker in the garden and played the mockingbird's song again, it was almost pathetic to watch the bird's amazement when he flew at the song but could find no bird on which to vent his wrath (page 188).

In Florida we were unsuccessful in our search for the ivory-billed woodpecker. If they still occur in this part of their former range it will take keener ears or luckier observers than we to find them.

So the last of March we started for Louisiana, where Dr. T. Gilbert Pearson had reported the finding of an ivorybill by Mason D. Spencer near the Tensas River in 1932.

On our way we stopped at Beachton, Georgia, at the charming home of Herbert Stoddard, the great authority on bobwhite quail. He had arranged with Col. L. S. Thompson to bait up a flock of wild turkeys on a chufa patch in a clearing on his plantation so that we could secure motion pictures and voice recordings of these shy, absolutely feral birds, uncontaminated by any domestic blood.

One familiar only with domestic turkeys little realizes the wariness of these grand old birds or the stealth necessary to get within camera distance.

Fortunately for us, Colonel Thompson had directed his superintendent, Albert Stringer, to build a blind of pine boughs before our arrival, so that the turkeys would have time to get accustomed to it.

Photograph by Arthur A. Allen

WILD TURKEY GOBBLERS STRUTTED UNCONCERNEDLY BEFORE THE MICROPHONE

With corn and peanuts the birds were baited to this clearing in the forest on the Colonel Thompson estate at Thomasville, Georgia, by Herbert Stoddard and Albert Stringer. The sound truck and cameras were concealed in blinds built two weeks before (page 195).

Corn and peanuts were scattered some 20 yards in front of the blind each day, and when we arrived we found many signs of turkeys, deer, quail, squirrels, and mourning doves that had been frequenting the spot.

NOT A GOOD GOBBLING MORNING

The day before we planned to make our record the sound truck was driven into the blind and completely concealed; the cable was stretched 250 feet to another blind where I could sit with Mr. Stoddard and aim the sound reflector at the gobblers when they should come off their roosts and advance toward the field. In the hope of attracting a gobbler within recording range, Stoddard armed himself with his turkey call and imitated the sound of a hen turkey.

But turkeys are capricious birds. Turkey hunters will tell you that certain days are "good gobbling mornings," and on other days not a gobble will be heard. Not one of the three days at our disposal proved to be a "good gobbling morning" and we had to content ourselves with mediocre sound, though

we secured good film of a flock of hen turkeys and two magnificent old gobblers.

It was interesting to watch from ambush their varying responses to the different morning sounds. To most they paid slight attention, but at anything suggestive of human presence they were extremely wary. Instantaneously they would change from full display, when they were the most conspicuous objects on the landscape, to sleek, trim creatures that miraculously disappeared into their environment, as if they had been swallowed by the earth.

Their eyes, which are extremely quick to notice any motion, are apparently not very keen at seeing objects at rest. On one occasion two old gobblers approached within thirty yards of Stoddard and me as we crouched immovable behind the sound mirror in full view.

RECORDING THE LIMPKIN'S EERIE CRY

From Beachton, at Stoddard's suggestion, we went south to the Wakulla River, Florida, where we hoped to get within recording distance of the limpkin, or crying bird, another of the main objectives of our trip.

Photograph by Arthur A. Allen

LESSER PRAIRIE CHICKENS CROUCH FOR ATTACK WITH FIERCE GOBBLES AND
WARLIKE DISPLAY

In spring the males repair to flat-topped knolls in groups of from four to as many as 40, and
each bird sets up a little domain of some 25 feet square and proceeds to fight with all his neighbors.
Thus the boundaries become fixed, and each learns to respect the rights of others, so that when the
females arrive after six weeks of battle, there is no grand rush (see page 203).

Here a magnificent underground stream, crystal clear, comes to the surface as a spring 185 feet deep and flows gently to the Gulf. Its waters teem with fish which can be observed easily even at considerable depth. The banks of the river are clothed with beautiful moss-covered cypress where hundreds of anhingas, or snakebirds, nest, as well as many herons, ospreys, and other fish-eating birds.

Most interesting of all, however, are the limpkins. About the size of bitterns but related to the cranes, they are dark brown spangled with white. They have been attracted to this beautiful stream by the abundance of a large aquatic snail (Pomacea), which is their principal food (page 150).

The snails are largely nocturnal, and so are the limpkins. At night the loud, wailing cries of the birds reverberate up and down the river, sending shivers down one's back. It would not be difficult even for the most prosaic person to imagine that some lost soul had come back to earth, or at least that some luckless black brother was losing his leg to an alligator.

Here, enthralled by the magical scenery which was rendered even more eerie by the hooting and laughing of the barred owls, we passed several days. We had little difficulty in recording the weird cries of the limpkin and filming its habits, as well as those of the snakebirds, ospreys, and Ward's herons.

From the Wakulla River our expedition proceeded to northern Louisiana, which we found largely under water, with all but the improved roads impassable for our trucks. The stickiness of this Louisiana mud, or "gumbo" as it is called, is exceeded only by its hardness when it is thoroughly dried out. Then it is as hard as stone, and in a dry season one can drive anywhere; but let a little water fall upon it and one sinks in it almost literally up to the knees.

So here our search for the ivorybill was greatly retarded, and had it not been for the kind offices of our friend Mason Spencer, the local representative in the State

Photograph by Arthur A. Allen

PART OF THE "ROAD" TO THE IVORYBILLS' NEST WAS UNDER WATER

Trucks were obviously of no use, and the party engaged a mule team and farm wagon; but two draft animals were not strong enough for the job, and another pair was required to help pull them out of the mud.

Photograph by Arthur A. Allen

PAUL KELLOGG HANDLES THE SOUND EQUIPMENT

To get to the ivorybills' nest, which was seven miles from an improved road in a forest 30 miles long and 18 miles wide, the party had to transfer all equipment to a farm wagon hauled by four mules. Arrived at the nest, the wagon became the sound laboratory and the camp was christened "Camp Ephilus," the generic name of the bird sought.

Legislature, and J. J. Kuhn, a member of the State Conservation Department, our hunt would probably have been in vain.

FOUND: THE ELUSIVE IVORYBILL

As it happened, however, we passed but three days tramping through the jungle before we not only located a pair of ivorybills but actually found the nesting cavity 43 feet from the ground in a dead swamp maple. Furthermore, the nest was only seven miles from an improved road, which, in an unbroken forest 18 miles wide and 30 miles long, was indeed fortunate.

It was obviously impossible to consider taking the sound truck, with its 1,500 pounds of equipment, into the swamp, but it was not beyond possibility to consider getting in with a wagon and a few mules.

The mayor and sheriff of the nearest town where electricity was available entered into the project with enthusiasm. They offered us the jail and its courtyard in which to dismantle the truck, unsolder all the connections, and set up the equipment in a wagon.

We furnished much amusement to the inmates of the jail as we worked, and when word of our objective got around, several of them volunteered confidentially the information that they could show us more of these "pecker-woods" if we could arrange a leave of absence for them with the jailer.

It required a day to eviscerate the truck and another day with four stalwart mules to haul the wagon into the swamp and set up our unique sound laboratory within 300 feet of the ivorybills' nest.

Here we camped for eight days, piling up palmetto fans on the roots of a giant oak to keep our blankets out of the water. Twenty-four-power binoculars, mounted on a tripod and focused on the nest tree, kept us informed of all the happenings, while the sound mirror brought us the calls. We christened our location "Camp Ephilus" in ivory-white bill, the glossy black plumage with the snowy-white lines from the head meeting in the glistening white of the wings, are as vividly pictured in my mind as if I were still sitting on that narrow board in the tree-top, not daring to shift my weight, but feeling the board gradually bifurcating me with wedgelike efficiency.

For five days we recorded all the happenings at the nest, taking turns with the glasses so that not a moment's observations would be missed, hoping we might discover some clue as to why the birds are apparently unsuccessful in rearing young.

But all the events were rather common-place. Each morning at 6:30 the male bird

Photograph by Arthur A. Allen

READY TO RECORD A RARE VOICE

James Tanner, "handy man," points the apparatus at the ivory-billed wood-peckers' nest so that all of their vocabulary could be recorded when they changed places. The microphone is hung at the focal point of the parabolic reflector, and the mirror is sighted at the birds through the telescope on one side.

honor of the scientific name of this rare North American bird—*Campephilus principalis.*

Gradually the birds became somewhat accustomed to our presence and we dared build a blind in the top of a rock elm on a level with the nest and only twenty feet away. It was a thrilling experience to sit and listen to the conversations and watch at such close range the exchange of courtesies as these strikingly beautiful birds changed places on the eggs.

The brilliant scarlet crest of the male, the gleaming yellow eye, the enormous

tapped on the inside of the nest hole; as he grew more impatient he stuck his head out and gave a few "yaps" or "kents" in no uncertain tone, but he never left his post until the female arrived.

MRS. IVORYBILL AWAY ALL NIGHT

A little intimate conversation then ensued and she entered, but before he took off through the forest he often passed 15 or 20 minutes arranging his plumage and scratching as if he were infested with mites. This, we later discovered, must have been the case.

Photograph by P. P. Kellogg

ARTHUR A. ALLEN STUDIES IVORYBILLS

For five days the members of the expedition made continuous observations, through a pair of powerful binoculars, of these rare American woodpeckers at their nest, recording all the happenings and endeavoring to determine reasons for the extreme scarcity of the species. The camp at the base of this large oak was surrounded by water, and palmetto fans kept the blankets out of the mud.

During the day the two birds took turns incubating in about two-hour shifts, but the female always so arranged it that she could leave for the night at 4:30 p. m. and not return until the following morning at 6:30. At least, this was the schedule every day for the week that we observed them.

We wanted to remain with the ivorybills until their eggs hatched and the young were reared, but we heard from our friend, Verne Davison, that if we wished to study and record the lesser prairie chickens in western Oklahoma we must hasten on so as to get there before the first of May.

So, torn between two desires and anxious to make the most of all opportunities, we sent for the mules and broke camp, planning to return in three weeks when the young should be nearly fledged. In two days we had our sound truck reassembled in preparation for the work in Oklahoma.

At this time, however, dust storms were raging on the prairie, and we delayed our journey to accept the kind invitation of E. A. McIlhenny to visit his beautiful estate and bird sanctuary at Avery Island, Louisiana. Here we passed three enchanting

days recording the daily life in his "Bird City."

This is an amazing object lesson in bird protection, showing what man can accomplish through thoughtfulness and kindness toward bird life. Beginning 35 years ago when the snowy heron had become quite rare, Mr. McIlhenny has gradually built up a large colony on an artificial pond of his own creation. At the time of our visit in late April it certainly numbered 10,000 birds, and as many again, we were told, were yet to come.

A BULL ALLIGATOR'S FEARSOME BELLOW

Here we recorded the curious froglike croakings of the snowy egrets, and, by unusual good-fortune, captured the bellow of a huge bull alligator. It is a thrilling sound—like the roar of a lion, but rendered more terrifying by the sight of the churning water, and it certainly must be effective in intimidating lesser male alligators and keeping them from the chosen territory.

The bull alligator lies at the surface of the water, inflating the large air sacs on the sides of his neck. He then submerges his

AN IVORY-BILLED WOODPECKER LEAVES HOME, AND HIS MATE TAKES HER TURN ON THE EGGS

The nest hole was 43 feet up in a dead swamp maple and measured 4½ inches in diameter. The great amount of white in the wings easily distinguishes this bird from the commoner pileated woodpecker, which is nearly as large.

ized that we were in the midst of a real "Panhandle" dust storm.

Furthermore, the storm continued without much abatement for seven of the eight days that we passed on the Davison Ranch near Arnett. It had scarcely rained for three years and from fields that had once been ploughed the surface soil and the very seed were blown into neighboring counties.

The Davison Ranch, itself, however, is largely covered with tiny oaks which the natives call "shinnery." Here in the dust-covered shinnery we were to study the lesser prairie chickens, photograph their curious courtship antics, and record their gobbling calls.

The cattle eyed us curiously when we first erected one of our observation blinds near the home of a burrowing owl. This blind was made of artificial grass mats, greener than anything in that whole country, greener than anything the heifers had ever seen. Instinctively they came lumbering in from all quarters to get a luscious meal.

ponderous body, while the armored head and tail protrude menacingly. Thereupon he emits his thunder while the heavy plates on his back seem to vibrate and cause the water above to dance and shoot spray into the air.

It was now the last of April and another message from Davison started us westward, though we were loath to leave our genial host and his marvelous bird sanctuary.

When we reached western Oklahoma a dull fog gradually obscured the landscape, and as the wind whipped across the barren fields and swirled across the road, we real-

The effect of habit on these same heifers was even more amusing after their first severe rain storm. The downpour not only laid the dust, but filled every depression in the ground with water, including those trodden by the cattle themselves around the drinking vats that were normally kept filled by windmills. Never before had they seen standing water except in these vats and never had they drunk out of anything else. So now, with the vats in the center of large ponds, they could be seen wading out to them to get a drink.

Each morning and again at evening during the spring on the Davison Ranch the lesser prairie chicken cocks assemble in groups of from four to forty on certain flat-topped knolls in the shinnery to compete with one another in a show of prowess, both of voice and of bodily vigor.

For six weeks the males engage in these matches before the females intentionally visit their gobbling grounds. Each male comes back to exactly the same spot every morning and gradually forces upon his neighbors a respect for his territory, some 25 or 30 feet square (page 197).

Photograph by Arthur A. Allen

IVORYBILLS CHANGE PLACES—THE FIRST PHOTOGRAPH EVER TAKEN
OF A NESTING PAIR

The ivory-billed woodpecker is now perhaps the rarest North American bird and from time to time has been thought extinct, though it formerly was found locally throughout the Gulf States and as far north in the Mississippi Valley as southern Indiana. The species is about the size of a crow, and the male has a flaming red crest, that of the female being black.

Many of the combats are mere gestures or feints of anger, but others are sufficiently severe to scatter feathers over the shinnery. Sometimes when the males jump at one another and strike with their wings, a hapless bird is flipped clear over upon his back by a stronger rival.

Each morning from April 25 to May 2 found us at the "gobbling grounds" of a group of 26 males with the microphone staked out in the territory of some aggressive cock. Seven of the eight mornings the wind howled in the microphone and the dust blew, but at last it was quiet and we secured a nearly perfect recording of the birds' sounds, from the pattering of their feet and the silken twitching of their tail feathers to the loud gobbling that follows.

COCKS ARE HEARD TWO MILES AWAY

This gobbling is accompanied by the swelling of the little balloons on the sides

Photograph by Arthur A. Allen

PERHAPS 20,000 SNOWY HERONS SEEK THE PROTECTION OF MC ILHENNY'S "BIRD
CITY," AVERY ISLAND, LOUISIANA

The expedition members were able to set up their microphone near several of the nests and record
some of the neighborhood gossip. It was far from musical.

of their necks, which serve as resonators.
These air sacs, really dilations of the
esophagus, swell up to the size of hens' eggs
when the mouth and nostrils are closed and
air is forced into them from the lungs.

The sound itself is produced by the vibra-
tion of tiny membranes in the syrinx, or
voice box, at the lower end of the windpipe.
Such resonance is given to the sound by the
neck sacs that the birds can be heard for
two miles on a quiet morning.

The strong winds made sound recording
very difficult in western Oklahoma, though
such clarion calls as that of the western
meadowlark and the *whip-whirr* of the
burrowing owls at dusk came through very
distinctly. We failed to record, however,
the white-necked ravens and Mississippi
kites which, while rare in many parts of
their range, are fairly common on the
Davison Ranch.

From Oklahoma our expedition moved
north and west through the barren, wind-
swept prairies of western Kansas into the
verdant irrigated stretches of eastern Colorado, and thence to Colorado Springs and
Denver.

Here we were met and generously assisted by Robert Niedrach, Curator of Birds
at the Colorado Museum of Natural History. Director J. D. Figgins kindly relieved
him of other duties so that he could help us
in our efforts to record and film the golden
eagles and prairie falcons which are still
not uncommon in the vicinity of Denver.

EAVESDROPPING AT AN EAGLE'S NEST

Never shall I forget the experience of lying prone on a flat rock at the edge of Box
Elder Canyon, near Fort Collins, for four
hours, watching and waiting for a golden
eagle to return to its eyrie.

Directly below me the cliff fell away 750
feet, while the nesting ledge was only 60
feet down. I was covered with one of our
grass blinds so that the eagle would not see
me and, unbeknown to me until I tried to
shift my position, the boys had piled so
many rocks on the edge of the blind to keep
me from falling off the cliff that I could
not even roll over.

At last the majestic bird sailed in with
a jack rabbit in his talons and the young
eagles screamed with anticipation at his ap-

Photograph by James Tanner

THE BELLOW OF THE ALLIGATOR WAS SUCCESSFULLY RECORDED

Through the courtesy of E. A. McIlhenny, who has made a life-long study of the curious beasts, the fearsome performance, which serves for them the same function as a bird's song, was caught by the microphone and photographed in motion pictures. During the call, the horny plates on the creature's back vibrate, causing the water to dance and shoot spray two feet above the surface. Air sacs resembling those of a huge leopard frog can be seen at the sides of the neck.

proach. The picture impressed upon my mind was well worth all the fatigue of the journey up the mountain and the long wait on the hard rock at the edge of the canyon.

A few days later Bob Niedrach led us to another eagle's nest in Willow Tree Canyon near Denver, where we could actually drive the sound truck nearly to the edge of the cliff above the nest.

We padded the microphone, lest it strike a rock, and let it down about 60 feet on its cable to the nesting ledge. Then, concealing the trucks in a grove of pines nearby, we passed the night on the bunks within them.

The next morning at daybreak we clamped on the earphones to learn what was happening at the nest, which, of course, we could not see. It was interesting to hear the many species of birds in the canyon below greet the new day with their various twitterings, screechings, or carols.

There was a canyon wren, too far away to record, whose song, a series of rich descending whistles, came through beautifully. A red-shafted flicker called close at hand.

A black-headed grosbeak and a western tanager, with songs almost exactly like those of our eastern rose-breasts and scarlet tanagers, could be heard faintly up the canyon. A long-crested jay screeched and a flock of violet-green swallows and white-throated swifts came forth from the crannies in the rocks and twittered past the microphone.

About 7:30 a loud crackling in the "mike" told us that the eaglets had arisen and were doing their daily dozen—jumping up and down on the nest and fanning their wings.

About 8 o'clock they began to scream and, looking out of the truck window, we could see one of the parent birds coming out of the east. In majestic circles it sailed over the canyon, looking the ground over to make sure that all was safe, with a large jack rabbit dangling from its talons.

Now the screams of the hungry eaglets became more and more excited as, in narrowing circles, the old bird dropped lower and lower. Finally, in one long graceful sweep, it disappeared below the rim of the

LOVELY LOGAN CANYON IS A HAPPY HOME FOR THE WATER OUZEL

There were plenty of these birds along this mountain torrent and they were not difficult to photograph, but the rush of the turbulent current over the rocks made so much noise that ordinary methods of recording their song were impossible. The microphone was therefore removed from its parabolic reflector and fastened to a rock at the edge of the stream where one little musician sang at daybreak.

canyon and a moment later we heard the crash of twigs as it landed on the nest. There were no cries from the old bird; silently she came and silently she departed. Only the calls of the young were recorded.

A more obliging creature was the dashing prairie falcon that had its eyrie on a similar vertical cliff at the mouth of a canyon near Denver. Its wild screams, whenever we approached the cliff, made it easy to record and photograph.

At the bottom of the same precipice under an overhanging cliff, long ages ago the home of cliff dwellers, a little canyon wren had built its nest, and the resounding whistles of the male were clearly recorded when once we discovered his favorite song perch on a near-by rock.

One of the most appealing experiences of the trip was at the home of a mountain plover in the arid prairie country east of Denver. It was one of those uncertain days when one can count a half-dozen rainstorms in different directions while the sun shines brightly overhead. Eventually, one of the storms headed directly for us, and soon we were being pelted with hailstones larger than marbles.

There was no shelter anywhere on the prairie, and as we hastened into the truck we noticed the alarm of the birds about us when the hailstones struck around them. We drove the truck to within 8 inches of the plover's nest to protect the eggs, and immediately the bird returned to the nest.

Then birds started flying to us from all

IN DASHING ROCKY MOUNTAIN STREAMS THE WATER OUZEL IS AT HOME

It gets a large part of its food from aquatic insects, which it captures by diving into the turbulent water and walking along the bottom.

Photographs by Arthur A. Allen

A SPIRIT OF THE SPRAY MADE MELODY IN LOGAN CANYON

With the microphone on the rock from which the water ouzel sang at daybreak, it was possible to catch the bird's voice in spite of the rushing water; for the singer's bill was sometimes less than two inches from the diaphragm. Sometimes the performer mounted to the instrument itself, but then its little claws made scratching sounds that ruined the recording (see page 209).

Photograph by Arthur A. Allen

WHITE-FACED GLOSSY IBISES AND FRANKLIN'S GULLS NEST TOGETHER

These two species join forces in large colonies in the tules of the Bear River Marshes, Utah. Apparently they do so for mutual protection rather than sociability, for the expedition learned, by watching them from blinds, that they pass most of their time fighting (see also pages 259-261).

directions, especially the showy lark buntings, and soon there were some twenty of them sitting beneath the truck.

HOW A MEADOWLARK SAID THANK YOU

Then came a western meadowlark, pitifully frightened. He longed for the shelter of the truck, but he was a timid bird and each time he approached within ten feet of the car, and could see us inside, his courage deserted him and he ran back. Three or four times he advanced as hailstones hit around him, but just as often he retreated.

At last, summoning all his courage, he made a rush for the car and slipped safely beneath with the other birds. And when he found himself secure at last, he loosed his feelings in one of those clear, beautiful songs that endear this bird to all westerners.

From just a few inches under our feet this

carol of thanks burst through the car and for a moment turned our thoughts to those countless natural dangers which constantly beset all wild creatures and to which we so seldom give heed.

Northward and then westward through arid Wyoming the expedition wound over the mountains to Logan, Utah, where I was scheduled to lecture at the Utah State Agricultural College.

We traveled through the beautiful Logan Canyon, where we had our first opportunity to get really acquainted with the water ouzels, or dippers, which live along most of the dashing Rocky Mountain streams. Famed for its mockingbirdlike song, often heard in midwinter, the ouzel presents a difficult problem for the microphone because, with normal amplification, the noise of the stream drowns out all other sounds.

Photograph by Arthur A. Allen

FRANKLIN'S GULLS AND WHITE-FACED GLOSSY IBISES BRING HOME THROATS FULL OF
GRASSHOPPERS, TADPOLES, AND MINNOWS

After being a death trap for waterfowl for a great many years, the Bear River Marshes of Utah
are once more a paradise for birds. The U. S. Biological Survey has eliminated the botulism
organism which formerly killed thousands of birds annually and has transformed the area into a
wild life sanctuary.

Hence, we studied intently a pair that had built their mossy nest on the side of a huge bowlder, to determine some method of capturing the song amid the rushing water. We often saw the little bird plunge head first into the whirling stream, using its wings as flippers and running along on the bottom in search of mayfly and stonefly larvae. The mountain torrent held no terrors for it and its dense plumage shed water like a duck's.

The song season was nearly over, but we soon discovered that this little ouzel had a favorite rock from which, early in the morning, it sang before going in search of food for its young.

NO "MIKE FRIGHT" HERE

It was a simple matter the next morning to fasten the microphone to the rock and have the bird's bill within two inches of the diaphragm while it was singing. Indeed, at times it mounted to the microphone itself to sing, but then the scratching of its tiny claws ruined the recording (page 207).

In the beautiful Cache Valley of Utah, into which Logan Canyon empties, we found many fascinating birds, and in our two weeks' stay added 15 species to our already long list of records. Birds like the long-billed curlew, the black-necked stilt, the western willet, and the avocet, which we think of as very rare in the East, are truly common there.

Even on the campus of the Utah State Agricultural College the lovely lazuli buntings, lark sparrows, Cassin's finches, and black-headed grosbeaks made bird observing a real pleasure.

Our normal method of recording at daybreak, however, was completely upset, for, with the setting of the sun, there poured down the canyons from the snow peaks above a strong, cooling breeze that

AMERICAN AVOCETS TAKE TURNS SITTING ON THE NEST

In this case the female was more timid than the male and after the observation blind was installed near by, she always waited for the male to take his position over the eggs before offering to do her share of the home duties.

MRS. AVOCET BUNTS HER MATE FROM THE NEST

When the female avocet finally made up her mind that all was safe, she sometimes had difficulty in dislodging her mate from the eggs. He seemed to have an overpowering sense of responsibility for their protection.

THE AMERICAN AVOCET MAKES CAREFUL PREPARATIONS FOR SETTING

Before settling upon the eggs, which are so large compared to the size of the brooders' bodies that it is difficult to cover all four of them, the birds usually turn them with their bills and adjust them so that their rather sharp ends are toward the center like wedges of a cut pie.

IN INCUBATING, THE AMERICAN AVOCET MUST BE A CONTORTIONIST

The long legs are now folded and straddle the nest. The pointed bill is admirably adapted to the bird's peculiar method of feeding on larvae sorted from the film of shallow water, for it is flat at the tip and as thin as a knife blade (page 296). Photographs by Arthur A. Allen.

FOR THE SNOWY PLOVER, THE STONE-SURFACED HIGHWAY OFFERS A NESTING PLACE

This little bird laid its protectively colored eggs in the middle of a gravel road leading out to the Bear River Marshes. It soon became accustomed to passing cars and would dart from its eggs just in time not to be run over, then would come back as soon as the car raced by.

Photographs by Arthur A. Allen

NOT EVEN AN AUTOMOBILE COULD FRIGHTEN THIS MOUNTAIN PLOVER

This species was formerly fairly common along the eastern edge of the Rocky Mountains, but has become rare because of excessive shooting. Shortly after this photograph was taken, near Denver, a sudden hailstorm threatened to kill the bird or break the eggs, and to protect it the party drove the truck within eight inches of it. Other birds then got beneath the shelter (page 206).

continued until 6 o'clock the next morning. T h i s was, no doubt, as delightful to the sleepers as it was a n n o y i n g and f r u s t r a t i n g to o u r recordings. It proved a blessing i n disguise, however, to some of the party, for Kellogg and Tanner c o u l d sleep that much longer while I continued to arise at 4:30 to lead my class of students afield to o b s e r v e the birds.

M a n y afternoons we drove to the Bear River Marshes, s o m e miles to the southwest, to see the innumerable waterfowl that had c o n g r e g a t e d there: ducks by the t h o u s a n d, Franklin's gulls, Brewster's egrets, w h i t e - f a c e d g l o s s y ibises, w e s t e r n a n d eared grebes, and others too numerous to mention and certainly too numerous to photograph satisfactorily in the short time at our disposal.

Photograph by P. P. Kellogg

HERE IS THE HOME OF ONE OF NORTH AMERICA'S RAREST BIRDS—THE TRUMPETER SWAN

The nest was about six feet across and two feet high, and was placed about fifteen feet from the open water of Lower Red Rock Lake, Montana, on one of the marshy islands which dot its entire surface.

Several pairs of snowy plovers had laid their eggs in the middle of a gravel road leading into the marsh from Brigham and would dash off their nests just long enough to let each car pass over and roll by. There were literally scores of these interruptions daily, but the birds continued to live in the middle of the road.

The last week of June found us headed northward toward eastern Idaho to look for trumpeter swans. It is thought that only about 75 individuals of this species remain alive in all the United States, though at one time it was not an uncommon bird throughout the West (page 96).

Arriving at Henrys Lake, we scanned its surface with our binoculars and discovered a pair of these birds swimming near a submerged island in the middle of the lake. Finding very comfortable quarters at the Bar L Ranch close by, we decided to stop for a few days.

Next morning we surveyed the lake more closely and found that there were 19 swans staying there, one of which had already molted its wing feathers and was unable to fly. None of the birds was nesting, however,

Photograph by Arthur A. Allen

FOR FIVE DAYS MICROPHONE AND REFLECTOR WERE VAINLY KEPT IN READINESS TO CATCH THE VOICES OF TRUMPETER SWANS

As a last resort the ornithologists placed a cylinder of screening in the lake in front of their blind and by cautious manipulation eased the cygnets into the cylinder. Within fifteen minutes these specimens, among the rarest of North American birds, returned to their youngsters and the men capsized the cylinder by a string running to the blind, at the same time recording not only the trumpets of the old birds but the lisping calls of the young as well.

even the mated pair in the center of the lake having been discouraged by the changing water level, for the lake was being used for water storage by a power company.

TRUMPETER SWANS REFUSE TO TRUMPET

We were hopeful that some of the flock might fly around and do some trumpeting which we might record, and we stayed for three days and kept our microphone and sound mirror ever ready. But it was not to be so simple, and we were doomed to disappointment.

Thereupon we moved on to Lower Red Rock Lake, Montana, where we were informed that a pair of swans had reared young the year before. This lake is about four miles long and three miles wide and is dotted with innumerable marshy islands.

At first we could see no signs of swans, but, climbing to the roof of the Montana Gun Club, with our powerful binoculars we soon located seven birds, two pairs of which seemed to be nesting.

A cruise around the lake in a duck boat showed that both had nests, though one was empty; the other contained two infertile eggs and the broken shells of two others from which the cygnets had hatched and been led away by their parents.

We were now quite hopeful of being able to secure a record of the voice of the trumpeter swan, though we could not get the sound truck within a half mile of the nearest pair. For four days we remained at the Montana Gun Club with the microphone ready, but, except for one trumpet call during the night, we heard nothing from the swans. Our time was almost exhausted and still we had failed to catch the voice.

TRUMPETERS TRICKED

When the last morning was at hand, we staked our all on one last scheme. We concealed the sound truck behind one of the buildings and ran the cable to the edge of the lake, where we set up the sound reflector and the blind with the Akeley camera inside. Then we made a little cylinder of fly-screening and set it among the rushes, fastening a string to the top of it and running it over to the blind.

Leaving Kellogg ready in the sound truck, Tanner and I then rowed two duck boats to the opposite end of the lake. We followed devious channels so as to avoid the swans until we could start drifting slowly toward them from the opposite side.

Swans are wary creatures and these kept moving away from us with the cygnets between them. But so slowly did we approach that they had time to feed as they went, and little did they realize that we had cut off their avenues of escape, except the one that lay past the blind. Never realizing, they fell into this simple trap and moved to the far side of the blind.

Now we increased our speed and rowed in more quickly than the cygnets could swim, cutting them off from their parents and edging them over to the blind. With the two boats this was easily done, and quickly we picked them up and placed them inside the cylinder of screening.

We now rowed back into the lake, and while Tanner diverted the attention of the old birds, I went ashore and sneaked into the blind. Jim then disappeared up the lake.

Within ten minutes the swans had found their youngsters and were talking to them —into the waiting microphone. In a few minutes we had the sounds of both young and old safely recorded. I then pulled gently on the string, capsizing the cylinder and releasing the young without their knowing just what had happened and without their realizing that we were anywhere around.

The little cygnets swam from one parent to the other, talking back and forth to each other, and gradually moving back up the lake. They were none the worse for having been our prisoners for a few minutes so that we could make a permanent record of their voices that will go down through the years, even though all their kind should vanish from the earth.

This was in very truth our swan song, though a happy one, and the end of our expedition. We had exposed ten miles of film, we had recorded the songs and calls of 100 species of birds, including the rarest in North America. We had filmed the home life of nearly as many and had filled our journals with observations that may help in the preservation of vanishing species.

By driving night and day and resting only while repairing a broken axle, we arrived safely at Ithaca just ahead of the greatest flood in the history of central New York. Two hours after we pulled in the deluge broke, and ten inches of rain fell in the next few hours. The hillside road leading to my home was entirely washed out, so that after a successful journey of 15,000 miles, our trucks finally became marooned in my own back yard.

Courtesy Canadian Department of the Interior

WILLOW PTARMIGAN CROWD AROUND A TENT IN THE LONELY BARRENS, NORTHWEST TERRITORIES

Dr. Helge Ingstad, Norwegian explorer, who lived for a year alone in this desolate region, reports that these birds are so tame that he could have killed them with a stick. Though it was unnecessary for him to take any for food, there are times when they save the native Indian Caribou-eaters from starvation.

Photograph by Associated Press from Keystone-Underwood

THIS WOULD BE A HUNTER'S PARADISE—BUT THE BIRDS ARE PROTECTED

Thousands of ducks annually pass the winter at the feeding grounds on a game preserve in Lake Washington, within Seattle city limits, where plenty of grain is provided for them and they are free from the fowler's gun.

Photograph by Arthur A. Allen

A POMPOUS WOODLAND DON JUAN DRUMS ON HIS FAVORITE LOG

By following the thunderous, far-carrying roar of his whirring wings, advancing when it is heard and halting when it stops, one may sometimes see a ruffed grouse in the act of drumming.

Photograph by Hamilton M. Laing

A TWO-DAY-OLD CALIFORNIA QUAIL MAKES LESS THAN HALF A HANDFUL

But its feet and legs are well developed, for these—together with its natural camouflage—are its only means of escaping danger. Chicks of this species have been known to run from the nest with pieces of the egg from which they were hatched still clinging to their backs. California quail raise large families.

THE TURKEYS, GROUSE, QUAIL, AND PIGEONS

These Game Birds of Prairie, Forest, and Tundra Are Important Assets In Our Wild Life

By Alexander Wetmore

THOUGH dawn was approaching, the blackness of night still lay over the wooded mountains of eastern Tennessee. With a mountaineer companion, I came quietly along a little path where near-by trees and bowlders were mere shadows against the sky, to the shelter of a windfall beside an opening in the forest.

We seemed so isolated from familiar things that my hand, resting on the rough bark of our sheltering log, brought a reassuring touch of reality in a world hidden in dim obscurity. The air was cold with the damp, penetrating chill of early spring.

A gray light that came slowly among the trees strengthened gradually until the wooded slopes about were dimly visible. Color touched the edge of distant clouds.

At that moment we heard low calls and then a rapid gobbling that made me quicken with tense excitement. Wild turkeys, traced to their roosting trees the night before, were coming to the ground.

My friend, skilled in woodland lore, with his turkey call began low notes in answer. As the birds continued, his imitations became louder and more varied, their invitation more urgent. The tone was deceptive even to me close beside him, and I listened with admiration for his skill.

Daylight now came quickly, so that my eyes no longer strained at shadows. Robins called and scolded from trees below, a Carolina wren sang, and in the distance I heard the loud drumming of a great pileated woodpecker. The turkey calls continued.

Soon dark shapes came walking quietly over the open ground before us. A little group of hen turkeys was approaching, pecking at the ground, and stopping constantly to look about with vigilant eye. The intermittent gobbling of the cock was louder, and in another instant he appeared.

PRIDE BEFORE A FALL

With spread tail, head drawn back, feathers erect, wings drooped, and body swollen, he strutted proudly before the seemingly indifferent hens. Light shone from the bronzed feathers of his back and breast. The bare, wattled skin of his head was red and purple, and his tail was tipped with brown. Truly he was a magnificent creature.

So intent had I become on the great birds that I had forgotten my hunter companion entirely, and the roar of his gun startled me almost as much as it did the turkeys. The hens disappeared instantly, running and flying among the trees, but the splendid gobbler lay prostrate where he had fallen at the shot.

In another moment I was admiring his rich colors and examining with interest the five-inch "beard" of hairlike plumes pendent from his heavy breast. His legs were armed with sharp-pointed spurs, and a fleshy wattle dangled from his forehead.

A half hour later, as we started home with the twenty-pound bird, we saw hen turkeys crossing a distant field while other gobblers called belligerently from the valley below.

In those days of abundant game it was considered entirely proper to hunt the turkey in early spring. In fact, this was the only time when the wily gobblers were to be found except by chance. Wisely planned game laws now restrict this sport to other seasons.

MOST IMPORTANT GROUP OF BIRDS

The great group of fowl-like birds (the Order Galliformes), to which the turkey and its relatives belong, is widely distributed through all the continents of the world and is the most important order of birds so far as man is concerned.

More than eight hundred kinds are known, ranging in size from the tiny oriental quail, no larger than a sparrow, to huge turkeys and long-tailed pheasants. Four of the seven families of the order are found native in North America, and members of a fifth, indigenous in the Old World, have been introduced in our continent.

The turkey (family Meleagrididae) is

the principal contribution of the New World to the domesticated birds kept by man. Captive turkeys were found among the Indians in abundance on the discovery of Mexico and were brought to Spain in 1519. From there they spread rapidly through Europe. Although at first a luxury, before the close of the century turkeys were a regular article of table fare among the better class.

PUEBLOS RAISED TURKEYS FOR FEATHERS, NOT FOOD

The Pueblo Indians of the Southwest kept turkeys in numbers long before the coming of the white man. At Pueblo Bonito, explored by a series of expeditions of the National Geographic Society, and at most of the other large pueblos that have been excavated, rooms were assigned to turkeys, as is indicated by the abundance of their bones.

These captive birds were kept not for use as food but for their feathers, which were used in ceremonial offerings to Indian deities. To the Pueblo Indians the turkey was a sacred bird and was seldom eaten.

The ordinary domestic turkey of the farmyard still shows its Mexican ancestry in the white or buffy-white tips on tail and rump feathers. This is a characteristic of the Mexican bird, these markings being brown in the race native to the eastern United States.

The only other living species of this family is the handsome ocellated turkey, of excellent flesh for the table, found from Yucatán to British Honduras and northern Guatemala. Seemingly this bird, of beautifully iridescent plumage, does not thrive in captivity, and is not known to have been domesticated except in a casual way.

A BIRD CALL HEARD A MILE AWAY

The low, mud-walled ranch house at Kilometer 80, west of Puerto Pinasco in northern Paraguay, is pleasantly located on the shore of a lagoon. The land about is level, with grass-grown prairies interspersed with groves of low trees.

After long hours afield during the morning, I sat each afternoon under the split palm roof of a broad porch, caring for specimens and writing. The heat at times was intense, tempered somewhat by warm winds that blew from the north.

At intervals from the forest there came a raucous, three-noted call that was given rapidly for several seconds. Immediately this was repeated from a distance, and often two or three of these voices called back and forth at intervals for an hour.

In walking along narrow forest trails, amid a dense ground growth of spiny plants, I sometimes caught sight of long-tailed birds, pheasantlike in form, that rested in trees or, rarely, fed on the ground. To them I traced the harsh calls that carried to the house, sometimes from a distance of a mile.

These were chachalacas (family Cracidae), of a group that is common in the American Tropics. One kind comes north across the Rio Grande.

The species of this family differ from other fowl-like birds of our fauna in living almost constantly in trees. They are marked by having the hind toe on the same level as those in front, to assist in perching, instead of elevated to a higher plane as in the grouse, quail, and the domestic fowl that live mainly on the ground. In addition to the chachalacas, the family includes the curassows, which are as large as turkeys, and the guans.

ONE OF A HUNDRED KINDS OF GROUSE

Above the village of Painscastle in southern Wales the hills rise in rolling, heath-grown moors that lie open to the summer sun. These elevated slopes are the home of the red grouse, famed as game, and the only distinct species of bird confined in its range entirely to the British Isles.

One warm July evening, in company with a friendly gamekeeper, I walked out through bracken and heather, eagerly anticipating my first sight of so renowned a bird. At one side was the traditional "keeper's larder"—a long pole, supported on two uprights, from which were suspended numerous carrion crows, a magpie or two, a kestrel, and a stoat. All had been killed by the keeper as "vermin" in his zeal to protect the game.

We passed several places where butts had been built of sod. In these, gunners stood in the shooting season to fire at the grouse driven by beaters.

Red grouse feathers were scattered about in abundance, but the day had been hot and birds lay close. I recognized the calling of male grouse from distant coverts at the first note, as the call is similar to that of the willow ptarmigan, but not until the keeper returned to the house for a dog did we find a bird.

As the dog, with waving tail, ranged through the bracken, a fine male grouse burst out suddenly with a startling roar of wings. As it sailed swiftly away, I had a fine view of its handsome red-brown markings and heard its cackling call. It was followed immediately by others.

The grouse (family Tetraonidae) are birds of the North, none of the hundred or more forms being found in the Tropics. In the Old World the black cock, the capercaillie, and the hazel grouse are representative of this well-known group, which includes also the ptarmigan and various grouse of North America.

In the mountains of northern Spain I found poachers hunting the capercaillie at night during the pairing season. Under the light of the moon the males call sonorously. They are said to close their eyes when calling, and by moving only when the note is heard it is possible to approach these shy birds near enough to shoot. At other times it is extremely difficult to see them.

The great group that includes the pheasants (family Phasianidae) has more than 550 forms distributed widely through the world. The domestic fowl, in this family, is without doubt the most valuable bird commercially that exists. Some of its relatives among the pheasants are strange and beautiful almost beyond the imagination of one who has not seen them.

SOME PHEASANTS HAVE FEATHERS FIVE FEET LONG

The largest individual feathers in the entire group of birds are found in members of this family. The decorative upper tail coverts of the peacocks, spread as a huge fan in display, are good examples, but even these are dwarfed by the tail feathers of Reinhardt's pheasant of Indo-China, which measure more than five feet in length and between five and six inches in breadth. The bird is an inhabitant of jungles, where it is seldom or never seen except when caught in snares.

It seems truly marvelous that such huge feathers, with their beautiful colorings, can be shed and renewed annually by birds with relatively small bodies.

Among the true pheasants, the common pheasant and its varieties are the most widely known. Originally the abundant common pheasant is supposed to have come from the ancient lands of Phasis, on the southeastern shore of the Black Sea; hence its name. It was well known to the Greeks and Romans, and may have been introduced into England during Roman occupation.

The pheasant is now one of the most important game birds of the world, as it is widely distributed in Europe and has been established in many localities in the United States. Hundreds of thousands are reared annually in captivity and then released to be hunted, and equally large numbers breed in a state of freedom.

In England pheasants are driven by groups of beaters past hunters stationed at strategic points. In America they are hunted with dogs, as are other upland game birds.

The rearing of pheasants for pleasure as well as for sale is now widespread and extends to many species. In recent years the great eared pheasants of western China, formerly known to few persons, have become common in captivity. Large aviaries often contain twenty or thirty species of pheasants of remarkable variety and beauty of plumage.

BOBWHITE CAN BE RAISED ON THE FARM

Though for many years the propagation of the bobwhite was regarded as difficult or impossible, the combined efforts of a number of game breeders have solved the difficulties one by one until the methods of handling quail are as well developed and as successful as those used for the ring-necked pheasant, writes W. L. McAtee.*

The Virginia State game farm, where propagation of this bird has been brought to a high degree of perfection, is well equipped, and is as methodically operated and efficient in production as any pheasant-rearing establishment. Several thousand bobwhites have been reared on this farm in each recent year and distributed to coverts in the State.

Production on a still larger scale merely awaits the demand that will justify it. Other species of native quail no doubt can be bred successfully under the same system as the bobwhite, with such minor modifications as climate and locality require.

The equipment and system used in quail propagation are similar in a general way to those long tried in the pheasant industry. Differences are chiefly those necessitated by

* From *Propagation of Upland Game Birds*, by W. L. McAtee, Farmers' Bulletin No. 1613, U. S. Department of Agriculture, page 48.

the smaller size of the birds and their non-polygamous nature, and to a less degree by their greater wildness and special dietary requirements.

The story of the quails that fed the Israelites in danger of starvation in the barren wilds of Sinai is well known to readers of the Bible. These were the small Old World quail that migrate south in winter to Africa and then return north into Europe in spring. In passage they are caught in nets by the thousands and shipped to European markets. So many have been taken that it has been necessary to regulate the practice by law.

JUNGLE PIGEONS IN WHITE CAPS

Before the cooling sweep of the trade wind, my little boat traveled easily across the head of Samaná Bay in the Dominican Republic. Terns and pelicans fished in the water, and flocks of screeching parrots passed over the green hills back of the shore.

Entering the mouth of the Yuna River, which drains the great valley called the Vega Real, I was soon in a heavily wooded swamp where the shade was a grateful relief from the intense rays of a tropical sun.

A huge sedge, eight or ten feet high with spreading head, grew along the river bank. On either side stretched the dense, green jungle with trees hung with vines and parasitic plants.

As I walked cautiously over the muddy forest floor, dozens of birds flew out overhead with loudly clapping wings and darted away over the trees. These were white-crowned pigeons, found here in greater abundance than in any other place I have been. Their guttural cooing came constantly to my ears, but in spite of their numbers I found it difficult to see them among the dense and heavy leaves.

From the balcony of the little hotel in Sánchez, all through the afternoon, as I wrote or cared for specimens, single birds and flocks of these pigeons crossed from the swamps to the wooded hills. At a distance they appeared entirely black until, as they turned, the light caught the white crown cap that gives them their name.

BOTH PARENTS GIVE "PIGEON'S MILK"

The group of pigeons and doves (family Columbidae) has more than eight hundred forms distributed through all the great continents and spread widely in the islands of tropical seas. The best-known member of the family is the common pigeon, native originally in the Old World. This species was domesticated many centuries ago and has been carried by the white race throughout the world.

Although raised extensively on a commercial basis, the pigeon, or dove, often ranges in a state of semi-freedom about barns and outbuildings. In every large city, flocks of them have reverted to a wild state, and live and nest about the ledges and towers of buildings, as they do about the rocky cliffs of their native habitat in Europe.

As one peculiarity, young pigeons, when first hatched, are fed on a substance called "pigeon's milk," which comes from the crop of both male and female birds. This is an easily digestible, creamy fluid formed by a fatty degeneration of the walls of the crop.

The most beautiful species of the group are the fruit pigeons of Polynesia and the Malay countries. In almost innumerable variety these display pleasing and unusual combinations of yellow, green, orange, and red, in varying shades and patterns. The orange dove (*Chrysoena victor*) of Fiji is deep, brilliant orange with an olive-green head. The handsome bleeding heart pigeon of the Philippines is named from a sanguinary spot of red spreading over the feathers of the breast.

Among living members of the group the largest are the great goura pigeons of New Guinea, the size of a domestic fowl. The crown has a filamentous crest which once was used so extensively for hat ornaments that the stately birds were in danger of extermination. The importation of these feathers into the United States and many other countries is now prohibited by law through the efforts of those interested in conservation.

THE DODO, EXTINCT SINCE 1681, WAS RELATED TO THE PIGEON

Larger than the gouras was the curious dodo that once lived on the island of Mauritius, a bird of the pigeon order but in another group (family Raphidae). The dodo was the size of a large goose, and had a heavy, hooked bill. Being unable to fly, it was soon exterminated by the sailors who invaded its haunts, so that the last living one was recorded in 1681.

Photograph by Hamilton M. Laing

FRANKLIN'S GROUSE, OF WESTERN MOUNTAIN FORESTS, SHOWS NOT THE SLIGHTEST FEAR

There are many tales of killing them with sticks or stones, or of shooting several from a flock, one by one, without alarming the others. They may even dodge missiles thrown at them, merely shifting position a bit without troubling to fly. This one posed for its picture in southern British Columbia (see page 239).

Turkey

(*Meleagris gallopavo*)
Average Length, Forty-nine Inches

The wild turkey, as the largest American game bird of its group, has enjoyed a renown that has come to few species of birds.

At the time of the discovery of the New World, turkeys were abundant through much of the vast area between eastern Mexico and New England. Because of their numbers and their excellent meat, they were a regular source of food to the Indians and became at once of importance to the early colonists.

As they were tame, they were killed with little difficulty and were a fair mark for the Indian with his bow. At this time the birds were said to range in large bands.

The introduction of guns made an immediate impression on their abundance. In 1672 in Massachusetts, turkeys were reported in lessened numbers, but as late as 1717 they were sold in Northampton at a shilling fourpence each. In 1788 the price had increased to threepence a pound and about 1820 it became tenpence and more.

The name "turkey" for this bird has a curious history. Originally the word was used for the guinea fowl which was brought to Europe from Africa by way of Turkey, and in early English was known as "turkey cocke." In the sixteenth century the newly imported bird from America was confused with the African guinea fowl, so that both were known as "turkeys." From this the American bird retained the name!

The turkey in a wild state ranges in extensive woodlands, where it is so shy that one may enter its haunts frequently without once seeing a bird. In large areas of their former range, both in New England and elsewhere, turkeys have now been completely exterminated. Where they persist they are carefully protected as game birds, and where there is sufficient wild land to afford them cover they may still exist in numbers.

Hundreds are killed each year in Pennsylvania during a short hunting season, and the birds are equally common in many areas in the South. A few remain in Virginia within a few miles of the city of Washington, though their presence is made known mainly through their tracks and the birds are seldom seen.

In spring the adult gobbler struts and gobbles in display before the hens. At this season a heavy pad of fat develops over the breast in the male, serving to sustain the bird, which is so occupied in display that he neglects to feed.

The wild turkey is polygamous. The nest, made by the female, is a hollow scratched in the ground, under cover of a log, dense brush, or other shelter. She lines it with grass or a few leaves, and lays from 8 to 15 cream-colored eggs spotted with reddish brown and lilac. She covers the eggs carefully with leaves and grass when she goes off to feed.

When the young turkeys hatch after four weeks of incubation, they are tender and delicate, and in wet seasons many are lost. They range with the mother through the summer and fall. The adult gobblers flock together, mainly apart from their families, during this period. When the young can fly, all roost in trees, often varying the sleeping place from night to night.

During the day the birds range on foot, feeding on acorns, berries, and in the warmer seasons on insects. Unless suddenly disturbed, they seldom fly except to reach their roost.

Ordinarily, grown turkeys range from 12 to 16 or 20 pounds in weight, while occasionally old gobblers weigh 30 or even 40 pounds. The male turkey has a spur on the side of the tarsus, or lower leg, above the toes, and is marked in addition by a pendent tuft of hairlike feathers called the "beard" in the center of the breast.

In adult birds this becomes five to ten inches long, so that it trails on the ground as the birds bend forward in feeding. Occasionally old hen turkeys develop beards.

As a domesticated bird the turkey has been carried throughout the world, since it has a wide tolerance for climatic differences. Gobblers strut and display in tropical farmyards with as much energy as in the extensive poultry ranges devoted to their raising in the North. And turkeys are found today in South Africa, Argentina, and New Zealand.

In English-speaking countries turkeys are prime favorites for holiday tables and tens of thousands of them are handled in our markets at festive seasons. They have come to be recognized in the United States especially as a bird of Thanksgiving and Christmas cheer.

Four varieties of the wild turkey are recognized, ranging from Pennsylvania and Colorado to Florida and Mexico.

Chachalaca

(*Ortalis vetula vetula*)
Average Length, Twenty-one Inches

Chachalacas live largely in the treetops, coming to the ground occasionally to feed, but retreating instantly to the branches at any alarm. Except to rise to such cover or to escape from isolated trees, they seldom fly far, preferring to run along the larger limbs. They are adepts at hiding and often disappear in seemingly scanty tree growth in a most astonishing manner.

A nest of sticks and moss is made in a tree. Usually three eggs are laid, buffy white, with an extremely hard shell that is finely corrugated. Eggs of the chachalaca are often hatched under hens, and the chicks are easily tamed.

The chachalaca is found in mesquites and chaparral in the lower Rio Grande Valley in Texas, ranging south to Vera Cruz. Related forms and species extend through tropical America to Argentina.

THE WILD TURKEY, BARNYARD BRED, HAS BECOME THANKSGIVING'S SYMBOL

In all his bronzed and brilliant glory, a big **Wild Turkey** gobbler struts and scrapes the ground for the edification of one of his wives in the background, who seems wholly unimpressed.   From this one hundred per cent American bird the common domesticated turkey of holiday tables has descended. Once friendly and seemingly stupid, the wild turkey has been "educated" by hunters until it is now among the most suspicious and unapproachable of all game birds.   In the tree is the elusive **Chachalaca** of southern Texas and northeastern Mexico, which lurks in woods and dense chaparral.   Through a U-shaped loop in its windpipe the male produces a resonant, far-carrying call.

Ring-necked Pheasant

(Phasianus colchicus torquatus)
Average Length, Thirty Inches

From where I rested in the pleasant warmth of the morning sun at the edge of a vineyard in western New York State, the land led down steeply to the blue waters of Canandaigua Lake. Beyond the lake lay a mosaic pattern of cultivated fields, pastures, and woodlands.

Suddenly I heard a curious crowing note, followed by a quick beating of wings. As this was repeated, I turned cautiously to see a gorgeous male pheasant posing at the edge of a thicket, with the red wattles about his eyes resplendent in the sun. The scene is one that may be repeated in many places, since this alien species is well established in our country.

In Europe pheasants have been kept in captivity for hundreds of years. The Greeks at the time of Alexander the Great reared them for food, and this propagation was continued in the days of the Roman Empire. Henry VIII employed a pheasant breeder in 1502. The birds are now bred in many countries.

The true pheasant (*Phasianus colchicus colchicus*) has no white ring about the neck. The Chinese, or ring-necked, pheasant (*Phasianus c. torquatus*) and the Mongolian pheasant (*Phasianus c. mongolicus*) have the neck ring well developed. These three have been much mixed in breeding, and in addition have been crossed at times with the dark, greenish-colored Japanese pheasant (*Phasianus versicolor*), so that the ordinary wild stock is of hybrid blood.

Pheasants were taken to America from England about 1790, by Governor Wentworth of New Hampshire. Early stocks soon died out, however, and successful establishment of the birds came nearly a century later.

In 1880 Judge O. N. Denny, United States Consul General at Shanghai, shipped Chinese pheasants to Oregon, where they were liberated near the mouth of the Willamette River. The following year he sent another shipment, which was freed in the Willamette Valley.

The birds established themselves at once, and increased so rapidly that when their hunting was permitted in 1892 fifty thousand birds were killed the first day.

The long tail, coupled with the size, distinguishes both sexes of the pheasant from any of our native birds. Pheasants feed regularly in cultivated fields and meadows, but at any alarm run to safety. It is astonishing to see so large a bird disappear completely in apparently scanty cover.

The cock pheasant crows mainly during the spring and early summer, though heard occasionally in fall. The birds are often, but perhaps not always, polygamous, and incubation normally is the duty of the female.

The nest is a slight hollow scratched in the ground under cover of vegetation. The eggs ordinarily are olive brown, though occasionally

sets are found that are pale blue. They usually number from 8 to 13 and hatch in from 23 to 25 days. Captive females often lay continuously for considerable periods.

At present the pheasant is established throughout much of the northern half of the United States, and in British Columbia and Ontario. It is resident, and if food is available it can withstand severe cold in winter.

European Partridge

(Perdix perdix perdix)
Average Length, Twelve and One-half Inches

This species, known often as the Hungarian partridge, has been introduced widely into the United States and Canada, and in many localities has now established itself definitely as a game bird, particularly in the prairie regions of the Dominion.

In Alberta, where the original stock was only 800 birds, conditions proved so excellent that a season for shooting partridges was opened five years after their introduction. Now they are common in Alberta, Saskatchewan, and parts of Manitoba.

With this success in mind, game commissions to date have released more than a quarter of a million of these partridges in various parts of the United States. They are now well established in Oregon, Washington, and Idaho, and are common in Wisconsin and Ohio. In other areas the experiment as yet is not wholly successful, but it is probable that the range will be considerably extended.

In the Old World the European partridge frequents cultivated lands, often where cover is scant. In America it has prospered most in sections devoted to fields of wheat and corn, interspersed with hay meadows and occasional areas of waste land.

In such haunts go afield some bright day in October, when the air is sharp with cold. In a weed-grown field, without the slightest warning, there is a sudden explosion of birds as twenty dark-gray forms rise together with roaring wings, and with tremendous speed dart away to new cover. The effect of a first meeting of this kind is more startling than any other I have experienced.

In spring these partridges separate in pairs. The nest is a little hollow in the ground, sometimes under shelter of bushes, but commonly in open meadows where it is sheltered by green vegetation. The 9 to 20 olive-brown eggs are placed on a slight lining of leaves and grass. Occasional sets are whitish or blue in color.

European partridges remain in coveys except during the pairing season, feeding and sleeping on the ground. Their tremendous speed on the wing and their secretiveness make them excellent game birds, and they are capable of thriving under conditions unfavorable to the native grouse of the prairie regions. In its native home this partridge ranges over most of Europe, including the British Isles.

ORIENTAL BLOOD PREDOMINATES IN A BRILLIANT WHITE-COLLARED IMMIGRANT

The showy **Ring-necked Pheasant** on the dead branch is of hybrid stock. Brought to America, these long-tailed birds are reared for game, for aviaries, and for fancy food markets. Ideal pheasant country has groves with underbrush and high grass, reed-sheltered pools, open fields and pastures. The modest female in the foreground contrasts sharply with the gaudy male (above). A dark, chestnut-brown horseshoe on the breast identifies the **European Partridge** (left, with his mate). This whirring flyer has been introduced in large numbers in the United States.

Bobwhite

(Colinus virginianus)
Average Length, Ten Inches

The bobwhite, ordinarily called "quail" in the Northern States and "partridge" in the South, is without doubt the best known of our upland game birds. It has wide range over the eastern half of the United States and in this area is a familiar inhabitant of fields and meadows, often living adjacent to farmyards.

During a large part of the year bobwhites range in coveys that often include members of several families. During the day these bands travel on foot through open fields or in the adjacent woodlands, walking quietly when somewhat protected by cover, or running rapidly, with necks erect and crest feathers slightly raised, as they cross little openings.

Flush them and they dart away to distant cover, from which, if there is no further alarm, in a few minutes they begin their "scatter" call, and under this guidance gradually reassemble. Imitation of this call may bring a bird or two in nervous alarm almost to your feet.

Toward evening the covey enters some thick cover, often in a weedy field, where the birds pass the night. To sleep they arrange themselves in a compact circle, with heads out and tails toward the center, resting closely against one another for warmth. If alarmed, all can fly straight without danger of collision.

In the North these coveys are sometimes covered with drifted snow and so sleep in warm protection. On occasion this is their undoing, for, if sleet forms a heavy crust over the snow, the birds are imprisoned.

In spring, when leaves appear, the coveys separate and each male bird selects an area in which he hopes to have a nest. Here, mounted on a stone, a clod of earth, or a fence post, for hours on end he whistles clearly *ah-bob-white* or simply *bob-white*.

This is a love song and at the same time a challenge. Let a rival male intrude and there is immediate battle. Sometimes this is merely a game of bluff and a chase, but on occasion the fight is bloody and may result in death to one of the combatants.

When a mate finally appears, the male puffs out his feathers, extends his wings, and turns from side to side to display his head markings. According to H. L. Stoddard, who has studied the bobwhite more intensively than any other naturalist, from two weeks to a month may elapse after birds are paired before there is a nest.

Contrary to popular belief, Stoddard has found that soon after males are mated most of them cease to whistle. The calls that continue so persistently through the summer are mainly the notes of mateless surplus males.

The nest is a slight cavity, excavated sometimes, perhaps usually, by the male alone. The hole is dug with beak and claws under shelter of vegetation and is lined with leaves, grass, and weed stems. The eggs are white and may number from 7 to 28 in a set. Incubation, in which the male may share, requires about 23 days. Nesting occurs from April to October, the usual period extending from May to August.

The eastern bobwhite (*Colinus v. virginianus*) is found from South Dakota and southwestern Maine to Texas and the Gulf coast, being more abundant in the southern half of the range. The Florida bobwhite (*Colinus v. floridanus*), smaller and much darker, occupies peninsular Florida. The Texas bobwhite (*Colinus v. texanus*), smaller and decidedly lighter colored, is found normally from southeastern New Mexico and southern Texas to Tamaulipas, but it has been introduced widely in many parts of the United States.

Masked Bobwhite

(Colinus ridgwayi)
Average Length, Nine and Three-quarters Inches

In this interesting quail the male has the markings of the head largely black, instead of white as in the common species, which it resembles in its call and general habits.

Before extensive settlement came, the masked bobwhite was common in a limited area along the southern boundary of Arizona, where it inhabited valleys and mesas covered with extensive growths of grasses. When grazing cattle destroyed the cover in its haunts, it disappeared, and is now known only from northern Mexico.

Mearns's Quail

(Cyrtonyx montezumae mearnsi)
Average Length, Eight Inches

Near Bar Foot Park, in the Chiricahua Mountains of southeastern Arizona, I heard at intervals the yelping calls of Mearns's quail, but the birds were shy and I found only their dust baths, in which lay a feather.

In the Dragoon Mountains, on the opposite side of the valley, I was more successful; one or two quail flushed almost beneath my feet and dashed away to be lost immediately from sight. Though now so wary, in early days they were frequently killed with stones. But the common name of "fool quail" for this bird today seems entirely misapplied.

At times this curious quail is more trustful, and may allow a view as it scratches for food or leads its young among the bushes. It is found ordinarily in bands of two to ten.

Its curious notes, uttered in descending scale and ending in a trill, are ventriloquial and offer little aid in locating the bird. It sometimes answers to a whistled imitation.

The nest is a slight hollow in the ground, and the white eggs number from 10 to 12.

This quail is found in semi-arid mountains and hills from central Arizona and central Texas south to Coahuila and Sonora.

FARMERS WELCOME CHEERFUL BOBWHITE, EATER OF INSECTS AND WEED SEEDS

Northerners name him "quail" and southerners "partridge," but the **Bobwhite** (right foreground with his mate) christens himself by his unmistakable call. This familiar inhabitant of eastern meadows is a shrewd game bird and a joy to the epicure. The odd-looking **Mearns's Quail** (upper right) is alert and wary throughout most of its range in the American Southwest and northern Mexico. The **Masked Bobwhite** (upper left), unable to cope with advancing agriculture, is now found only in northern Mexico, though it formerly frequented southern Arizona as well.

Gambel's Quail

(*Lophortyx gambeli*)
Average Length, Nine and Three-quarters Inches

The lower slopes of Bill Williams Mountain in northern Arizona are grown with piñons and cedars, with much rough terrain cut by rock-strewn arroyos. Here I had my first view of Gambel's quail, which was common over the brush-grown flats and about the scattered water holes. My first one stood in the shade of a little bush, watching me alertly.

After admiring its erect pose and soft coloration through glasses, I walked toward it slowly, expecting it to fly in usual bobwhite fashion. Instead it suddenly walked back among the bushes. As I came nearer it ran swiftly away, easily outdistancing me, and was lost among the rocks. Only rarely did I see the birds in flight, when I found that they traveled with great rapidity.

Gambel's quail is the most important game bird in considerable areas of semi-arid country, particularly in Arizona, for it is common and widely distributed. Except when nesting, the birds are found in coveys, which, when food is abundant, may join with others to form bands of a hundred or more individuals.

The nesting season begins in April and continues through the summer, one family being reared. Males whistle from some commanding perch for hours on end, but, like the bobwhite, are believed to stop these calls soon after being mated.

The nest is a hollow scratched in the ground under suitable cover. This is lined with grass or other fragments of dry vegetation from near at hand. Rarely, these quail occupy nests of other birds in trees and bushes.

From 10 to 12 eggs constitute the usual set, though occasionally double that number are found. They vary from dull white to pale buff, spotted with brown and drab.

Seeds of various kinds form the principal food, those of the mesquite bean being especially favored. Grasshoppers, ants, and various other insects are eaten in small quantity, as are spiders. The birds also are fond of salt, and come regularly to peck at the supplies placed for domestic stock.

While Gambel's quail come constantly to water holes and drink copiously, the birds, like many other desert creatures, have the capacity to go for weeks without water. Their nests are often located where it is not possible for the birds to travel daily to water holes.

Gambel's quail (*Lophortyx g. gambeli*) ranges from the desert region of southeastern California and southwestern New Mexico to extreme western Texas and south into Sonora. A form called the Olathe quail (*Lophortyx g. sanus*), found in southwestern Colorado, is believed by some ornithologists to be native in that region and by others to have developed from introduced Gambel's quail.

Scaled Quail

(*Callipepla squamata*)
Average Length, Eleven Inches

Low hills grown with yucca and bunches of coarse grass border the bench lands along the Arkansas River where that stream emerges from the mountain foothills in Colorado. Irrigated lands lie below, but the rougher area above is invaded mainly by grazing animals.

As I crossed a dry wash between low hills, a curious barking call, uttered at regular intervals, arrested my attention. On climbing carefully up a steep slope, I saw a grayish quail with a light-tipped crest standing on the edge of a bank sixty yards away.

While I looked, the bird threw back his head and uttered the call that had started my search. For some time he continued, occasionally walking about nervously while keeping a sharp lookout all around. At the rattle of a pebble displaced by my foot he was instantly alert, and in another moment ran swiftly away.

Rock-strewn hills and open flats grown with cactus and various thorny shrubs are the chosen habitat of this pale-colored bird, whose plumage seems to match this desert background. Its haunts include lands more barren than those selected by any other American species in this group of game birds.

Amid the intense light of such harsh surroundings, the "cotton top" or "blue quail," as it is usually known, ranges in little flocks that at times gather in larger bands where food is abundant.

Though swift when on the wing, they seldom resort to flight. Their speed on foot is most amazing, and a covey disappears through the bushes with a celerity that is often a surprise even to those who are familiar with them.

Frequently they are the despair of sportsmen, particularly when they have been much hunted.

At any alarm, however slight, they dash away with raised crests, running swiftly, sometimes in single file and sometimes scattering, with no pause or hesitation that might give opportunity for a shot.

Though ordinarily shy, they are sometimes found in the irrigated lands of ranches, and then, with quiet trust in their human hosts, may come about the very door.

The nest is the hollow usual among quail, scratched in the ground and lined with bits of such vegetation as is conveniently at hand. The 9 to 16 eggs vary from white to buff and are spotted with brown.

The chestnut-bellied scaled quail (*Callipepla s. castanogastris*) is found from southern Texas to Tamaulipas and Coahuila. The Arizona scaled quail (*Callipepla s. pallida*), with the abdomen buff instead of brown, ranges from central Arizona and western Oklahoma to Sonora and Chihuahua.

THORNY SHRUBBERY PROTECTS DESERT QUAIL FROM ENEMIES

Dwellers among mesquite and cactus, these southwestern members of the family rarely take wing when flushed, but sprint to safety under spiny undergrowth. The plumed **Gambel's Quail,** on the rock with his mate, lives in desert regions of the southwestern United States and northern Mexico. Across the foreground, seeking their dry fare of dusty weed seeds and scrawny insects, comes a pair of **Scaled Quail,** whose coveys range over both arid and irrigated lands from Arizona to Texas and from southern Colorado to the Valley of Mexico.

IN THE FAR WEST LIVES THE LARGEST OF AMERICAN QUAIL

Upland districts of the Pacific coast from Washington to central California are inhabited by the big, handsome **Mountain Quail** (on the rock), which wears a long plume and utters a clear, plaintive call. Flocks of these birds walk down the mountain trails into the valleys when winter chills the heights. A favorite game bird in the West is the **California Quail** (foreground pair), which posts sentinels while the flock is feeding or dusting. A single nesting each year is the usual thing in the quail family, but broods are large.

Mountain Quail

(*Oreortyx picta*)
Average Length, Eleven Inches

On the ground beside a spring in the Greenhorn Mountains of California, I saw brown feathers handsomely marked with white, indicating the presence of the mountain quail.

A moment later a low call came from one side, and I went out carefully through dense cedars until finally I saw a brown bird with gray breast standing beside a log. As he called he nodded his head, shaking the long, graceful plume that formed his crest.

Others, hidden in the brush, ran with a pattering sound over dry leaves. At an alarm all dashed across a little opening, with heads erect and crest feathers streaming in the wind, and when safe behind cover flew with whirring wings to a distant shelter.

This species, known sometimes as "plumed quail" or "mountain partridge," is one of the most handsome of its group, both in its color and in its decorative crest. Male and female are alike, except that the female usually has a shorter crest and slightly duller colors.

The nest is a hollow in the ground, lined with grass, leaves, pine needles, and other vegetation. Usually it is placed beneath the overhanging cover of logs, rocks, or bushes. The eggs are reddish buff without markings, and vary from 5 to 15 in number. Rarely there are more. In the lower part of their range the birds sometimes lay in nests of valley quail.

Family parties of mountain quail pass the summer quietly, being often found about little springs at the heads of gulches. In the higher mountains in September the birds become restless, and come down the slopes to pass the winter below the region of heavy snows. This migration is performed on foot. The birds follow ridges or at times come out on mountain roadways in little companies. This quail, in fact, usually trusts to its legs to escape its enemies.

While these quail pick up some grasshoppers and other insects, the bulk of their food is composed of various seeds.

The coveys break up in spring and the birds begin their mating in late March or early April. Those that have come down from higher altitudes to winter usually return singly or in pairs, traveling upward as the snow disappears.

The mountain quail (*Oreortyx picta palmeri*) is found from southwestern Washington near the coast to San Diego County, California. It has been introduced on Vancouver Island.

Another form, called in books "plumed quail," but familiarly "mountain quail" (*Oreortyx p. picta*), somewhat darker in color, ranges from northwestern Oregon along the Sierra Nevada and inner Coast Ranges through California and to western Nevada. The paler colored San Pedro quail (*Oreortyx p. confinis*) occurs in the Juárez and San Pedro Mártir Ranges of Baja California.

California Quail

(*Lophortyx californica*)
Average Length, Nine and One-half Inches

To Californians this sturdy-bodied quail with jaunty crest is the most familiar upland game bird. During most of the year it ranges chaparral-covered slopes in the mountain foothills, or brush-grown draws and thickets in the lowlands, in flocks that vary in size according to the extent the birds are hunted.

Though these quail run swiftly, they ordinarily hide when alarmed, to burst out with disconcerting suddenness and dart away.

In the early years of settlement these quail were very abundant; flocks of hundreds were not unusual. They still remain common, but, through cultivation and grazing in their haunts, coupled with much hunting, they are reduced till their bands now range between 10 and 50.

The birds are highly adaptable, and with increased settlement have established themselves in many places in suburban gardens and even in parks in some cities. The bird lover, visiting in California, may be thrilled by male quail calling from roofs or chimneys in Pasadena, or may encounter pairs or bands in Golden Gate Park in San Francisco.

This quail has proved adaptable to transport elsewhere, so that I have been delighted to hear its pleasant notes in the Salt Lake Valley in Utah, on the island of Oahu in Hawaii, and near Valparaiso in far-distant Chile. In the eastern United States, however, attempts to naturalize it thus far have failed.

The nest is a hollow, usually hidden beneath some cover. On a lining of grass and other soft materials there are placed from 6 to 28 eggs. When more are found, the nest is used by two females. The eggs are white or cream color, spotted with brown, and, like other quails' eggs, are strongly pointed at the smaller end. They hatch in 21 to 23 days.

Though nests are found from spring to fall, only one brood is raised. The later broods are believed to be those of birds that have lost an earlier setting. In exceptionally dry seasons these quail remain in bands through the summer, and many do not nest at all.

The California quail is one of the most strictly vegetarian of our birds, and approximately 97 per cent of its food is made up of seeds and other vegetable matter.

The typical California quail (*Lophortyx c. californica*) is found from southwestern Oregon near the coast to Monterey County, California, and has been introduced in the State of Washington and on Vancouver Island. The valley quail (*Lophortyx c. vallicola*), which is lighter colored, ranges from Upper Klamath Lake, Oregon, through California to northwestern Baja California. The Catalina quail (*Lophortyx c. catalinensis*), like the last but larger, is confined to Catalina Island, and there are two additional forms in Baja California.

DEEP WOODS RESOUND WITH THUNDEROUS DRUMMING OF THE RUFFED GROUSE

The male drums with his wings to summon his mates, to challenge other cock grouse to battle, and sometimes just to wear off excess energy. Ranging widely in Canada and the northern and eastern United States, this hardy bird thrives on nuts, grain, seeds, buds, fruit, and insects. During the unexplained "crazy season" in the fall, many **Ruffed Grouse** kill themselves by flying into obstacles. As winter approaches, they grow "snowshoes," horny, comblike projections on the toes, which help support their weight in deep snow.

Ruffed Grouse

(*Bonasa umbellus*)

Average Length, Seventeen Inches

Admiring the view from the slopes of Spruce Knob, highest mountain in West Virginia, I suddenly sensed rather than heard a slow, throbbing sound, like the beat of a great heart. This was repeated, at first slowly, then with increasing speed, until it became a muffled roar of sound that ceased as abruptly as it had begun.

Immediately answer came in kind from farther away, and again from another side. Ruffed grouse, under the inspiration of the cool air of fall, were drumming, a thrilling sound that gave the proper accompaniment for the wild panorama before me.

In my mind I could see the drummer, as I had on other occasions, standing proudly on a prostrate log, with neck ruffs glistening in the sun. Suddenly he throws the body erect, with the tail at an angle, and begins the beats of his wings that produce the sound. The movement is so rapid as to defy the eye, until at the close the swiftly moving pinions show as a hazy blur about his body. The sound, a resonant drumming whose tones may carry far, is produced by the beat of the stiff wing feathers against the air.

The ruffed grouse in the North is often known as "partridge," while in the southern mountains many call it "pheasant." It is an inhabitant of extensive woodlands, where it ranges in little bands that crouch and hide at any disturbance. It is a bird dear to the heart of many a sportsman, and with its quick get-away under cover is one of the most difficult to kill of any of our game birds.

Walk through its haunts and the birds lie close until you have passed, when they rise with a resounding roar of wings that startles the novice into complete forgetfulness of his gun. The grouse dodge at once behind some tree or thicket and dart away, to set their wings finally and sail rapidly to safe coverts.

In spring drumming begins in earnest, and it is then that at times it is possible to approach and watch the drummer. Move forward cautiously when the drum is heard, and stop motionless the instant it ceases. With fortune you may see the bird before it takes alarm.

Nest making and incubation fall entirely to the female. The nest is a hollow made in the ground, usually near the foot of a tree. It is lined with dried leaves and contains from 7 to 16 eggs, rarely more. These are buff or brown, occasionally slightly spotted with reddish brown. When not alarmed the female covers the nest completely with leaves before leaving, at times laying some gently on her back and wings so that they settle over the eggs as she slips from under them. There is some evidence that this grouse is polygamous.

The grouse is a model mother, guarding her family carefully, and with bristling feathers rushing to their defense, like a little hen, at any danger. The chicks hide instantly and the mother bird then attempts to lead the enemy, be it man, dog, or fox, to a distance by feigning injury and tumbling over the ground.

The wings of the young grow rapidly and by the time they are half grown they are able to fly for short distances.

Though subsisting largely on seeds, fruits, and buds, the ruffed grouse in the warmer months eats a great variety of insects and other animal food. Sylvester D. Judd, who made a detailed examination of stomachs of this bird, found that they ate hazel nuts, beechnuts, and small acorns with a great variety of seeds. The fruits of wild grapes, sumac, partridge-berry, blueberry, raspberry, and wild cherry are taken in abundance at the proper season. I have seen them feeding on wild strawberries and on a great variety of small wild fruits.

In winter when other food is scarce they eat the buds of trees. When apples are planted at the edge of woodlands these are favorites, with buds of many other trees.

In summer all feed on a variety of insects as well as snails, slugs, and spiders. When grasshoppers are abundant family flocks of the grouse wander out from the woods into the borders of open fields to profit by this food supply.

In late summer and fall these birds roost in trees, and they may continue to sleep in conifers in mild winter weather. Regularly, however, at that season they sleep on the ground beneath low protecting branches, sometimes burrowing under deep snow.

Periodically there is great reduction in numbers among ruffed grouse, for reasons that are not clearly apparent.* Increasing settlement has brought about their extermination in many areas, but where there are extended forests, and hunting is properly restricted, the birds still remain in fair numbers.

When undisturbed these grouse become as tame as chickens. Having been for many years unmolested on the estate of the late Alexander Graham Bell in Cape Breton Island, Nova Scotia, the older birds now occasionally take refuge on the porch when caught out of the woods by a heavy shower. Gilbert Grosvenor reports that the family often stumbles over them on the garden paths.

Six geographic varieties of the ruffed grouse, differing in size and color, are at present recognized in a range that extends through wooded areas from Labrador to Alaska, and south to Pennsylvania, Tennessee, Colorado, and northern California. In the mountains the birds go to northern Georgia, and formerly were found south into eastern Kansas.

* George Shiras, 3d, gives interesting data on this subject in *Hunting Wild Life with Camera and Flashlight,* National Geographic Society, 1936.

TO CHARM THEIR MATES, THESE WESTERN GROUSE STRUT IN PROUD DISPLAY

With inflated skin sacs which push aside their neck feathers, these grouse produce a deep, booming sound, a vocal effort audible at a great distance. The **Richardson's Grouse** (male and female.
above) inhabits coniferous forests of the Canadian Rockies, ranging south to Montana and Wyoming,
where it clings to the edges of timber and open glades along streams. Pacific coast mountains are the
habitat of the foliage-eating **Sooty Grouse** (foreground pair), which is noted for the great yellow sacs
of the male.

Dusky Grouse

(*Dendragapus obscurus*)

Average Length, Twenty Inches

Travelers in the Rocky Mountain region may encounter little bands of large gray grouse in the bushes along streams or in more open sections under pines and spruces. These are dusky grouse, the "fool hens" of the ranchmen. The name is often merited, as in remote sections the birds are tame and fearless.

Flocks of nearly grown young may rest on logs within a few feet, or may fly into low trees where they remain quietly. When game birds were more abundant, it was often possible to shoot several from such a flock with a pistol or small rifle without causing alarm among the others.

In spring a low hooting call may attract attention to a male dusky grouse as he struts along the ground with drooping wings. On either side of the swollen neck an area of bare, dull-reddish skin, covering a distended air sac, is outlined by an oval ring of pure-white feathers.

The nest is a shallow basin beside a log or under the shelter of bushes, with a scanty lining of pine needles and other vegetation. The eggs vary from 7 to 10, occasionally more, and are buff, spotted with brown.

When the young are hatched, the female is highly solicitous for their welfare, and is often fearless in her anxiety for them. Later, the entire family often flies into trees, and it is not unusual to discover suddenly that a little group of them is eyeing you quietly from a few feet away. Their flight is accompanied by a roar of their stiff-feathered wings, and as they dart away the gray band at the end of the tail is often a prominent mark.

In Colorado and New Mexico these grouse are usually found in the mountains at 7,000 feet altitude and above. Farther north they range at lower elevations. In winter their tracks are often seen in snow when themselves are not discovered.

In summer these birds eat many grasshoppers and other insects, but their food for most of the year is entirely vegetable. Strawberries and fresh fruits are eaten in season and the dried berries and drupes of various shrubs and plants with leaves, small twigs, and buds form part of their fare. In winter when other food is buried beneath deep snow the leaves and buds of spruces and other coniferous trees become a staple in their diet.

The true dusky grouse (*Dendragapus o. obscurus*) is found from Utah, southern Idaho, and Colorado to New Mexico, Arizona, and central Nevada. The form called Richardson's grouse (*Dendragapus o. richardsoni*), figured on the color plate, with the terminal gray tail band less distinct, frequents the mountains from central British Columbia and western Alberta to eastern Oregon and Wyoming.

Fleming's grouse (*Dendragapus o. flemingi*), of darker color, ranges from northern British Columbia to southern Yukon and District of Mackenzie.

Sooty Grouse

(*Dendragapus fuliginosus*)

Average Length, Seventeen and One-half Inches

This large grouse is an inhabitant of conifers, and though it nests on the ground and feeds there to some extent, a good part of the life of adult birds is passed in trees.

My first meeting with them was in northwestern Washington. As I traversed wet undergrowth, sodden from nearly constant rains, I heard resonant, hooting notes, repeated with varying accent.

After long listening, I traced these calls to a group of tall firs, where, after much watching, with aching neck, I made out the dark form of the bird. Secure in its remoteness, the grouse continued to call at intervals, paying little attention to my movements on the ground below.

The sac on either side of the neck in this species is yellow, and is larger than in the dusky grouse. The skin above it also is considerably thickened. The greatest difference comes in the call of the male, for that of the sooty grouse carries for long distances, while the notes of the dusky grouse have much less force and power.

As it calls the great bird poses with drooping wings and spreading tail, while the neck sacs are inflated to display their color.

To nest, this grouse descends to the ground and prepares a slight depression under the cover of a rock or log, or beneath bushes. This is lined scantily with grasses and leaves, and contains from 5 to 12 eggs, buff in color, spotted with reddish brown. As incubation continues, a few feathers from the bird are usually added to the nest lining.

The mother bird seems to care for the young alone, the males joining in little groups at this season. As in other grouse the wing feathers grow quickly and it is not long until the chicks can fly sufficiently to escape from enemies upon the ground.

In forests remote from human intrusion, when the birds are not disturbed they are tame and unsuspicious. When disturbed they soon become wild.

Various kinds of berries are favorite food, together with leaves, soft stems, and seeds. In winter the birds feed extensively, if not entirely, on the needles of pines and firs, which give a strong flavor to their flesh and make it unpalatable to many persons.

These grouse are hunted with considerable difficulty, since, when in lofty trees, they remain motionless and cannot be seen.

Four varieties are recognized in the area from Alaska to the mountains of California.

LIVING IN LONELY FORESTS, THEY HAVE NOT YET LEARNED FEAR OF MAN

Full-grown **Spruce Grouse** (lower pair) have been caught by hand, and hunters often kill them more easily with a stick than with a gun. This naïve vegetarian frequents the vast Canadian spruce forests and tamarack swamps from the eastern base of the Rockies to the Atlantic. The equally fearless and confiding **Franklin's Grouse** (above), of the mountains of Alaska, western Canada, and northwestern United States, is almost a twin of the spruce grouse, but lacks the orange bar at the tip of the tail.

Spruce Grouse
(*Canachites canadensis*)
Average Length, Fifteen Inches

The spruce grouse is a bird of the far northern forests and can live only in undisturbed wilderness. With any development of natural resources by civilized man it becomes rare and ordinarily is soon exterminated. Because of its long isolation it has little fear so long as it is out of actual reach, and is often captured with the greatest of ease.

Boys kill them with sticks and stones, or catch them in snares. Often a flock in a low tree will watch quietly while their members, one by one, are snared by a noose on the end of a long pole, never seeming to realize that they are in danger. This is another of the grouse that often bear the local name of "fool hen" (page 237).

The male spruce grouse has a curious display, which, though given during most of the year, has its greatest expression in the mating season. The bird rests on a low branch at the border of a little opening. At intervals it flies across to another perch, pausing for an instant in the air to beat its wings rapidly, producing a drumming, rattling sound.

Sometimes a bird may rest on the ground in a little opening, jumping into the air at intervals to drum. Again, the male resorts to a leaning spruce up which he walks, frequently springing into the air to drum. Such drumming trees become well known, as the bark is worn and rubbed through constant use.

The birds are not at all shy and continue their display fearlessly, with little regard for curious human eyes.

Years ago the spruce grouse was more abundant, and was said at times to gather in large bands. Such flockings now are a thing of the past, as the birds are found mainly in pairs or family parties. Often male and female are found together through the winter.

The numbers of this bird are always difficult to judge, since they remain quiet on most occasions when their plumage blends with their background in such a way that they are not seen. In summer their tracks may be found in sand or earth, but in winter, when ptarmigan travel everywhere through the snow, the spruce grouse remains aloft in the spruces where it is concealed except when encountered by chance approach.

The nest is placed on the ground under bushes, or beneath the low-hanging branches of a spruce. As the birds sit close, their homes are discovered with considerable difficulty. Often the female will not rise until trodden upon. The eggs, which number from 10 to 16, are buff or cinnamon, boldly marked with varying shades of rich brown. They are among the handsomest in color and marking of the entire family.

The care of the young falls to the female, as with other grouse. She cares solicitously for her brood, often remaining on the ground to scold with ruffled feathers after the youngsters, able early to fly, have taken refuge in the trees.

Aside from the drumming of the males that has been described this grouse is a silent species. Females cluck excitedly when their nests or young are threatened, and the chicks have little high-pitched calls. Other than this there is no record of their notes.

The spruce grouse spends much time in trees and bushes, where it secures its principal food of leaves and buds. The birds are resident even in the far north. In winter they live almost exclusively on spruce needles, so that their flesh acquires a strong, resinous flavor.

The four geographic forms are distributed through northern forests from the Labrador Peninsula across to Mount McKinley and the Yukon region in Alaska. They range south to New England, northern Minnesota, and southeastern Alaska.

Franklin's Grouse
(*Canachites franklini*)
Average Length, Fifteen Inches

This is the western counterpart of the spruce grouse, from which it differs principally in lacking the buff-colored tip on the tail. It is an inhabitant of mountain forests of conifers.

Like the eastern bird, Franklin's grouse has no fear at all of man. Aretas A. Saunders relates that once he climbed a small pine and seized one of these grouse by the foot, merely to see if this was possible. When released, the bird merely moved a few feet to a higher limb.

There are many tales of killing them with sticks, or of shooting several from a flock, one by one, without alarming the others into attempt at escape. They may even dodge missiles thrown at them by shifting position a bit, not troubling to fly.

The male in display, according to T. T. McCabe, struts with spread tail, drooping wings, and head drawn back with the red combs over either eye prominently erect.

The nest and eggs, seen seldom by naturalists, resemble those of the spruce grouse.

Care of the eggs and young falls entirely to the female, and the males at this season remain apart. The mother bird often is little alarmed when the young are approached, merely clucking or calling softly as warning or threat to the one intruding.

Franklin's grouse feed largely on needles of pines and firs, and in winter remain almost constantly in trees. They do not migrate, but during the colder season are difficult to find because of their arboreal habits.

In late summer they eat berries of various kinds, but the bulk of their food comes from coniferous trees, a fact that gives their flesh a strongly resinous flavor.

Franklin's grouse ranges in the northwestern United States and southwestern Canada, from southeastern Alaska, British Columbia, and Alberta to central Idaho and northern Oregon.

PRAIRIE CHICKENS ARE VAIN AND JEALOUS LOVERS

Struggling to preserve itself by keeping ahead of civilization, the **Prairie Chicken** (female and male, below) may now be found, in greatly diminished numbers, from the southern Prairie Provinces of Canada to Colorado, Texas, and eastward to Indiana. The orange air sacs of the male, here pictured in mating display, are violently deflated after the resonant *boom-ah-boom* call with which he challenges all rivals is uttered. The **Lesser Prairie Chicken** (above), which occupies the more southerly part of his cousin's range, is similar in plumage, but paler.

Prairie Chicken

(*Tympanuchus cupido*)
Average Length, Eighteen Inches

The coming of spring in the haunts of the prairie chicken is signalized by a resounding booming, whose insistent repetition is certain to arouse interest. Follow the sound and eventually you will find a number of gray-brown birds resting a short distance apart on the ground in open field or prairie.

Suddenly one begins a curious dance in which the rapidly moving feet make a little pattering sound on the ground. It then droops the wings, erects the tail, and throws the pointed feathers on the sides of the neck forward like little horns, while the body swells, and two yellow sacs like oranges are inflated on either side of the neck. The bird runs forward a few steps and then expels the air from the sacs after uttering a hollow, booming sound.

Immediately the challenge is answered by another male a short distance away, and the two approach with threatening mien to rush at one another. The combat is no sham battle, as feathers fall and the birds strike viciously with bills and feet. Females near by look on with seeming indifference.

The booming of the prairie chicken may begin in March, but reaches its climax in May, which is the height of the mating season. Like the ruff of Europe, the birds visit the same areas each year for their mating, even though the ground has been plowed and the original sod replaced by growing crops. Their booming is one of the sounds of the prairie countries that, heard once, are never forgotten.

The prairie chicken lives entirely in the open, and where it has been given reasonable protection has persisted in many localities in the face of extensive cultivation. With the sharp-tailed grouse it is the most characteristic upland game bird of the interior prairie regions.

Nesting duties fall entirely to the female, as the male is too engrossed in his displays to have interest in such affairs. The nest is placed on the ground, where it is hidden by dense vegetation. Rarely is it located in the shelter of groves of trees. The eggs vary from 7 to 17 in number. They are olive buff in color, spotted with brown in varying degree, some being almost without markings. Incubation requires approximately 24 days.

After the young hatch the birds range for the rest of the year in family parties wherever food and cover are found. While insects are eaten extensively in summer, during most of the year the prairie chicken depends on leaves, buds, and seeds for its nourishment.

In the northern part of their range these birds migrate southward at the approach of cold weather, traveling north again in spring. During these movements they sometimes fly at a considerable height above the ground.

When colonists came first to the area between Massachusetts and New Jersey, they found a bird called the "heath hen" that ranged in large flocks in open country. This eastern race of the prairie chicken, marked by wider dark bars and slightly darker color in general, was hunted to such a degree, and was so molested by increasing settlement that finally all disappeared except a small colony on the island of Martha's Vineyard off the coast of Massachusetts. In spite of careful protection this group steadily dwindled in number, until the last survivor disappeared in the fall of 1931.

The true prairie chicken (*Tympanuchus cupido americanus*) ranges from Alberta and Manitoba to eastern Colorado, Arkansas, and Indiana. Attwater's prairie chicken (*Tympanuchus c. attwateri*), smaller and darker, is found in the coast region of Texas and southwestern Louisiana.

The heath hen (*Tympanuchus c. cupido*), now extinct, formerly ranged from southern New Hampshire to New Jersey, probably extending to the shores of Chesapeake Bay in Maryland.

Lesser Prairie Chicken

(*Tympanuchus pallidicinctus*)
Average Length, Sixteen Inches

This interesting species, marked by small size and pale coloration, is a bird of the Great Plains area that formerly was found in tremendous numbers. Early travelers in this section describe flocks ranging from fifty to five hundred individuals, whose wings, as they rose in sudden flight, made a noise like thunder.

These great flocks have disappeared, and for a period of years this species seemed on the way to extinction. With more carefully planned game laws that have afforded better protection, the birds have increased in number, and, though absent over much of their former range, are still found in some sections in fair abundance.

In spring the lesser prairie chickens resort in droves to their booming ground, often a low elevation grown with buffalo grass. Here they go through antics similar to those of their larger cousins. The booming sound differs decidedly in tone, and the sacs on the neck of the male are reddish instead of yellow.

The eggs are somewhat less spotted than those of the larger prairie chicken, some being almost immaculate.

Their flight is swift and the birds afford much sport to the hunter, though some consider them as inferior for the table.

In summer and fall they feed extensively on grasshoppers, but for much of the year they subsist on seeds. Formerly they ranged through the bunch grass of the plains country, but with burning and grazing much of this has disappeared. Now the lesser prairie chicken finds winter food and cover in fields of cane, Kaffir corn, and other similar crops.

The lesser prairie chicken ranges from southeastern Colorado and Kansas to central Texas and southeastern New Mexico.

LARGEST OF THE GROUSE, THE SAGE HEN CLINGS TO SAGEBRUSH PLAINS

Large flocks of male **Sage Hens** (in foreground with female) assemble in earliest spring to croak, strut, and posture. This vainglory is punctuated with frequent vicious fights. These birds, also known as "sage grouse," are found from southwestern Canada to California and Nebraska. At the top is a female **Columbian Sharp-tailed Grouse** (left) with two males. Much grayer plumage and a more southerly range distinguish the Columbian from the northern sharp-tailed grouse.

Sharp-tailed Grouse
(*Pedioecetes phasianellus*)
Average Length, Seventeen and One-half Inches

In quest of food the sharp-tailed grouse may come out into the open fields of corn and wheat where its cousin the prairie chicken is at home, but it regularly ranges in and near the thickets of brush and the groves of trees that are scattered here and there throughout the prairie countries.

Low, rolling hills grown with plums and wild roses, with stands of poplar and willow about little lakes, are especially favored haunts.

In spring the sharp-tail resorts to certain knolls where for some weeks it is occupied in the spirited dancing and fighting that accompany the mating period.

Males droop the wings, elevate the tail, puff out the feathers, and with lowered head strut and run about in circles, often springing into the air. Their feet make quick, stamping sounds, and at intervals they expel the air in the swollen, feather-covered air sacs on the sides of the neck as they produce a hollow boom.

These activities soon trample the ground, leaving it hard and bare. Fifty birds may congregate in one spot, and the same knolls are sought year after year, regardless of their cultivation in wheat or other crops. These are the ancestral mating grounds and to them the grouse must repair, in spite of man's intrusion.

The nest is a hollow on the ground, lined with whatever vegetation is at hand. The eggs usually number from 10 to 15, and are olive buff speckled with small spots of brown. Some are almost entirely unmarked.

In the hunting season these grouse are favorite game, as they usually lie well to dogs, and to one with steady nerves, not disturbed by their roaring wings on their sudden rise, they offer excellent shooting.

At the approach of winter sharp-tailed grouse often move to regions with more timber, and at this time come into areas where they do not occur in the nesting season. Though in summer they live on the ground, in winter they spend much time in trees, where they eat dried berries and buds. At this season they often come about farmhouses and into small towns, where wheat may be found about grain elevators.

They sleep on the ground, in winter burrowing into loose snow in the shelter of thickets where the wind has not packed the drifts.

The northern sharp-tailed grouse (*Pedioecetes p. phasianellus*) ranges from central Alaska across to northern Quebec. The Columbian sharp-tail (*Pedioecetes p. columbianus*), which is grayer, is found from the interior lowlands of British Columbia to Utah and northern New Mexico. The prairie sharp-tail (*Pedioecetes p. campestris*), of paler, buffier hue, is found from southern Alberta and Manitoba to eastern Colorado and western Wisconsin.

Sage Hen
(*Centrocercus urophasianus*)
Average Length, Male, Twenty-eight Inches;
Female, Twenty-two Inches

Walk through the aromatic growths of sage in the Great Basin region, and you may be startled by the sudden flight of a huge grouse. It rises without warning and whirls quickly away to disappear in the shelter of the gray-green shrubs that extend for miles in every direction.

This is the sage hen, better called "sage grouse," the largest of its group in America. Old males weigh from four and one half to eight pounds, and with their long tails and striking markings are truly magnificent birds.

Formerly sage hens were abundant, but with extensive settlement they have been reduced in many parts of their former habitat, and without protection would soon become extinct.

A strong, muscular gizzard, like that of the domestic chicken, is so usual among grouselike birds that it is curious to find in the sage grouse a stomach that is merely a thin-walled sack. Feeding as it does on insects and soft vegetation in summer, and on the leaves of sage in winter, the sage grouse apparently digests this food without the need of a strong grinding organ.

In spring, sage grouse gather in certain favored localities for a strange display. This begins before dawn, often when it is too dark for human eyes to see. The male bird spreads its tail so that the pointed feathers stand out in a semicircle, and inflates the sacs on the breast and sides of the neck so that they come nearly to the ground. These distended sacs are thrown quickly up and down, while the stiffened feathers on the neck and breast rasp against one another and against the wings to produce a rattling noise. Finally air is expelled in a curious sound difficult to describe.

In addition to the noises produced by this display these grouse utter a guttural note, given as they rise on the wing. The females have a rapid, scolding call when alarmed about their young.

Like other grouse of this group, the present species makes its nest in a scantily lined hollow on the ground. The 7 to 13 eggs (occasionally more) are olive buff spotted with brown.

The sage grouse is polygamous and the care of nest and young fall entirely to the female. Incubation requires 22 days and the young grouse are active immediately on hatching.

As they attain their growth the family flocks gather in companies that feed along the creek bottoms, and the adult males, which during the summer have ranged apart, join the others.

In earlier days the winter flocks sometimes included thousands of birds, but that is something no longer seen.

This species ranges from British Columbia and southern Saskatchewan to California and northwestern Nebraska.

CHAMELEONLIKE, PTARMIGAN SUIT THEIR DRESS TO THE BACKGROUND

The two **Willow Ptarmigan** on the ground at the left (male above, his mate below) are flecked with white to merge with a sparsely snow-strewn autumn landscape. Spring decks the males (on the wing and on the rock) in striking finery, but protects the mother bird with sober plumage. In winter they all match the snow. These ptarmigan range over the Arctic and subarctic regions of the North, migrating southward in winter, casually to the border of the United States. They form an important food supply for northern natives.

Willow Ptarmigan

(*Lagopus lagopus*)

Average Length, Fifteen Inches

As Elisiy and I put up our tent in the doubtful shelter of low dunes near the end of the Alaska Peninsula one July evening, I heard on all sides curious cackling calls that my Aleut companion said were those of *alladēk,* or ptarmigan.

The following morning as I walked across the hummocky tundra, wet from rain, a reddish-brown bird as large as a bantam suddenly ran ahead of me with neck extended and breast brushing the ground, so that it seemed more like a crouching reptile or mammal than like a bird. This was a cock willow ptarmigan.

After moving a short distance in this fashion, the bird rose with a startling roar of stiffly feathered wings, and to the accompaniment of loud cackles dashed away a few feet above the ground.

At that instant, from the corner of my eye, I caught the movement of a brown hen bird stealing quietly away to one side, and sprang forward to surprise a little brood of newly hatched chicks that instantly disappeared in the deep moss. One that I captured nestled quietly in my hand while I admired the buff and brown markings of its tiny, down-covered body.

This was the season of hatching, and several times in the next few hours this little scene was repeated, with the parent ptarmigan attracting my attention until the young were hidden. The birds were abundant, and I was fully aware that unless they were directly in my path they simply remained motionless, hidden from my eyes by the blending of their colors with that of their tundra background.

The handsome willow ptarmigan of subarctic tundras and barrens is the outstanding land game bird through the vast region of the north, though hunted for sport in only a small part of its extended range. To various races of men, as well as to predatory birds and mammals, it is an important source of food.

The seasonal changes in color are most interesting. In late fall the willow ptarmigan is in clear white plumage except for a black bill, dark eye, and black tail feathers, the latter mainly concealed except in flight. The birds match perfectly their winter background of snow.

In spring, as soon as snow begins to leave the ground, dark feathers appear on head and neck, so that the birds are parti-colored. As summer arrives, the ptarmigan become entirely dark, but almost at once white feathers begin to replace the darker plumage, so that through the fall the birds are in mixed dress. When winter snows come again, new white feathers have replaced all dark body plumes.

At all seasons these birds match their background, the mixed dark and white plumage of spring and fall simulating the patches of snow that then are scattered through their haunts.

In winter, ptarmigan grow long, hairlike feathers on the feet that serve as supports in walking in soft snow. At this season the willow ptarmigan perform regular migrations to valleys and river bottoms where willows, alders, and other trees project above the snow. On the buds of these the birds feed when all other supplies of food are hidden. In their migrations the birds often move in flocks of hundreds of individuals. Many killed by hunters are preserved frozen for later use.

In spring these ptarmigan return to their breeding grounds, where each male selects a bare spot of ground, and, with swollen red comb, begins to strut and call. Frequently he flies a few feet into the air, to utter his barking notes as he flutters down to earth. Battles in which feathers and blood may fly are frequent when the birds are numerous.

The female ptarmigan places her eggs in a hollow in the ground, covering them carefully with grass whenever she leaves them, until incubation begins, when she seldom wanders far. The male remains close by and flies viciously at gulls that attempt to steal the eggs, often striking them hard with his firm, heavy body.

From 7 to 10 eggs are the usual number, with variation from 5 to 17. They are handsomely marked with brown that is brighter when the egg is first laid and becomes darker as the coloring matter hardens.

While tame and unsuspicious when they are unfamiliar with man, these ptarmigan learn fear in time, and then adopt the secretive habits of other grouse. Under such conditions they rise from the ground without warning with resounding wings and cackling calls, to dash away to safety with rapid speed.

At these times their hunting is truly sport, as the ptarmigan live on open ground where they can see for long distances. Most shots that offer are at long range and it takes a steady hand and eye to hit these fast-flying birds.

Snowy owls, foxes, and other predatory creatures kill many ptarmigan, and many are taken by natives with snares and nets. When these birds, with other wild creatures of the North, decrease in their periodic cycles there is a definite food shortage among men and other predators that require meat.

Five forms of this ptarmigan are now recognized, their combined ranges extending from the western coast of central Greenland and the eastern Aleutian Islands to Newfoundland, and in the mountains to central Alberta and British Columbia. Accidentally they occur in the northern United States from North Dakota to Massachusetts.

PTARMIGAN WEAR WARM "STOCKINGS" OF FEATHERS ON LEGS AND FEET

They nest on the ground, and so fully do they trust their protective coloration that they may not stir until almost trampled. The **Rock Ptarmigan** (male and female in fall plumage, above) breeds throughout Arctic America and the barren lands of Alaska and Canada. The dapper **White-tailed Ptarmigan** (male and female in summer dress, lower right and left, and young bird in fall plumage in the foreground) is smaller than other ptarmigan and is found in the Rocky Mountains.

White-tailed Ptarmigan

(*Lagopus leucurus*)

Average Length, Twelve and One-half Inches

Climb over the rough, rock-strewn slopes above timber line in favored parts of the Rocky Mountains and you may be fortunate in finding a medium-sized, grayish-brown, grouselike bird. Often it shows no fear, permitting the closest approach without alarm.

This is the white-tailed ptarmigan, smallest of our three species of this group. In addition to small size, it differs from the others in having the tail feathers white instead of black. It is one of the rarer mountain birds and from difficulty of access to its haunts is known only to the hardier among naturalists.

The white-tailed ptarmigan live permanently on the higher slopes of the mountains and for much of the year are found above timber line. Only when snows cover their food supply do they descend into the timber or along the creeks where buds from bushes projecting above the snow furnish sustenance.

This ptarmigan is a master in the art of hiding, aided by its coloration, which through its changes in summer and winter always resembles the background against which the bird is found. Relying on this it often chooses to move away over the ground rather than fly even when closely approached. When it is pursued as game, however, it becomes alert and flies rapidly and far.

The nesting period comes in June, and the nest is placed in a depression on the ground. The eggs vary considerably in number, from 4 to 15 being recorded as complete settings. From 6 to 8 seem to be the usual number. They lack the rich coloration of other ptarmigan eggs, being buff more or less spotted with brown. Some eggs are nearly plain.

Their food consists of leaves, buds, and fine browse from mountain shrubs and herbs, varied in summer by insects, tender shoots, and flowers.

In winter when strong blasts sweep the mountain slopes the ptarmigan feed behind the shelter of sticks and stones, always facing toward the wind. To rest they sometimes dig little hollows in the snow where they may lie secure while the rushing air whistles overhead.

Four closely allied forms of this bird are recognized by scientists, extending on mountain ranges from central Alaska and the District of Mackenzie to New Mexico.

Rock Ptarmigan

(*Lagopus rupestris*)

Average Length, Thirteen Inches

Leaving the little valleys, where willow ptarmigan tended their young, I climbed slowly up for several hundred feet over the rock-strewn slopes of a low mountain. Below me were the waters of Isanotski Strait, at the western end of the Alaska Peninsula. The lush grass of the lower valleys soon disappeared and on these high slopes the stony ground in part was bare and in part was covered heavily with dense growths of moss.

Suddenly with a roar of wings a cock ptarmigan rose with a harsh, cackling call and started away at rapid speed, to be tumbled over by a quick shot at long range. In another moment I was admiring a fine male for which I had climbed laboriously to search.

In the hand the smaller size and duller colors that distinguish this species from the willow ptarmigan were easily apparent. I admired the little comb above the eyes and the closely feathered feet as I removed the skin to preserve this bird for the collections of the National Museum in far distant Washington.

The rock ptarmigan is found almost entirely in open country, ranging regularly in the hills and mountains above the haunts of the willow ptarmigan.

They are birds of strong, swift flight and when startled may travel as much as a mile before alighting. The wings move so rapidly as to make a blur about the body until sufficient momentum has been gained, when the pinions are set and the bird glides away at high speed.

In fall, in the far north, this ptarmigan makes extensive migrations, often gathering in flocks of several hundred. These travel on foot and on the wing, sometimes crossing wide expanses of water.

In summer they feed on insects, berries, and green vegetation. In winter they frequent slopes where the wind sweeps the ground bare, to search for frozen berries and buds. Or where the snow is not deep, they dig it away with strong claws to expose their food. The Eskimos often trap them by placing nets on bare ground where they gather to feed.

In the Aleutian Islands in early summer I often saw the cock birds rise thirty or forty feet in the air, to descend slowly, giving a cackling, crowing call. Their lookout posts usually overlooked the nest site. When flushed, the male frequently flew low over the female on the nest, so that I found nests on several occasions by approaching the cocks and then searching along their line of flight.

The nest is the usual depression on the ground, lined with grass, sometimes with vegetation arching overhead as a protection against the sharp eyes of marauding gulls and ravens.

The eggs number ordinarily from 6 to 9, occasionally more. They are buff in color, strongly marked with black and brown. The female sits very close. On one occasion I stepped on the tail of one on the nest before I saw her in the grass.

There are eleven recognized forms of the rock ptarmigan in the vast region extending from Attu, at the western end of the Aleutian Islands, to Greenland. Closely allied forms are found in northern Europe and Siberia.

Ptarmigan in Winter

The vast expanses of winter snow that cover the North for much of the year make a hard and difficult background for life of any kind. Among the few birds that exist under these bleak and rigorous conditions the most interesting are the ptarmigan.

These grouse of the snow through countless ages have developed the ability for life in an environment where only the most hardy may survive. They are not "game" in the sense of civilized man who hunts for sport. To the primitive peoples that find their homes in these distant regions they are often the means of life itself.

At the approach of fall ptarmigan molt the dull plumage of summer and come out in a dress of snowy white. The feathers are dense, heavy and abundant, far more so than in the summer dress, to guard against the winter's cold. Long, closely set, slender feathers cover the legs and even the toes to guard these exposed parts against freezing chill. The generic name *Lagopus,* given by the French naturalist Brisson to ptarmigan, means "rabbit-footed," and rabbit feet they have to all external appearance.

The claws grow long and pointed as spikes for walking over icy slopes, and the openings of the nose at the base of the bill are set with dense, close feathers to keep out frost and fine snow. No other bird, except the snowy owl, is so well fitted for life under these rigorous conditions. Thus equipped the ptarmigan can brave the winter, being under necessity of finding only where shrubs and low trees project above the snow to give browse and buds for food.

The change to white in winter is a peculiarity of the northern kinds of ptarmigan, including those of America. The red grouse of the British Isles remains dark in color the year round, though sometimes, especially in Scotland, birds spotted more or less with white are found.

To sleep the birds fly into banks of soft snow, sometimes going in out of sight, and sometimes merely making little forms in which they lie. Dozens may sleep close together, but none walk in to their roosts. To do so would leave telltale tracks to guide fox or lynx to the sleeping birds. In morning they also fly on awakening, perhaps so that they may return for another night to the same shelter.

On Southampton Island, on one occasion George M. Sutton found willow ptarmigan sleeping in depressions in the snow made by his footprints, where the birds found relief from the sweep of the wind. These shelters seemed much to their liking, as the ptarmigan returned a second evening to roost in the newer tracks made in examining their sleeping quarters of the night before.

A supply of food in the form of twigs and buds of willow or other shrubs is necessary for the life of these grouse, and when heavy snows come many are under the necessity of making extensive migrations toward the south. At such times they move in flocks, usually toward dusk, flying swiftly near the ground. From the great Arctic islands ptarmigan have to cross considerable stretches of water to reach the mainland tundras. Their flight is strong and swift and they can cover long distances with ease.

INVISIBLE WHEN MOTIONLESS

Against the white expanse of winter ptarmigan clad in equally white plumage are invisible so long as they remain motionless. Black tail feathers in the willow and rock ptarmigan are folded under coverts of white. Only the eye and bill are dark, small points of black that are not noticed.

When flushed the birds rise with a roar of wings and appear so conspicuous that there is wonder that they could be overlooked. As they drop back onto the snow at a distance, there is even greater wonder as they disappear as if into the ground. With all these artifices enough survive to carry through until the spring.

As the sun advances once more toward the north male ptarmigan develop little red combs above the eye; they become noisy and pugnacious, and fight much among themselves.

With the arrival of spring dark feathers begin to appear once more in the ptarmigan's plumage and for a time the birds seem conspicuous. This is due mainly, however, to their active motions in display, for at rest they still merge into their partly snow-covered background.

The Eskimo, sagacious in the ways of birds, sometimes places the stuffed skin of a ptarmigan in some conspicuous place, surrounding it with his fine-meshed bird nets. Concealed near by he imitates the crowing challenge of the cock bird until living ptarmigan rush to attack the supposed intruder and are entangled in the nets.

During their migration flights, natives equipped with long nets often station themselves toward dark in little hollows where they watch until flocks of ptarmigan come skimming along just above the ground. The nets are raised at the proper instant, and the birds dash into them, to be pressed down against the snow until they can be killed.

In Labrador ptarmigan obtained during their migrations are stored in a frozen condition in caves dug into the sides of banks, where they keep perfectly for months. Others are preserved by being salted down in barrels.

Winter-taken birds from Norway are often imported for sale in American markets, where they are offered especially at the holiday season.

IN SPOTLESS WINTER DRESS, PTARMIGAN ARE HARD TO SEE

When snow flies, ptarmigan plumage changes as completely as the face of nature. Black tail feathers tipped with white identify the single bird in the foreground and the flying pair as **Willow Ptarmigan.** **Rock Ptarmigan** (center pair) may be recognized by smaller bills, or, in the adult male, by a black stripe from the bill to behind the eye. They also flirt black tail feathers. Only black bills and dark eyes interrupt the uniform snowy winter costume of the **White-tailed Ptarmigan** (upper pair on the ground).

White-crowned Pigeon

(*Columba leucocephala*)

Average Length, Thirteen and One-half Inches

Within the limits of the United States this handsome pigeon is found only in the lower Florida Keys and the adjacent mainland. Formerly it was abundant, but hunting has considerably reduced its number.

Its loud, strongly accented cooing betrays its presence in forests where otherwise it would not be seen. I have wondered often at the ease with which such large birds concealed themselves in the leafy tree tops, where I could not see them until with loudly clapping wings they darted away in flight.

The nest is a simple collection of twigs that holds one glistening white egg. Many that I have seen were placed on parasitic plants growing on the branches and trunks of forest trees. The bases of the leaves of these plants form cups that collect water from the frequent rains, so that in climbing to the pigeons' nests I was continually drenched as I bent or broke the plants aside.

The white-crowned pigeon ranges from extreme southern Florida to the Bahamas and to a large number of other West Indies islands, and on coastal islands as far as western Panama.

Band-tailed Pigeon

(*Columba fasciata*)

Average Length, Fifteen and One-half Inches

Through December fog, with occasional showers of rain, I walked slowly among the live oaks of a scattered grove near Stockton, California, watching eagerly for strange birds. A large pigeon passed at a distance, its direct, swift flight resembling that of a hawk.

A little later one of the same kind flushed quickly from a tree top, only to be stopped by a shot as it darted away, and a moment later I held in my hand my first band-tailed pigeon.

Its body was heavy, far more so than I had supposed, and its handsome markings seemed to me to make it one of the finest birds that I had ever seen. Its crop was filled with acorns swallowed whole to be ground to pieces in its strongly muscled stomach.

The band-tailed pigeon is important as a game bird in various parts of the West, and for this reason has had its difficulties in maintaining its numbers. Years ago great flocks came in winter to the valley lands of California when acorns were abundant, and thousands of them were killed by hunters.

With increasing population, there was danger that these birds might follow the passenger pigeon to extinction. Fortunately, wisely planned hunting regulations intervened and the birds were protected to a point where they are again abundant in many localities.

The nest of the band-tail is a loose structure of twigs built in a tree. Normally it contains one white egg, though rarely there are two.

Nests on the ground have been reported. The nesting period ranges from April to June. Ordinarily the birds breed in scattered pairs, though at times they have been known to colonize.

By the novice in ornithological matters the band-tailed pigeon is often mistaken for the extinct passenger pigeon, formerly so abundant. The band-tail, however, is easily told by its square-ended tail.

The true band-tailed pigeon (*Columba fasciata fasciata*) ranges from southern British Columbia and Montana to western Texas, Mexico, and Guatemala. It remains in winter as far north as the southwestern United States. Viosca's pigeon (*Columba f. vioscae*), which is somewhat paler, is found in lower Baja California.

Red-billed Pigeon

(*Columba flavirostris flavirostris*)

Average Length, Thirteen Inches

To find the red-billed pigeon it is necessary to visit the densely wooded bottomlands of the Rio Grande in southern Texas, for this is another of the interesting southern species that come barely within American borders.

This bird is an inhabitant of trees, in which it makes the frail nest usual among pigeons to contain a single, pure-white egg. It is like the domestic pigeon in build, with heavy body, and strong wings that make a clapping sound as it rises in flight. The call is a loud cooing note.

This pigeon ranges from El Salvador and Guatemala north to the lower Rio Grande Valley in Texas. A closely allied form is found in Nicaragua and Costa Rica.

White-fronted Dove

(*Leptotila fulviventris angelica*)

Average Length, Twelve Inches

Another species of southern affinity is the white-fronted dove, which ranges with the red-billed pigeon in the forests of the lower Rio Grande in Texas.

Ordinarily this is a bird of the ground, where it walks about sedately under the dense cover of trees and shrubbery. It is also found in tall trees on occasion, often at a considerable height.

Flush it suddenly, and it rises with a peculiar whistling sound, probably produced by the outermost primary feather of the wing. This is narrowed at the tip, so that it is shaped like a little, curved sword.

The white-fronted dove differs from our other pigeons in the deep sounding notes of its call. Its nest, larger and bulkier than ordinary in this family, is placed in bushes or low trees. It lays two creamy buff eggs which usually fade in a short time to dull white when preserved in collections.

The species is found from the lower Rio Grande Valley in Texas south through Mexico.

SOME PIGEONS ARE FOREST DWELLERS, WHILE OTHERS PREFER OPEN COUNTRY

Before Federal protection of the **Band-tailed Pigeon** of the West (lower right), its flocks were easy prey for numerous hunters and the bird was threatened with the fate of the passenger pigeon. The shy **White-crowned Pigeon** (upper left) comes north as far as southern Florida. Densely timbered areas in the lower Rio Grande Valley and Mexico are frequented by the **White-fronted Dove** (lower left and flying). The **Red-billed Pigeon** (upper right) lives along the Mexican border and southward to Central America, favoring groves of large trees close to water.

Passenger Pigeon

(*Ectopistes migratorius*)

Average Length, Sixteen and One-quarter Inches

The passenger pigeon, the widely known "wild pigeon" found in almost fabulous abundance at the time of the discovery of America, is now extinct.

As indication of the hordes of these birds that formerly existed, Kalm wrote of a flock that he observed in flight in Pennsylvania in March, 1740, that was three to four miles in length and a mile in breadth. A more graphic description is that of Alexander Wilson, who told of columns of the birds eight or ten miles in length, and of flocks continuing for more than an hour in steady procession.

Alexander Wilson reports a nesting colony near Shelbyville, Kentucky, that covered an area a mile wide and more than thirty miles long. S. S. Stevens described to William Brewster a nesting near Petoskey, Michigan, in 1876 or 1877 that, with an average width of three or four miles, extended 28 miles.

It was not unusual to see a hundred nests in a tree, and the heavy-bodied birds often crowded in desirable groves until large limbs were broken by their weight. The ground in their colonies was strewn always with fallen nests, eggs, and young, and was covered with the droppings of the multitudes of birds.

The decimation of this most remarkable of North American birds has been commonly attributed to some storm or other natural catastrophe, but in my opinion and that of many others it is to be charged directly to ruthless slaughter by the white man.

One account says 990,000 dozen pigeons were shipped in three years from western Michigan to New York City. Another tells of three carloads a day, each car containing 150 barrels of pigeons, shipped from one town for forty days. The birds sold for from twenty cents a dozen upward. Roney reports shipments of one and one-half million birds from Petoskey, Michigan, between March 22 and August 12, 1878. In addition, more than 80,000 birds were shipped alive for use in trap shooting.

The last wild bird for which there is certain record was one killed in April, 1904, though there is account of one identified positively in 1907. I believe that I saw two in flight near Independence, Kansas, in April, 1905, but since the birds were at a little distance this is not entirely certain.

The end of the species came when the only surviving bird of a flock long in captivity died in the zoological gardens in Cincinnati, Ohio, at 1 p. m. Central Standard Time, on September 1, 1914. This bird, mounted, is now on exhibition in the U. S. National Museum.

The nest of the passenger pigeon was a flimsy structure of twigs, placed in a tree, and ordinarily contained a single egg. Sets of two are reported, but this was unusual. The egg hatched in fourteen days (some report a longer period), and the squab rapidly became fat and heavy. When grown it was crowded from the nest by its parents.

The passenger pigeon fed on nuts, seeds, and berries, beechnuts being especial favorites. It migrated south when snow covered its food supplies in the north, and returned again in spring when the ground was bare.

In the West the band-tailed pigeon is sometimes confused with the extinct wild pigeon, but can be told at a glance by its square-cut tail. There are many stories of the passenger pigeon having migrated *en masse* to unknown forests in South America, but in more than a hundred years of investigation naturalists have never had record of this bird beyond Cuba and central Mexico. It formerly nested from the District of Mackenzie and Nova Scotia to Kansas, Kentucky, and Pennsylvania. In winter it ranged from Arkansas and North Carolina to Texas and Florida, casually farther south.

Mourning Dove

(*Zenaidura macroura*)

Average Length, Twelve Inches

Stand at a desert water hole in Arizona, and usually it is not long until there is a whistling of wings as a mourning dove comes swiftly in to drink, offering a good view of its elongated form, accentuated by the slender neck and long tail as it passes quickly overhead.

In the East one more often identifies this dove by its gently modulated coo, coming from a distant bird quietly at rest on some high tree limb, or by a hasty glimpse of its contrasted black and white tail markings as one or two rise in confusion from the roadside.

While the mourning dove frequents groves and gardens in the better-watered sections of our country, it is equally at home in the open plains and treeless valleys of the more arid regions. It feeds on the ground, its food being composed almost entirely of seeds. Cut grain fields draw it in abundance.

In fall and winter the mourning dove gathers in little flocks where food is abundant, but in its nesting it is solitary. The nest is a fragile structure of twigs, ordinarily placed in a shrub or tree, but often found upon the ground, particularly in regions where trees are few.

The mourning dove nests somewhat irregularly, especially in regions where the weather is not too severe. In California occupied nests have been found in every month from February to December.

Mourning doves require definitely regulated seasons for their protection because of the small number of young they produce.

The eastern mourning dove (*Zenaidura m. carolinensis*) nests from Nova Scotia and Wisconsin to Kansas and the Gulf coast. In winter it migrates south as far as Panama. The western form (*Zenaidura m. marginella*), somewhat paler, is found from British Columbia and Manitoba south into Mexico.

FABULOUS FLOCKS OF PASSENGER PIGEONS ONCE DARKENED THE SKY

Long extinct, the strong-flying **Passenger Pigeon** (upper) was once one of the most abundant birds in the world and its flocks were measured by the square mile. It inhabited the whole forested area of eastern North America, fifty or more pairs commonly nesting in the same tree. Branches broke under the weight of breeding birds. They were easy to kill and indiscriminate slaughter for food wiped them out. Observers who report passenger pigeons today see either the band-tailed pigeon or the **Mourning Dove** (male and female, lower). The latter is similar to its extinct cousin in form, but much smaller.

White-winged Dove

(*Melopelia asiatica*)

Average Length, Eleven and One-half Inches

At dawn on a morning in June in Arizona, the softly modulated voices of doves came to me through my open window, and a little later, with arrival of the sun, I heard the birds on every side. As one crossed the sky in rapid flight, a flash of white came from its wings and I knew that these were white-winged doves.

Entering a large mesquite grove, I found myself in the midst of a breeding colony of these doves. Loose nests of sticks and weed stems were placed on inclined limbs where the forking of the smaller branches gave firm support. Sometimes two or three nests were placed in one tree, but there was no crowding, and often one pair occupied a tree alone. The nests contained two eggs that varied in color from buff to white.

As I passed under the low trees, whitewings flushed about me constantly with loudly clapping wings. Birds were continually arriving and departing, their excursions for seeds and waste grain covering many miles.

Although the males did not coo in unison, the effect of hundreds calling at one time was truly remarkable. Save for the notes of one or two birds near at hand, the whole blended in such a way that it was difficult to pick out individual songs. The volume of sound carried to me easily at a distance of a mile, but the tone was soft, so that it was not deafening even near at hand. The notes formed a continuous undertone, filling the air as completely as the noise of rushing water from a stream. The effect was most remarkable and still lingers in my memory.

In recent years these birds have decreased greatly and large colonies like the one described are said to be a thing of the past. The doves are still common, though they require protection in order to maintain them as game birds.

The eastern white-winged dove (*Melopelia a. asiatica*) is found from the lower Rio Grande in Texas into Mexico, occurring casually in Florida and Louisiana. The larger, paler, western form (*Melopelia a. mearnsi*) is found from New Mexico and southeastern California southward to Guerrero and Puebla.

Inca Dove

(*Scardafella inca inca*)

Average Length, Eight Inches

A monotonous, insistent repetition of cooing notes, coming from a hidden source in shade trees or shrubbery, to many is the only recognized sign of the tiny, long-tailed Inca dove. Others more observant may see the attractively formed little birds walking hurriedly with tiny steps in search of food, or at rest on some shaded porch. To see their pretty bodies is to forgive the monotony of their call.

The Inca dove is most common about houses, and even comes into thickly populated towns. I have seen them in the State Capitol grounds in Phoenix, Arizona, and in Tucson have found them common at the State University. In Texas they have extended their range recently to the northward.

The nest, which contains two white eggs, is more compactly built than in the case of most other members of the family of doves. Usually it is placed in a tree or shrub, from 4 to 25 feet from the ground. Occasionally when opportunity offers, the Inca relines the old nest of a mourning dove, mockingbird, or other bird for a safe foundation.

The Inca dove is found from southern Arizona, New Mexico, and central Texas south through the warmer parts of Mexico to Honduras.

Ground Dove

(*Columbigallina passerina*)

Average Length, Six and Three-quarters Inches

Walk quietly between the rows of trees in a Florida citrus grove, or follow some brush-bordered path near cultivated fields in more arid regions, and you may see a pair or more of tiny, gray-brown birds that walk rapidly with quickly nodding heads.

At a noise they crouch immobile, and then, in sudden alarm, rise with a bright flash of reddish brown from the underside of the wings. In an instant they are gone.

To watch these ground doves, try to attract them with food and water so that they may be easily seen. Your reward will be much pleasure in the sight of their trimly graceful forms and soft colors. But observe them awhile and you will be certain that the phrase "gentle as a dove" is sometimes to be used in irony, for males constantly advance toward one another threateningly, strike quickly with their wings, and hustle one another about. Probably the rather misleading adjective so often applied to these birds has reference to the softness of their voices and the quietness of their colorings.

While this bird is well named in that it spends much time on the ground in search of its food of seeds, it perches regularly in trees, and on or about buildings.

While its nest may be placed on the ground, it is located frequently in a bush, on a stump, or in a low tree. It ordinarily contains two white eggs, rarely three.

The eastern ground dove (*Columbigallina p. passerina*) is found from South Carolina to eastern Texas. The paler Mexican ground dove (*Columbigallina p. pallescens*) ranges from western Texas and southeastern California to Guatemala and Baja California. A related form is in Bermuda and the Bahamas, and additional ones inhabit other West Indies islands.

THOUGH THEY SYMBOLIZE PEACE, SOME DOVES ARE HIGHLY QUARRELSOME

Fierce and angry conflicts during the mating season belie their reputation for gentleness. The **White-winged Dove** (upper) is one of the best-known birds of the torrid cactus and mesquite deserts of the Southwest. Smallest of our pigeons is the dainty **Ground Dove** (male lower right and female alighting) of Florida, the Gulf coast, and the Southwest. The amorous little **Inca Dove** (lower left) is equally at home along country roads and on city lawns throughout the Southwest, Mexico, and Central America. It is not easily disturbed as it searches unconcernedly for grain and weed seeds.

Photograph by Arthur A. Allen

THINKING THE PHOTOGRAPHER HAS GONE, THIS EASTERN GOLDEN PLOVER VENTURES BACK
TO ITS NEST

This amazing traveler, which makes an annual round trip between the pampas of Argentina and the Arctic coasts of North America, does not attempt to conceal its nest, a mere hollow in the open tundra at Churchill, Manitoba, on Hudson Bay. The protective coloring of the eggs makes it difficult to find them against the white and grayish moss.

THE SHORE BIRDS, CRANES, AND RAILS

Willets, Plovers, Stilts, Phalaropes, Sandpipers, and Their Relatives Deserve Protection

By Arthur A. Allen

Professor of Ornithology, Cornell University

FIVE hundred miles due north of Winnipeg one leaves behind the last outpost of the spruce forest and for a few miles travels the open tundra before approaching that great expanse known as Hudson Bay. It was a sea of ice when we arrived the first of June, with no cracks or other evidence of weakening, though spring had already arrived on the tundra and back home, in northern United States, summer was not far away.

We had journeyed thus far to study ptarmigan—those Arctic grouse whose periodic epidemics we hoped might throw some light on similar cyclic mortality in our native ruffed grouse. The ptarmigan, all about us, were now in their spring garb, white bodies and red heads, and dotted over the tundra as far as the eye could reach were white wings and scattered feathers bespeaking high death rate during the winter and early spring.

STRANGE BIRD CALLS A MYSTERY

But even more impressive than the ptarmigan were the strange sounds that filled the air. I counted myself fairly familiar with the songs and calls of North American birds, but here was bird music I had never heard before and all of it apparently coming right out of the sky. I pictured to myself the thousands and thousands of square miles of the Arctic tundra that no civilized man ever sees, and I thought of the tens of thousands of vibrant throats pouring forth their melodies for ears not akin to man's, and realized how insignificant a part I really was of this great Northland I had come to study.

Here were dozens of new songs being poured forth by birds that in my country are nearly mute, for at last I had come, not only to the home of the ptarmigan, but to the breeding ground of the Hudsonian curlew, the golden plover, the stilt sandpiper, the lesser yellow-legs, the northern phalarope, and many more of those alluring shore birds whose very names had always thrilled me; birds whose nearly silent, ghostlike forms frequent our shores and mud flats for brief intervals on their journeys between their mysterious Arctic breeding grounds and their glamorous South American wintering resorts. For the shore birds are our greatest travelers.

Many a time in years gone by on stormy nights in September I had awakened to the mellow whistles of the greater yellow-legs and black-bellied plovers as they were hurrying southward ahead of the approaching winter, and at daybreak I would hasten to the lake shore expecting to find it teeming with the graceful waders, but I usually arrived just in time to see the last flocks heading south leaving only a few stragglers behind them.

Very gradually I had become familiar with the simple little whistles uttered as they took flight, and I had learned to recognize the several shore birds at sight even in their obscure winter plumages. But here at last was something different. Here on the tundra at Churchill on Hudson Bay I could stand in one place and have shore birds all about me—here, there, and everywhere, but mostly in the air.

Some on vibrating wings were hovering over definite spots on the tundra, giving vent to their passions in loud, buzzing sounds like swarms of bees; others were chasing each other about in crazy courtship flights, and still others were flying in great circles uttering the strangest notes I had ever heard.

One that I finally identified as our demure little stilt sandpiper was braying like a jackass as he circled about overhead. *Wheep! Wheep! Wheep! Hee-haw! Hee-haw! Hee-haw!* The notes rolled across the tundra as if our democratic emblem had suddenly taken wings and gone in search of Santa Claus.

There was the lesser yellow-legs cavorting in the same way and instead of giving the two or three little whistles that we always associate with him on migration, he was vocalizing the syllables *keep-a-going! keep-a-going! keep-a-going!* as if he were the official traffic policeman of those vast Arctic prairies.

THE RAILROAD UNLOCKED SECRETS

Before the Canadian Government extended its thread of steel from Winnipeg to Churchill on Hudson Bay and built the gigantic grain elevator that stands as the last outpost of civilization at the mouth of the Churchill River, this springtime orgy of the shore birds was a closed secret. It was practically impossible to reach the barren grounds by the first of June when the courtship of the shore birds is at its height, unless one started the year before and passed the winter in the Arctic. Consequently the songs of these northern breeding sandpipers, which are restricted to the nesting period, are practically unknown.

Certainly they came as a great surprise to me. The courageous engineers who conceived the railroad to Hudson Bay to shorten the route to Liverpool from the Great Northwest and succeeded in laying a thousand miles of rails over ice and muskeg little dreamed of this boon to ornithologists nor the thrills they were to provide for bird lovers when this easy access to a formerly almost forbidden land should become available.

Among the Arctic birds that chased the flies and midges about the lagoon near the grain elevator, however, there were certain ones that were almost silent. There were pectoral and white-rumped sandpipers, there were black-bellied plovers and turnstones that never produced any notes other than those we hear in the States.

Very soon I began to realize that even though I had come 2,500 miles I had not traveled far enough to reach the breeding grounds of all the shore birds. Some there were, like the white-rumps and turnstones, that would not be satisfied until they had crossed Hudson Bay, at least to Southampton Island, while still others, like the knot, would continue on to Baffin Island and Ellesmere Island and even to the very edge of the polar ice sheet.

Homogeneous as the tundra may seem to us, apparently it is not so to the birds, for they recognize various degrees of "Arcticness" just as other birds farther south seem to recognize certain life zones in the more temperate regions. Thus along our Atlantic beaches the Wilson's plover is found nesting from Florida to Virginia, where it is replaced by the smaller and paler piping plover. This species occurs in summer from North Carolina northward to Nova Scotia where it, in turn, is replaced by the semipalmated plover, which nests from Nova Scotia northward to the Arctic coasts. In winter, or on migration, all three species may mingle on our Gulf coast, but when the time comes for them to raise their families each species searches out its respective zone where it finds its own most congenial conditions for nesting.

As I stood there on the rock ledge overlooking the vast ice sheet of Hudson Bay to the north, and listened to the varied notes of the courting shore birds behind me, I could see flocks of turnstones resting on the rocks of the lagoon or flicking over pebbles and bits of drift in their search for food, and flocks of white-rumped sandpipers circling about. Both were awaiting sufficient impulse to start over the great sea of ice that separated them from their nesting ground 300 miles to the north.

THE GOLDEN PLOVER A GADABOUT

A single golden plover flew over heading northwest as if bound for Alaska, calling *to leeit* as he passed, and I thought of what a year and what a journey he had before him. Somewhere between Churchill and Alaska he would stop for the summer and raise his family during the few short weeks of July and August. For less than two months would he know the anchorage of home and family before it would be time to start back, and by the first of September we might see him flying southeasterly over Churchill with others of his kind headed for the great tidal flats of James Bay.

There he might play around for a week or more before undertaking the next lap of his journey to the berry-covered tundra of southern Labrador or the shrimp-strewn beaches of Nova Scotia. There he would feed and rest and store up energy for the 2,500 mile flight due south over the Atlantic for South America. High over the Bermudas and the Bahamas and even the mangrove-fringed coast of South America he would wing his tireless way until he could see below him the llanos of Venezuela, 150 miles inland, with grassy plains and mud-fringed estuaries.

There he could stop, feed, and rest for

perhaps a couple of weeks before starting off again—this time over the 1,500-mile forest of the Amazon, heading for the pampas of Bolivia or Argentina. With shorter flights he might proceed into Patagonia, but the year is short and already he would sense the urge to turn about and start northward.

He would not, however, retrace his flight over the Amazon to Venezuela. Instead he would head northwestward over the Andes of Peru and across one corner of the Pacific for the high plateau of Guatemala. Then his course would lie due north across the Gulf of Mexico, never faltering, for Louisiana and the mouth of the Mississippi where in days gone by thousands of his kind were shot for the market.

Happily, this practice is now forbidden by law, and by easy stages the golden plover can now proceed up the Mississippi Valley, arriving in the vicinity of St. Louis by the last of March or early April.

There would be no rush then to the nesting grounds, for these would be icebound for another two months, and in this interim the birds must change all their body feathers from the gray winter plumage to the variegated gold and black of summer. By the first of June, once again, he might be winging his way over Churchill; that is, provided he escaped the perils of the 12,000 miles over mountains and sea and successfully passed the barrage of gunners who have little thought for anything save the sport of marksmanship and the savory bit of breast muscle that propels those tireless wings.

There is a fascination in the study of shore birds which lays hold of one as one's knowledge of them increases—an allurement that spreads a charm wherever ornithological opportunity offers. The debris-littered mud flats exposed by the receding waters of late summer and strewn with dead and dying fish might well cause my over-sensitive nose to revolt, but when my ear catches the mellow note of a semipalmated plover, I am transported in thought to the rock-ribbed shores of Labrador.

Salt air stings my cheek; there is a lifting fog, the yelping of gulls, the screeching of terns; and the wailing of red-throated loons fills my ears. Long black and white lines of eider ducks wing past, ungainly murres and curious puffins circle close, and the surf pounds on a rocky reef where harlequin ducks are playing preparatory to their flight inland to their nesting grounds. Sticky mud and odorous fish are forgotten as I visualize the little plover among its Labrador associates that I learned to love.

Perhaps I spy a solitary sandpiper jerking his head at the water's edge, and I am reminded how for years, despite its abundance, its home life remained a mystery until finally Evan Thompson discovered its eggs in an old robin's nest in a tamarack bog in Saskatchewan. A trim little stilt sandpiper, resembling very closely in its fall plumage a lesser yellow-legs, takes me back once more to Hudson Bay and a train of recollections of most pleasant experiences with the Arctic birds.

UTAH PROVIDES A SUMMER HOME

Lest it seem that all shore birds belong to the Northern Plains, and before we consider them individually as Major Brooks has brought them to us so realistically in the following plates, let us take a short trip to the Cache Valley of Utah or 50 miles farther westward to the Bear River marshes, just north of Great Salt Lake. Here is an area where vast numbers of migratory waterfowl of all kinds assemble and where, after the Arctic species have gone north, other species equally interesting are content to pass the summer and rear their young (see pages 208-213).

One need not even leave the car to watch by the roadside the strikingly marked avocets and stilts with their long legs wading in the shallow pools, or the long-billed curlews, with their sicklelike bills, circling overhead and waiting to fly at the intruder who leaves his car and tries to catch their ungainly youngsters. The snowy plovers and the widely distributed killdeers nest in the middle of the gravel roads.

Western willets, with their black and white pinions conspicuous in flight, fade from sight even in the open when they fold their wings, but they continue to call attention to themselves with their loud cry of pilly-willy-willet until they decide to sneak off to their nests by the side of some pond near by. Graceful little Wilson's phalaropes, jerking their heads as they swim about like miniature ducks, whirl about in circles and stir up the bottom of the shallow pools so that midge larvæ are brought to the surface in the vortex created and they can pick them up without having to submerge their dainty heads.

The phalaropes are remarkable among

all birds in that with them the coloration and the respective duties of the sexes seem to be reversed. With most birds, if the sexes are different in color, the males are the brighter in plumage. This is not true of the phalaropes, however, for the females in all families are brighter than the males.

It is likewise the female phalarope that is the aggressor in the courtship, while it is the male that builds the nest and incubates the eggs. Once the eggs are laid, the female seems to lose all interest in home and family and sports about with others of her kind in scattered flocks, leaving the luckless male to hatch the eggs and raise the children.

VARIATIONS IN PLUMAGE DURING THE BREEDING SEASON

One of the most difficult avian phenomena to explain is the difference in closely related birds in the matter of changing their garb in the course of the breeding season. Among the plovers, for example, the killdeer wears the same colored feathers winter and summer, and the young resemble their parents. The golden and black-bellied plovers, on the other hand, are so different in summer from their appearance in the fall as to appear to be an entirely different species. Indeed the same holds true for all of the shore birds that are brightly colored in breeding dress; they have a winter plumage that is distinctly different, and the immature birds resemble their parents in winter.

The majority of shore birds, as the name implies, frequent only the most open places away from trees or concealing vegetation of any kind. The Wilson's snipe, however, prefers grassy marshes; the solitary sandpiper prefers woodland pools; and the woodcock selects alder thickets and seldom ventures into the open fields except at dusk.

The real marshes of cattails and sedges are shunned by the shore birds, except where mud flats become exposed in the shallow ponds. Marshes are, however, preferred by the rails and gallinules.

It was after midnight on the last day of May when I stood knee-deep in one of these swamps with the sedges waving about me. Before me on a tripod stood a parabolic reflector, three feet in diameter, with a microphone hung at its focal point.

We were recording the calls of the marsh birds, photographing the sounds on motion-picture film so that they could later be transferred to phonograph records or made available to bird students in other ways.

The redwings had long since ceased their scolding; the liquid notes of the bitterns no longer rolled across the marsh, though the cuckoolike notes of the least bittern occasionally sounded from a clump of cattails. The marsh wrens, however, had been roused to new activity by darkness, and the explosive notes of gallinules, and the wails of the pied-billed grebes vied with those of the bullfrogs for ascendency.

It was my job to get the sound reflector pointed directly at the spot where the bird was calling and tell my colleague, Paul Kellogg, in the sound truck, when to start the film running through the recorder. We had already recorded the notes of the grebe, the gallinule, and the wren, and what we wanted most was to catch the whinny of the sora or the *ticket-ticket* call of the Virginia rail. Both were calling intermittently about the marsh, but apparently never twice from the same spot, so that I was beginning to despair of ever getting one directly in the sound beam.

LOOKING FOR "DICK MC GREER"

Suddenly came a strange call, the like of which I had never heard before. *Dick-Dick-Dick McGreer!* it seemed to say, over and over again, and very insistently.

"Here is a new bird," I whispered to Kellogg through the microphone. "Catch its voice and we will find out later what it is."

The film started running through the recording camera and each time the call struck the microphone it set the galvanometer with its little mirror to vibrating in the truck and sent light messages to the edge of the film. Thus "Dick-Dick-Dick McGreer" was photographed and written down in sound-recording history.

The next task was to find the author of the call. One after another I thought over the various calls of all the marsh birds with which I was familiar and eliminated them one by one until only the tiny black rail and the small yellow rail remained. These two I had never heard call, and one of them, I was sure, must be our "McGreer" bird.

But to sneak through a sedge marsh after midnight and hope to find a rail the size of a sparrow has its difficulties. There were ditches and bottomless holes to be avoided, and the sound of my approach must not alarm the bird which was calling a hundred yards away. Step by step I edged toward the sound, expecting momentarily to slip into some black hole, for I didn't dare use my flashlight for fear of alarming the owner of the voice.

Halfway to my quarry I stumbled into a flock of immature redwings and starlings that had been asleep in the cattails for four hours and they went up with such a roar of wings that I was sure they would alarm the rest of the marsh, but my little bird went right on calling as if nothing had happened.

A little farther on a great lumbering bittern got off the roost he had made for himself by twisting together the tops of the sedges with his long toes, but his going did not alarm my bird either and he kept right on calling for Dick McGreer.

ONLY THE VOICE RECORDED

Finally he was calling not six feet from me and I flashed my light on the spot. So dense were the sedges, however, that the light did not penetrate to the level where my bird had been calling, and I could see nothing. I waited a moment to see if he would call again, but in vain.

I rushed toward the spot to flush him— and up he went, but not from the exact place where he had last called. I heard him leave and I heard him drop back into the marsh ten feet away, but my light flashed in the wrong direction and I did not see my bird.

Thus we have recorded the voice of a rail that we have neither seen nor identified. Diligent search by day failed to find the bird, though examination of ornithological literature seems to point to its having been a yellow rail.

Similarly, to many of my readers who may become interested in marsh birds, the voices which emanate from the cattails during the day and far into the night may long remain unidentified. So seldom do the rails venture into the open where we can see them, even where they are common, that we can only guess at the authors of many of the mysterious sounds that issue from a cattail marsh.

There are two calls, however, made by members of this group that would be difficult to confuse, especially since the birds themselves are quite conspicuous. One is the rolling *garoo* of the sandhill crane, which, like the honking of wild geese, can be heard after the birds themselves have disappeared in the clouds, and the other is the *aow* of the limpkin in certain Florida swamps, which calls to mind quite unmistakably the full-toned exclamations one sometimes hears from a dentist's chair

and which may well be responsible for some of the ghost stories that center about these cypress and saw-grass glades (see page 194).

SHORE BIRDS AND MARSH BIRDS AS GAME

During the early history of this country any bird or animal that was good to eat was considered legitimate game, and the more food a species supplied, and the less effort required to procure it, the more highly was it esteemed.

Quite naturally the deer and the turkey received the most attention. Gradually, however, they became scarce, and the attention of those who supplied food to the ever increasing populace turned toward the smaller species, such as the grouse, the heath hen, the wild pigeon, and waterfowl.

All kinds of devices were employed for harvesting these cheaply and in great quantities. The heath hen and the wild pigeon, unable to withstand the slaughter, were exterminated; the whooping crane is so near the precipice of extinction that it is apt to topple over any moment; the Eskimo curlew, Labrador duck, and great auk are gone forever, and perhaps 75 trumpeter swans are left in the entire United States.

Gradually we have come to our senses. Let us hope it is not too late. We no longer feel that a bird is legitimate game just because it is good to eat; we no longer offer strings of robins and meadowlarks for sale in the markets just because they make good potpies.

Today, if a bird is to be considered game it must serve its best function as game; it should not have greater value as a destroyer of insects, nor should it have greater esthetic value, and it should be prolific so that its numbers can withstand the added strain of hunting. Any bird, like the crane, that lays only two eggs, or like the shore birds that lay only four, or the swans that do not breed until they are two or three years old, will never again be considered satisfactory game birds.

Furthermore, to be really suitable, a game species must render the greatest amount of sport for the number killed. Tame, trustful species, like the shore birds, that can be easily approached or decoyed, and that travel in compact flocks, making it possible to kill large numbers at a single discharge of the gun, will never be satisfactory game birds. We might just as well accept as permanent the temporary removal of all these species from the game list.

WARY SANDHILL CRANES GUARD AN EGG AND A NEWLY HATCHED YOUNGSTER IN A BLUE FLAG MARSH, FLORIDA

Unlike the herons, which they resemble in form, sandhill cranes are landlubbers. They usually choose a shallow pond overgrown with marsh vegetation as a site for their bulky nests. Their food includes roots, bulbs, and grains, including corn, of which they are especially fond, as well as insects, small reptiles, and rodents. Herons prefer a fish diet.

Photographs by Arthur A. Allen

A MALE WILSON'S PHALAROPE GETS BACK ON THE JOB

In all the phalaropes the males do the work of hatching the eggs and rearing the young. Photographed in Manitoba.

HOW CAN SHE COVER THOSE FOUR LARGE EGGS?

The eggs of all shore birds are very large for the size of the bird. A stilt sandpiper photographed at Churchill, on Hudson Bay.

American Oyster-catcher

Haematopus palliatus
Average Length, Nineteen Inches

Formerly found all along the Atlantic shores as far south as Brazil, and on the Pacific coast from Mexico to Colombia, the American oyster-catcher has been greatly reduced in the northern part of its range, so that although Audubon found these birds a century ago in southern Labrador, they are today rarely seen north of Virginia. The subspecies found on the coast of Baja California and adjacent Mexico is called Frazar's oyster-catcher (*Haematopus p. frazari*).

The oyster-catcher breeds locally throughout its range, laying two or three large ovate eggs, buff in ground color, sparingly blotched with black or dark brown. The nest is a little depression, usually on a low mound above high tide on the broad beaches of small coastal islands or reefs. There is usually no nesting material, although some "nests" seem to be decorated about the rim with pieces of shells.

The oyster-catcher derives its name from its habit of flying to the oyster reefs at low tide to feed. Inserting its flattened bill between the partly opened shells, the bird deftly cuts the adductor muscles so that they cannot close, and then feeds on the oysters at leisure. It likewise feeds on other mollusks, shrimps, sea urchins, and small creatures of the shores or tidal pools, sometimes thrusting its long, red bill full length into the sand.

Black Oyster-catcher

Haematopus bachmani
Average Length, Seventeen Inches

This black counterpart of the American oyster-catcher is found from the west coast of Baja California northward to the Aleutian Islands in summer and often winters as far north as southern Alaska. In all its habits it is similar to the American oyster-catcher, though perhaps less wild and more sluggish.

When approached, it often squats in a depression in the rocks or stealthily creeps to the top of some large bowlder, where, if alarmed, it utters a piercing chatterlike note, somewhat similar to a policeman's whistle. Other birds near by answer, and the din is ear-splitting.

The black oyster-catcher nests the last of May in California and ten days later in Alaska, often lining a depression in the gravel or rocks with fragments of stone and occasionally even with grasses or seaweed. Both species of oyster-catchers wear the same colored plumage winter and summer, and the sexes are indistinguishable. The eggs hatch in a little more than three weeks, and the downy young, which are grizzled and protectively colored, run from the nest almost as soon as hatched, and start searching for food.

Ruddy Turnstone

Arenaria interpres morinella
Average Length, Nine and One-half Inches

The ruddy turnstone never tires of trotting along the beach, flipping over shells, pebbles, and bits of seaweed that might give shelter to a scud, a beetle, or a worm. What a life he must lead, starting from Alaska or Baffin Island in August and flipping stones all the way down to central Chile or southern Brazil, only to turn and flip them all the way back again!

Turnstones are found throughout the Arctic regions during the summer. The Old World birds, since they are a little larger and darker than those in the New World, are considered subspecifically distinct. They nest chiefly north of the Arctic Circle, laying their four large olive-buff eggs, boldly marked with brown, in a well-lined depression in the tundra.

They seem not to indulge in flight songs even on their nesting grounds, but perch on a hummock and sound not unmelodiously their rapid challenge of *kye-ute cat-tat-tah*.

Black Turnstone

Arenaria melanocephala
Average Length, Nine Inches

The black turnstone is a bird of the Pacific coast, rarely, if ever, found in the interior, for it prefers the coastal islands to the mainland. In summer it nests along the coast of Alaska from the Bering Strait south to the Sitka district and in winter it wanders as far south as Baja California.

On migration it often associates with the ruddy turnstones, but is not so much a wanderer and never visits the Pacific islands.

In its summer home, instead of singing from the ground it mounts high in the air and, like the Wilson's snipe, produces a curious winnowing sound—perhaps with its tail feathers.

Its nest is only a little depression, without lining, near the water's edge. Often the eggs are discolored by the mud on which they rest.

Surf-bird

Aphriza virgata
Average Length, Ten Inches

For 46 weeks of the year the surf-bird frequents the rocky coasts and islands from Alaska to the Strait of Magellan. Then for six weeks it disappears.

The species was first described by Gmelin in 1789, but it was not until 1927 that its nest and eggs were found in the Mount McKinley area on a rocky ledge a thousand feet above timberline. Unlike all others of its family, when it arrives in Alaska it deserts the seacoast and flies scores of miles inland to nest on the tops of the mountains.

The eggs of the surf-bird resemble in color those of a falcon with a buff ground color heavily marked with reddish brown.

LEARN THEIR NAMES BY WATCHING WHAT THEY DO

The **American Oyster-catcher** (lower left) and the **Black Oyster-catcher** (lower right) clip the muscles of partly opened oysters so that they cannot close again. The smart birds then feast at leisure. In the search for insects and tasty crawling morsels, the **Ruddy Turnstone** (right center pair; adult in summer garb above young in fall plumage) continually flips over shells, stones, and debris, a habit shared by the Pacific's **Black Turnstone** (upper left pair, in winter and summer plumage). The **Surfbird** (upper pair, in winter and summer dress) spends most of the year close to the pounding breakers.

Black-bellied Plover

Squatarola squatarola (Linnaeus)
Average Length, Eleven Inches

The black-bellied plover is one of the few birds found over almost the entire world. It nests in Arctic Russia, Siberia, and North America, and winters as far south as Africa, India, Australia, and South America. Wild and sagacious and not given to traveling in such dense flocks as some of the other species, it has met more successfully the inroads of the gunners, though always much sought after as a game bird.

The black-bellies in their striking breeding dress begin to appear on our southern beaches in March and April. Indeed, many pass the winter on our Gulf coast, but they do not reach the Northern States until late May. June, and most of July, they pass on the barren grounds in and about the same region as the ruddy turnstone, but not so far south as the golden plover. By the last of July some of the old birds, still in full dress, appear on our New England beaches, but the main flight passes through in August and September, the young birds apparently leaving later than the adults.

In nesting habits the black-belly is similar to the golden plover, but the eggs are paler and more evenly speckled. Its courtship is largely aerial, the birds flying at great speed.

The loud whistled *whe-or-ee* call of the black-belly is easily imitated, and the birds decoy so readily to it that I have frequently brought specimens down from so high in the sky or so far away that I could not see them when the call was first made.

Males and females both wear the showy plumage during the breeding season, the males being perhaps a little brighter. Both molt in August and September into the dull winter plumage in which they are scarcely distinguishable from the immature birds.

Golden Plover

Pluvialis dominica dominica (Müller)
Average Length, Ten and One-half Inches

In the fall golden plovers are seen along the Atlantic coast, chiefly during September after strong easterly gales, when they are blown in from the sea. In the spring they frequent ploughed fields and old pastures in the Mississippi Valley, feeding on grubs and crickets. They scatter while feeding but usually rise in a body when alarmed and soon gather in a compact, swiftly moving flock.

The first birds seen in the fall still retain some of their old breeding dress, and the last ones to leave in the spring have started to regain their new nuptial plumage, but for the most part birds seen in the United States are in the dull winter plumage.

The nest of the golden plover is a shallow depression in the reindeer moss of the tundra, scantily lined with fragments of moss, and the four buff eggs are heavily marked with brownish black. The downy young are thickly covered with a marbled black, golden, and gray down, and like other species of plover leave their nest at hatching and find their own food, being dependent on their parents only for brooding.

The golden plovers which nest on the Bering Sea shores of Alaska and thence westward along the Arctic shores of Siberia are somewhat smaller and more brightly colored than the more eastern birds, and have been separated as a subspecies called the Pacific golden plover (*Pluvialis d. fulva* Gmelin). The European golden plover, however, breeding from Great Britain and central Europe to Iceland and northwestern Siberia is a distinct species. The Pacific golden plover makes a direct flight from Alaska to Hawaii for the winter.

Killdeer

Oxyechus vociferus vociferus (Linnaeus)
Average Length, Ten and One-half Inches

The killdeer is as well known to the schoolboy of California as to the golfer on Cape Cod, and his vociferous cries are heard in summer on the tundra near Hudson Bay and on the shores of Lake Okeechobee in Florida.

In the Northern States during March and earlier in the South, the male makes the air resound with loud-whistled *kill-deer—kill-deer* cries as he circles a wide area with a curious erratic flight. In no uncertain terms he proclaims his presence to the female and tells her that he will soon scratch out a little depression in a suitable gravelly spot where she can lay her four large, tan, spotted eggs, and that he will gladly do the lion's share in hatching those eggs and protecting the family.

If one comes suddenly upon the sitting bird, which is scarcely possible until the eggs are nearly ready to hatch, the killdeer will dramatize a feigned decrepitude and flutter along the ground with tail spread and wings drooping, leading the enemy away from the nest.

Male and female and immature killdeers look exactly alike winter and summer, and even the downy young resemble their parents except for having only a single black band, instead of two, across their breasts.

Mountain Plover

Eupoda montana (Townsend)
Average Length, Eight and Three-quarters Inches

The mountain plover is not very appropriately named, except in that it is confined to the Rocky Mountain region, for it inhabits only the semi-arid plains from northern Montana and western Nebraska south to western Kansas, northern New Mexico and northwestern Texas. In winter it moves to the border States and Mexico, and avoids the lakes and shores sought by other shore birds.

FEATHERED COSMOPOLITES OF TWO AMERICAS MEET ON A NORTHERN BEACH

Unlike the **American Golden Plover** and the **Black-bellied Plover** (right foreground, left and right, in summer plumage; young of each flying above), the **Killdeer** (left foreground and flying bird above) wears the same costume winter and summer. In the center background stands a western **Mountain Plover.**

Semipalmated Plover

Charadrius semipalmatus
Average Length, Six and Three-quarters Inches

The semipalmated plover breeds throughout Arctic North America, and as far south on the Atlantic coast as Nova Scotia, and winters from the Gulf coast to Chile and Patagonia. It has a wide migration route through the interior as well as on both coasts, so that in suitable places along lake shores and mud flats one can expect to see this species almost anywhere in North America during its migrating periods of August, September, and October and again the following May.

In flight its long, pointed wings give it an apparent size quite at variance with its tiny body, and many a sportsman in the old days when all shore birds were considered game, was disappointed at the tiny morsel of meat afforded by what seemed a good-sized target.

On taking wing these birds often utter a melodious *cher-wee*, especially when coming in to join a flock of other shore birds, but on migration they are regularly so silent and unobtrusive that I was amazed upon visiting their Arctic nesting ground to see the male birds dashing around on wild, erratic flights, voicing their feelings in loud, harsh, whinnylike songs.

To see two of these gentle creatures face each other, puff out their feathers and crouch low with spread tails, and then jump into sharp combat like a couple of gamecocks was even more amazing, but such is the keen and determined competition for nesting territory and mates on the Labrador coast.

The nest is a mere hollow in the sand or gravel, like that of a killdeer, and the eggs, too, seem like small models of the killdeer's.

Piping Plover

Charadrius melodus
Average Length, Seven Inches

Forty years ago this dovelike little plover was almost exterminated by gunning, but now, after 25 years of protection, it has come back to much of its former range and is locally common, especially on Long Island and New England beaches beyond the reach of dogs and summer boarders.

On some of the beaches of our Great Lakes and westward even to southern Alberta it occurs locally in summer and as far south as North Carolina. In winter it retires to our southern beaches from South Carolina to Texas and northern Mexico.

Being just the color of the sand, it escapes detection by the casual observer, and it often relies upon running rather than flying to avoid intruders, speeding along with such rapidity that one scarcely notices its swiftly gliding legs. It nests like Wilson's plover, but the black-speckled tan eggs are somewhat smaller.

Snowy Plover

Charadrius nivosus
Average Length, Six and One-half Inches

We were driving one June day to the Bear River Marshes north of Great Salt Lake in Utah. Suddenly a few feet in front of the car, a queer-looking pebble rolled off to the side of the road. I stopped the car as quickly as I could and watched my rolling stone turn into a pale, graceful little snowy plover—now much perturbed.

It was not until after a half hour of diligent search that we realized our objective and found the protectively colored eggs between stones of about the same size and color halfway between our front wheels.

The real center of abundance of the snowy plover is the sandy beaches of California and southern Washington, where it takes the place of our eastern piping plover. These birds are really the western snowy plover. An eastern form called the Cuban snowy plover *(Charadrius nivosus tenuirostris)* is found along the Gulf coast from Florida to Texas and on the salt plains of Oklahoma and Kansas.

Wilson's Plover

Pagolla wilsonia
Average Length, Seven and One-half Inches

It was on the beach at Mosquito Inlet on the east coast of Florida that I first became acquainted with the Wilson's plover. I had been watching a flock of black skimmers hollowing out little depressions for their nests by twisting and turning their plump breasts in the sand.

Further from the water's edge where the dunes began, I had noticed this little plover behaving somewhat nervously.

Whenever she seemed to realize that I was watching her, she would trot a few paces and busy herself twisting and turning in the sand like the black skimmers, as if she were just beginning to think about building a nest. Knowing from experience that this is often a misleading trick of the plovers, I withdrew and watched her through binoculars.

No longer did she seem interested in building a nest but trotted to one particular spot about 50 feet away and settled down. I soon realized that she was incubating eggs.

There was no nesting material whatsoever, and the eggs were half buried by the drifting sand. I later learned that if the little bird remained away from her eggs as long as 30 minutes they would be almost completely covered, and she would have to excavate them.

The Wilson's plover is found in summer as far north as Virginia and south only to the Gulf coast of Texas. In winter many remain from Florida to Texas, but some wander to Brazil. They sometimes live in scattered colonies but more often are found singly or in pairs. Belding's plover *(P. w. beldingi)* ranges from Baja California to Peru.

MILD-MANNERED LITTLE BEACHCOMBERS OF NORTH, SOUTH, EAST, AND WEST

Usually silent and unobtrusive, the **Semipalmated Plover** (right background, young alighting) swoops and sings ecstatically in its Arctic nesting grounds. The South's **Wilson's Plover** (foreground pair, female and male) skillfully decoys intruders from its nest. The **Piping Plover** (left-hand figure with yellow legs) frequents eastern beaches, while the **Snowy Plover** (adult and young, extreme left) abounds on southern and western shores.

American Woodcock

Philohela minor

Average Length, Eleven Inches

The American woodcock, which is somewhat smaller than the European species, enjoys all the fame and mystery of its cousin: its nocturnal habits, its curious courtship flights, the fable of the carrying of its young, its erratic migrations, the sport of hunting it, and its savoriness upon the table.

Woodcocks move northward early in the spring and often are overtaken by late freezes and snowstorms. Indeed the birds are sometimes incubating early in April in New York and New England and sometimes are covered with snow while on the nest. The eggs hatch in three weeks and the young grow so rapidly that they attain their full size in 25 days. They sometimes eat twice their own weight of earthworms in a day.

This species nests from Manitoba and Nova Scotia to northern Florida, wintering south of the lines of winter ice.

Wilson's Snipe

Capella delicata

Average Length, Eleven and One-quarter Inches

Of all the shore birds that were formerly on the game list, the snipe and the woodcock are the only ones for which there is still an open season and for which there is no immediate danger thereby of extermination.

The Wilson's snipe has a very extensive breeding range—most of which has not been at all affected by the march of civilization. In summer it is found nesting on the tundra, as well as in suitable grassy marshes, from western Alaska to Newfoundland and south as far as California and Pennsylvania.

These birds never travel in the compact flocks of the other shore birds, and seldom is more than one bird killed at each discharge of the gun. They frequent grassy marshes, where they are usually invisible until flushed, when they rise with a startling bleat and fly swiftly on a zigzag course.

The bill of the snipe, like that of the woodcock, is covered with soft skin rather than horn, and upon drying, in a mounted specimen, it reveals the pits in the bone underneath in which lie the tiny sense organs which enable the bird to locate worms in the soil.

The snipe builds a grass-lined nest in a tussock, often surrounded by water, and lays usually four olive-buff eggs marked with dark brown or black.

The courtship "song" of the male is one of the mysteries of the bird world that have never been fully explained. Flying in great circles high overhead, he sets his wings, spreads his tail, and pitches slightly toward the earth, producing a winnowing sound that gradually grows louder and then dies away.

Upland Plover

Bartramia longicauda

Average Length, Eleven and One-half Inches

Formerly abundant from northwestern Alaska to northern Virginia during the summer, and wintering on the pampas of Brazil and Argentina, the upland plover is now a rare bird through much of its range. Some 25 years ago it was thought to be on the verge of extinction, but it was placed on the protected list in 1916, and has staged a gradual comeback.

Even in well-settled country where there are pasture lots, we can still hope to hear again the eerie whistle *whip-whip-whee-ee-ee-ou-u* of this gentle bird as it sails in great circles. We may find its grass-lined nest in a bed of clover or wild strawberries or see its downy young once more tottering across the road.

Long-billed Curlew

Numenius americanus

Average Length, Twenty-four Inches

The history of the long-billed curlew, our largest shore bird, parallels that of the bison, the prong-horned antelope and the trumpeter swan. Until the middle of the last century it was a common wintering bird on our South Atlantic coasts; on migration it occurred frequently as far north as Massachusetts; and it nested as far east as Ohio and throughout the prairies of the Mississippi Valley and the Rocky Mountain country.

Today it is greatly reduced, except in a few favored localities, and it has not been seen east of the Mississippi for a great many years. You can imagine my delight, therefore, when not long ago I found it still a common nesting bird in the beautiful Cache Valley of Utah, about the edges of the Bear River marshes, and again in southeastern Montana.

The birds breeding in Wyoming and South Dakota north into Manitoba and Alberta are somewhat smaller than the Utah birds and have been separated into a distinct subspecies called the northern curlew (*Numenius americanus occidentalis*). The curlews winter in the southwestern States, especially Texas and California, and thence to Guatemala.

The curlew's long curved bill is very efficient in fishing fiddler crabs and even crayfish from their burrows on their Texas wintering resorts, but in summer a large part of the bird's food consists of grasshoppers, crickets, and other insects.

The curlews lay four large eggs, resembling those of gulls, in a poorly lined depression on the prairie where the grass is not high enough to obscure the birds' vision. They seem to nest in scattered colonies, and when the young have hatched they bring them together in a more or less communal manner.

ELUSIVE SNIPE AND WOODCOCK TEST THE SHOOTER'S SKILL

The early-migrating **American Woodcock** (lower right) sometimes incubates under a blanket of snow. Still fairly abundant is the widely distributed **Wilson's Snipe** (left foreground and distant flying bird). The **Upland Plover** (upper right) and the **Long-billed Curlew** (flying center) are both rare except in favored places.

NO REASON HAS BEEN FOUND WHY GODWITS' BILLS TURN UP WHILE CURLEWS' CURVE DOWNWARD

The once abundant **Eskimo Curlew** (on one leg, center background) is now apparently extinct. The **Hudsonian Curlew** (extreme right) and the **Hudsonian Godwit** (wading pair, in winter and summer plumage) nest in Arctic tundras. Two others are the rare **Marbled Godwit** (extreme left in summer

Hudsonian Curlew
Phaeopus hudsonicus
Average Length, Seventeen Inches

If we can judge from the accounts of such ornithologists as Audubon and Wilson in the early part of the 19th century, the Hudsonian curlew has increased in numbers during the last hundred years, while every other species has been on the downgrade. This species still holds its own on the tundra from Hudson Bay to Alaska, and both the Atlantic and Pacific coasts know it as a regular migrant on its way to the west coast of South America for the winter, although it is rather uncommon in the interior of the United States.

To the wariness of this bird I can personally attest from trying to find its nest on the tundra near Hudson Bay. The birds would come flying to meet me half a mile away, and when I concealed myself and watched them through binoculars it was almost impossible to determine in which direction they went when they finally decided to return to the unconcealed nest depressions in the moss. The four large eggs are brown-spotted olive green.

Eskimo Curlew
Phaeopus borealis
Average Length, Thirteen and One-half Inches

The Eskimo curlew, or "dough bird" or "prairie pigeon" as it was called by the gunners, apparently rivaled the passenger pigeon in numbers prior to 1885. At that time as many as 2,000 were reported killed in a single day by a party of 25 or 30 men, and it was no uncommon experience to shoot a wagonload in a day during their migration through the Mississippi Valley in April. In such compact flocks did they fly that as many as 28 were brought down by one shot from an old muzzle-loader.

The last Eskimo curlew to be taken was killed in Argentina January 11, 1925. Since then there have been a few possible sight records, but the species is in all probability extinct. It once flew to Labrador and then directly south 2,000 miles over the Atlantic, except when easterly storms drove it to the New England shores. It wintered in Argentina where it was a favorite game bird, and in sadly reduced numbers it returned to its summer home by way of the Mississippi Valley where the greatest carnage of all took place.

In general appearance the Eskimo curlew resembled the Hudsonian curlew but was smaller, weighing only about a pound when fat, and it had a shorter bill. An immature Hudsonian curlew might easily be mistaken for an Eskimo curlew but that its primaries are barred beneath, and its axillars are pointed.

The nesting habits of the Eskimo curlew were apparently similar to those of the Hudsonian curlew except that its calls were distinctly different—one a melodious whistled *bee, bee* and one a blackbirdlike chatter.

Marbled Godwit
Limosa fedoa
Average Length, Eighteen Inches

Next to the long-billed curlew this is our largest shore bird and its size, along with its limited breeding range and the encroachments of agriculture, have caused its near extinction. One hundred years ago it was not an uncommon migrant on the Atlantic coast as far north as New England, and it wintered in large numbers in Florida and on the Gulf coast.

Today, if it occurs at all east of the Mississippi, it is the rarest straggler. At present the relatively few birds that remain nest in North Dakota and central Saskatchewan, with a few in western Minnesota and other prairie country as far south as South Dakota.

Its name comes from its call *god-wit, god-wit, god-wit*. In habits it is like the curlews, lining a depression with grass and laying four greenish-drab spotted eggs.

Hudsonian Godwit
Limosa haemastica
Average Length, Fifteen Inches

For some unknown reason the Hudsonian godwit has apparently never been a common bird, and since it follows the golden plover in its migration directly from Labrador to South America, it is seldom seen in the fall on the Atlantic coast and still less frequently during the spring when it returns from Argentina by way of the Mississippi Valley. Audubon himself never saw one of these godwits alive. The nest and eggs, as discovered by Roderick McFarlane around the mouths of the Mackenzie and Anderson Rivers, are apparently similar to those of the Hudsonian curlew.

The female Hudsonian godwit is somewhat larger than the male, with lighter barrings on the breast, and both appear very dark in flight with conspicuous white rumps. In winter plumage they somewhat resemble willets, but lack the conspicuous wing pattern.

Pacific Godwit
Limosa lapponica baueri
Average Length, Fifteen Inches

This eastern representative of the European bar-tailed godwit will remain unknown to the American bird-lover unless he journeys to northwestern Alaska where it is a common summer resident. In migration it cuts southwestward to Japan and the Philippines, and winters in the Malay Archipelago, Australia, and New Zealand.

According to Herbert Brandt, who has studied them on their nesting ground, they are very conspicuous and noisy, both in their courtship flights and in defense of their young. Their nesting habits are not very different from other godwits and curlews, the birds preferring dry ridges on the rolling tundra and placing their nests between clumps of bunch grass.

THE UBIQUITOUS "TIP-UP" GREETS FOUR LONG-LEGGED COUSINS

The teetering **Spotted Sandpiper** (lower left, adult in summer plumage above young in fall garb) bobs a welcome to the summer-clad **Lesser** and **Greater Yellow-legs** (center), the tree-nesting **Eastern Solitary Sandpiper** (right foreground), and the **Eastern Willet** (behind, with extended wings).

Eastern Willet

Catoptrophorus semipalmatus semipalmatus

Average Length, Fifteen Inches

The willet is one of the characteristic sights of the tidal marshes of our southern coasts. In March or early April the larger, longer-billed birds start northwestward for Utah and points north, for they represent a western sub-species (*Catoptrophorus s. inornatus* Brewster), and some of the others move up the coast as far as New Jersey. Still others jump over Long Island and New England, from which willets were long since extirpated, to form a summer colony in Nova Scotia.

Those that remain on our southern coasts about the same time become much noisier, calling their name *pilly, willy, willet* over and over again as they circle overhead or dart at any intruder who dares to approach the nesting territory. In May they scoop out hollows in the sand above high tide, especially on coastal islands, often lining them well with grasses, and lay four large olive-buff eggs, boldly and irregularly marked with dark brown. Some of the western birds wander to Peru and some of the eastern birds to Brazil.

Greater Yellow-legs

Totanus melanoleucus

Average Length, Fourteen Inches

The greater yellow-legs is found in summer from Newfoundland to southern British Columbia, northward to central Alberta and southern Ungava, but it seems to shun the Prairie Provinces which are favored by so many of the other shore birds. It does not extend its range so far north as the lesser yellow-legs but stops far short of timber line. In winter some birds remain as far north as South Carolina, but others wander southward, even to Patagonia. It moves northward earlier than other species and sometimes appears on the New England coast and the shores of the Great Lakes by the last of March.

It nests on the ground, but seems to prefer gravelly ridges among scattered trees and fallen logs rather than open muskeg and tundra.

Lesser Yellow-legs

Totanus flavipes

Average Length, Ten and Three-quarters Inches

This smaller edition of the greater yellow-legs resembles it so closely that when there are no other birds about with which to compare the size, it is difficult to identify it with certainty unless one has had considerable experience or unless it takes wing and calls. The two-syllable note of the lesser yellow-legs is much more like that of the solitary sandpiper than like the longer series of its larger cousin.

Like the larger species it occurs singly or in flocks of as many as a hundred, though small groups are the rule. It goes farther north for the summer, even to the limit of trees, and seldom winters north of South America. It avoids the Atlantic coast in the spring.

In nesting habits it resembles the greater yellow-legs and is equally noisy, having a remarkable territorial song resembling the syllables *keep-a-going, keep-a-going.*

Solitary Sandpiper

Tringa solitaria

Average Length, Eight and One-half Inches

Here is another relatively small-size species whose solitary habits have preserved it in undiminished numbers, although it never has been so abundant or widespread as the spotted sandpiper.

Passing the summer from the limit of trees southward to the northern United States east of the Rocky Mountains, and wintering from Texas to Argentina, it goes through most of the United States during April and May and again from July to September where it is often seen about the edges of woodland pools.

The solitary sandpiper is the only North American shore bird that regularly nests in trees. Relatively few of its eggs have ever been found, however, and these have always been placed in old nests such as those of robins and rusty blackbirds, from five to twenty feet from the ground in larches and firs usually standing in or near water. A western form (*T. s. cinnamomea*) breeds in Alaska.

Spotted Sandpiper

Actitis macularia

Average Length, Seven and One-half Inches

This is our most ubiquitous and best known species of shore bird. From the Atlantic to the Pacific and from Alaska to South Carolina nearly every pond, stream, or lake shore has its "tip-up" or "teeter-tail," as it is familiarly called. Though it occasionally wanders into barren fields or pastures, it is best known as it flies up along the lake shore with short, quick strokes of the wings, skimming just above the water.

Spotted sandpipers never assemble in large flocks and during the winter they are scattered along the streams of South America as far south as southern Brazil, Bolivia, and Peru. I have seen them along the Cauca River in Colombia behaving exactly as they do along the Potomac or the Hudson River at home.

When nesting time comes, they frequently move back a considerable distance from the water and line a little depression with bits of grasses and weed stems and lay four large tan eggs heavily spotted about the large end with black. The downy gray youngsters follow their parents to the shore on wobbly legs as soon as hatched.

During the courtship period the male bird responds very quickly to a whistled imitation of its call—*sus-a-weet, sus-a-weet, sus-a-weet, sweet, sweet, sweet, sweet, sweet.*

THEIR ASTONISHING TRAVELS MAKE UP FOR CONSERVATIVE APPAREL

From South Sea lagoons, the **Wandering Tattler** (upper left) makes an annual cruise to Alaska. The **American Knot** (lower left, adult in summer finery left, young right) nests within a few hundred miles of the North Pole. In winter, the **Aleutian Sandpiper** (center pair, in winter and summer plumage) resembles the hardy **Purple Sandpiper** (on rock, right). A notorious gypsy is the **Sanderling** (lower right pair, young left; also flying bird).

Wandering Tattler

Heteroscelus incanus
Average Length, Eleven Inches

From the coral-fringed South Sea islands most of the wandering tattlers start northward over the 2,500 miles of open sea in March to the rocky headlands of California and Washington. Some, however, remain in the Hawaiian Islands until April or May; indeed yearling birds may remain there all summer.

By the last of May the tattler reaches northern Alaska, but for more than 150 years after the bird itself was known no one had ever seen its eggs. It was not until July 1, 1923, that Olaus J. Murie made the important first discovery of a set of eggs. The nest was on a gravel bar of the Savage River. Rather well-built and about five inches in diameter, it contained four greenish-gray eggs irregularly spotted with dark brown, chiefly about the larger end.

Aleutian Sandpiper

Arquatella ptilocnemis couesi
Average Length, Nine Inches

Three varieties of this little sandpiper inhabit the Pribilof Islands, the Aleutians, and the Commander Islands, respectively. In winter they so resemble the purple sandpiper that at one time they were thought to be subspecies of it. In summer plumage, however, they are more suggestive of red-backed sandpipers.

The Aleutian sandpipers build their nests in little hollows in the tundra moss, and the males have a charming courtship performance—rising 30 or 40 feet in the air, then fluttering down with a delightful twittering song. They likewise produce a loud "bleating" call from the ground, so similar to that made by the Wilson's snipe in the air as to convince Dr. Leonhard Stejneger that the sound of the snipe is also produced vocally instead of with its tail feathers, a belief commonly accepted.

American Knot

Calidris canutus rufus
Average Length, Ten and One-half Inches

When Admiral Peary returned from the North Pole to his winter base near Cape Sheridan in northern Ellesmere Island about 600 miles from the Pole, he announced discovery on June 27, 1909, of the first authentic nest and eggs of the knot. The species is circumpolar in its summer distribution.

The knots leave the Arctic in July, appear on our coasts in August, move gradually southward, and leave Florida by November for Argentina and other points south. In the fall and winter they wear white underparts, but in April the adult birds once again have red breasts, and the sexes are alike.

In the old days the knots passed down our coasts in enormous numbers, flying in close formation and making easy targets for the market hunters. By 1916, when the treaty with Canada was signed giving them complete protection, they were much reduced, but since then they have increased considerably.

Sanderling

Crocethia alba
Average Length, Eight Inches

From its nesting place on the northernmost Arctic islands on both sides of the world, the sanderling wanders southward in August and September until it has visited nearly every beach from Patagonia and South Africa to Australia and the Polynesian islands, including Hawaii.

In their pale winter plumage these birds are the whitest of our small sandpipers, with large white patches in their black wings, nearly white heads and pure white underparts. In the spring their heads and throats become suffused with cinnamon brown, and they appear much darker.

Sanderlings usually travel in small flocks, frequenting the sand beaches where they pursue the receding waves to snatch tiny mollusks and shrimps from the seething waters and trot back just in time not to be overtaken by the oncoming line of foam.

The sanderling returns to our northern beaches between the middle and the last of May, and arrives on its nesting ground the first week in June. The nest is a hollow in the tundra, often in the center of a recumbent plant of the Arctic willow or dryas, and the eggs vary from pale yellowish white to olive buff in ground color, with small, often inconspicuous spots of brown or black.

The courting male is said to have a flight song, but he does not rise high into the air and his notes are described as a "snarling or slight neighing sound."

Purple Sandpiper

Arquatella maritima
Average Length, Nine Inches

The purple sandpiper is perhaps the hardiest of the whole tribe, passing the winter even as far north as southern Greenland only a few venturing south of Montauk Point, Long Island, no matter how severe the winter. These birds do not generally appear on the reefs and rocky ledges off the New England coast until November or December, and they usually leave again by March for their nesting ground on Baffin Island and in Greenland.

The species has a very limited range in North America and is not ordinarily seen except by bird-lovers who make a special trip to its inhospitable haunts. It has a somewhat wider range in the northern parts of the Old World.

Its dark bluish-gray color is rather unusual among shore birds but hardly merits the designation of purple which has given it its name.

TRIM SANDPIPERS FOLLOW THE RECEDING TIDE, PROBING FOR LARVAE IN THE OOZE

Present are: **Baird's Sandpiper** (left center in summer plumage, young on wing); the abundant **Least Sandpiper** (left foreground; adult in summer plumage left, young in fall feathering right); the **Red-backed** (center pair and distant flying bird; winter-clad flying left and on the wing, summer style right); and the **White-rumped Sandpiper** (right-hand pair; young in fall dress below adult in summer plumage).

Red-backed Sandpiper

Pelidna alpina sakhalina
Average Length, Eight Inches

During the late fall when this species is migrating from its Arctic breeding ground west of Hudson Bay, and during the winter months when it is feeding along our coastal beaches from New Jersey and Washington southward, one looks in vain for its red back or any other distinguishing characteristic except its rather long and slightly decurved bill. During March and April, however, a complete molt of the body feathers produces a striking breeding dress.

The red-backs are hardy little birds, slightly larger than spotted sandpipers. They travel in rather compact flocks, which although apparently leaderless, show remarkable unity. They migrate later than most other shore birds, and I have seen belated individuals wandering around on the ice at the head of Cayuga Lake when a November freeze had closed all the shallow water.

At the eastern edge of the breeding range at Churchill on Hudson Bay I found these birds nesting very similarly to the northern phalaropes in tussocks of sedges more or less surrounded by water. Like most of the other shore birds the males indulge in a flight song, a musical trill of a peculiar liquid quality which suggests the ordinary call of a toad.

Our red-backed sandpiper is the New World representative of the Old World dunlin (*Pelidna alpina alpina*), which is a familiar bird on the moorlands of the Netherlands, northern Germany, the British Isles, Norway, and Russia. The two subspecies are almost indistinguishable.

White-rumped Sandpiper

Pisobia fuscicollis
Average Length, Seven and One-half Inches

After nesting from northern Alaska to Baffin Island the white-rumped sandpiper migrates for the winter to Paraguay, southern Patagonia, and the Falkland Islands. As it follows the route of the Baird's sandpiper down the Mississippi Valley, it is therefore rather uncommon on the Atlantic coast. It migrates somewhat later than the other small species, most often being seen in October.

The call of the white-rumped sandpiper reminds one more of some sparrow's song than the note of a shore bird. As the bird hovers on rapidly beating wings over its tundra home, its flight song can scarcely be heard.

Mr. J. Dewey Soper, who heard the song of the white-rumped sandpiper on Baffin Island, writes concerning it: "Given in a very low tone and slow tempo, the notes are weak and inclined to be squeaky, with a weird, dripping quality like the sound of water oozing and dripping in a small cavern."

Baird's Sandpiper

Pisobia bairdi
Average Length, Seven and One-half Inches

Baird's sandpiper is more a bird of the interior than of ocean beaches. It nests along the Arctic coast from western Alaska to Baffin Island and migrates directly southward to Chile and Patagonia, using the Mississippi Valley as its highway both fall and spring. It is thus comparatively rare on the Atlantic and Pacific coasts.

In appearance it resembles a small pectoral sandpiper, but has black instead of greenish legs. Since the latter species varies considerably in size, the bird student often overlooks the Baird's sandpiper. It more often associates with least and semipalmated sandpipers than with pectorals, so that, by contrast, it appears larger than it really is. Indeed, when seen in the company of "sandpeeps," it looks like a large, light-colored least sandpiper, with the streaked breast characteristic of the breeding plumage of that species.

Least Sandpiper

Pisobia minutilla
Average Length, Six Inches

The least sandpiper is the smallest and one of the most abundant of our shore birds, nesting throughout the Arctic from northwestern Alaska to Newfoundland, and known as a migrant throughout the United States and Canada. Collectively with the very similar but somewhat grayer semipalmated sandpiper, least sandpipers are commonly called "sandpeeps" or just "peeps." They sometimes occur in flocks of hundreds on our shores and mud flats.

They are confiding little birds as they trot along the shore, probing in the ooze for midge larvæ and the like, and sometimes they will allow one to approach within a few feet of them without taking alarm. At such times it is easy to distinguish them from the semipalmated sandpipers, even when the color difference is not so apparent, because the least has greenish legs instead of black and its bill is more slender.

The two birds are not so closely related as one might think from their similarity of appearance, but they are always associated in nesting as well as in migration except that the least sandpipers extend their nesting somewhat farther south. Together they continue their migrations southward, even to Patagonia, though many remain as far north as our Gulf States.

On the Northern Plains both species indulge in flight songs, hovering fifteen or twenty feet over the tundra and voicing a curious buzzing sound. The nests and eggs of the two species are practically indistinguishable, although the eggs of the least are perhaps somewhat grayer and more heavily marked with reddish brown.

BETWEEN PRODIGIOUS FLIGHTS, THEY SPEND MOST OF THEIR TIME ON THE GROUND

A giant among his small neighbors, the **Bristle-thighed Curlew** (center) commutes between Tahiti and central Alaska. The **Sharp-tailed Sandpiper** (right foreground; young left, adult in summer plumage right) is the Old World representative of our grass-loving **Pectoral Sandpiper** (left pair; adult left, young right). Market hunters once nearly exterminated the confiding **Buff-breasted Sandpiper** (upper right; young left, adult in summer plumage right).

Pectoral Sandpiper

Pisobia melanotos

Average Length, Nine Inches

The pectoral sandpiper usually frequents the grassy parts of marshes and shores. To the gunners it was formerly known as the "grassbird." While it generally travels in more or less compact flocks, it scatters while feeding and often lies close upon approach like a snipe, rising with a harsh call that has given it the name of "krieker."

It nests on the Arctic coasts from Siberia eastward to Southampton Island and winters in South America from Peru to Chile and central Patagonia. It seems to avoid the Pacific coast in its travels and also the Atlantic coast in the spring, and the Mississippi Valley is its favorite route through the United States.

When the pectoral sandpiper arrives on the nesting ground, the male, which is appreciably larger than the female, develops a large sac on the throat by the dilation of the gullet. This he fills with air as a sounding board for his call, a prairie-chickenlike *tōō-û, tōō-û, tōō-û, tōō-û, too-û, too-û, too-u, too-u, too-u.*

Upon filling his gular sac until it is fully as large as the rest of his body, he may call from the ground, run about the female with his bill horizontal and the sac pendent, or fly 40 feet into the air and sail to the ground on set wings, jerking his head as he gives the call.

The nest is built of grass and is usually placed in a tussock of grass in a fairly dry situation.

Sharp-tailed Sandpiper

Pisobia acuminata

Average Length, Eight and One-half Inches

This Old World representative of our pectoral sandpiper nests in eastern Siberia and winters in New Guinea, New Zealand, and in Australia, where it is especially abundant. Our only claim to birds of this species lies in the fact that before their long migration southward many of them take a little jaunt over to Alaska and even to the coast of British Columbia. The nest and eggs of the sharp-tailed sandpiper have never been found.

Buff-breasted Sandpiper

Tryngites subruficollis

Average Length, Eight and One-half Inches

This is another bird of the interior of North America with a comparatively limited breeding range in northern Alaska and northern Mackenzie, a migration route through the Prairie Provinces of Canada and the Mississippi Valley, and winter quarters in Argentina and Uruguay. On the Pacific coast of the United States it is unknown, and on the Atlantic coast it is very rare.

Despite its limited range, it formerly occurred in countless thousands, but so confiding was its disposition and so closely massed were the flocks with the unfortunate habit of returning time and again to wounded companions, that it was nearly exterminated by hunters.

In general habits and appearance the buff-breasted sandpiper is a small edition of the upland plover (which is really a sandpiper), and like that species it frequents the prairie far from water.

Professor Rowan has observed an unusual nuptial display by these birds in the course of their migration through Alberta. During the most characteristic and amusing performance both wings are raised, with the under surfaces facing to the front but with the primaries perpendicular and the tips practically touching each other over the bird's head. The body is held absolutely vertical, the legs are stretched to their uttermost, and the tail is cocked out horizontally, while the call *tick, tick, tick, tick* is sounded at top speed for about a second. A bird may suddenly stop in its hunt for food in order to go through this ridiculous feat and then proceed as if nothing unusual had happened.

The nest and eggs of the buff-breasted sandpiper on the tundra are similar to the golden plover's but considerably smaller.

Bristle-thighed Curlew

Phaeopus tahitiensis

Average Length, Seventeen Inches

When Dr. George Sutton discovered the first authentic nest and eggs of the Harris's sparrow at Churchill on Hudson Bay in 1931, he left only two birds of our North whose eggs have never been seen by man—the Ross's snow goose and the bristle-thighed curlew.

The curlew was first described from Tahiti in 1785 and is best known from this and other islands of the South Pacific group where it passes the winter. Until 1869 these islands were thought to be its summer home as well, but now ornithologists believe the species goes for the summer somewhere into the interior of northern Alaska.

Toward the last of May it makes the long 2,500-mile flight from the South Pacific over the open sea to the Kenai Peninsula of Alaska, the majority of birds not even stopping there but continuing on into the interior. Again in August they appear on the coast with their young fully grown, but where they have been in the meantime is still a mystery.

The bristle-thighed curlew derives its name from the lengthened shafts of some of the flank feathers, which are without barbs and project like bristles or stiff hairs from its sides.

On Laysan Island, where Dr. Alexander Wetmore and Donald R. Dickey made observations, these birds were remarkably tame and had developed the strange habit of stealing and eating the eggs of terns and frigate birds—an unusual habit for a shore bird but one shared by the turnstones on this island.

ON THEIR NORTHERN NESTING GROUNDS, AMOROUS HOVERERS GIVE VOICE TO BUZZING, INSECTLIKE LOVE SONGS

Above are two **Stilt Sandpipers** (left, young alighting) and a trio of the **Eastern Dowitcher** (adults in winter and summer plumage, young in fall dress). The **Semipalmated Sandpiper** (two lower right, young left) often associates with the **Western Sandpiper** (lower left-hand pair, young left).

Eastern Dowitcher

Limnodromus griseus griseus

Average Length, Ten and One-half Inches

Wintering from Florida and the West Indies south to central Brazil and Peru, these dowitchers or "red-breasted snipe," as they are sometimes called, move northward during April and May, especially along the coasts, to their breeding grounds. Sooner or later they have to cut northwestward, for they pass the summer from central Alberta to the west side of Hudson Bay and northward.

The birds which nest from the delta of the Yukon to Point Barrow and northwestern Mackenzie have somewhat redder breasts and longer bills than the eastern birds, and have been separated as a distinct subspecies called the "long-billed dowitcher" (*Limnodromus griseus scolopaceus* Say). There seem to be many intermediates, however, and the long-billed birds are sometimes seen on the Atlantic coast. They regularly winter in Florida and Louisiana with their shorter-billed cousins, as well as in California and points south.

On the nesting ground dowitchers are noisy, one of their chief call notes resembling the word "dowitch." At times they strut like woodcock and at other times indulge in pursuit of the female and give a musical flight song on hovering wings.

Nests of typical eastern dowitchers have not yet been found, but birds of intermediate characteristics in central Alberta, and long-billed birds in Alaska and Mackenzie, place their eggs in slight depressions in hummocks of moss, through which sedges are growing and around which water is standing. The eggs are olive or bluish gray strikingly marked with dark brown.

Stilt Sandpiper

Micropalama himantopus

Average Length, Eight and One-quarter Inches

To be able to distinguish the stilt sandpiper in its fall plumage from the lesser yellow-legs, and the western sandpiper from the semipalmated, requires a keen eye. In spring plumage, however, the species are distinct.

When A. C. Bent published his monumental work, *Life Histories of North American Shore Birds,* in 1927, he wrote that he had never seen a stilt sandpiper alive. He could find only three definite nesting records for it and these in northern Mackenzie about the middle of the last century.

At Churchill on Hudson Bay in 1934, however, I found the stilt sandpiper fairly common and discovered nearly a dozen nests. Its curious courtship song was a familiar sound all about us, and nearly every shallow pond had at least one of the conspicuously barred birds feeding along its margin.

The species probably nests all the way from Churchill to Mackenzie, just beyond the limit of trees. The nests which we found were shallow depressions in the tundra with scarcely any pretense at nest building; and the large eggs were olive, boldly marked with black.

Western Sandpiper

Ereunetes maurii

Average Length, Six and One-quarter Inches

The western sandpiper, which passes the summer in Alaska from the Yukon Delta to Point Barrow, regularly makes a long flight southeastward in the fall to our Atlantic coast on its way to South America. In winter plumage it closely resembles the semipalmated sandpiper and is easily overlooked. It is told mainly by its longer bill.

In the spring it seldom ventures up the Atlantic coast beyond North Carolina before cutting northwestward to its breeding ground. At this time of the year its upper parts are considerably brighter than are those of the semipalmated sandpiper.

A considerable number of western sandpipers winter on our Gulf coast, though the majority continue on to South America. The largest number migrate down the Pacific coast and winter from Washington to Peru.

In courtship and nesting habits the western is very similar to the semipalmated sandpiper.

Semipalmated Sandpiper

Ereunetes pusillus

Average Length, Six and One-third Inches

This most abundant species of the shore bird group passes the summer throughout the Arctic from northeastern Siberia to northern Labrador; it winters from South Carolina and the Gulf States to Patagonia, and migrates through the United States and Canada mainly east of the Rockies.

Very often associating with the least and western sandpipers and together with them being known as "peeps," they are the most numerous sandpipers on our coasts and mud flats during August and September and again during late April and May. They often assemble in suitable places in flocks of hundreds or even thousands, and usually are very tame.

It was once considered legitimate sport to fire into these enormous flocks, killing dozens at one discharge of the gun and crippling many others for the sake of a none too savory potpie of tiny breasts. Fortunately that day is gone, and the little sandpeeps will continue to grace our shores and inspire such poems as that by Celia Thaxter, "One Little Sandpiper and I."

The call of the semipalmated sandpiper is somewhat hoarser than that of the least sandpiper, but its courtship and nesting habits are similar. Over the tundra at Churchill early in June dozens of these little birds could be seen at almost any time hovering in the air, voicing their amorous feelings in loud buzzing sounds more like cicadas or bees than birds.

PLAINER AND SMALLER THAN THEIR MATES, MALE PHALAROPES ALSO BUILD THE NESTS AND INCUBATE THE EGGS

The trio at the left are the **Wilson's Phalarope** (female in summer plumage right, male left, young in winter garb above). At the right are the **Red Phalarope** (showy female in center, winter-clad young alighting) and **Northern Phalarope** (young on one leg in front of male and female in summer plumage).

Wilson's Phalarope

Steganopus tricolor
Average Length, Male, Eight and Three-quarters
Inches; Female, Nine and One-half Inches

Phalaropes are swimming sandpipers whose toes are lobed rather than webbed. They can swim like miniature ducks and do not hesitate to do so. Indeed, two of the three species making up the family pass the winter months largely on the open sea where their dense breast feathers and undercoating of down are fully as waterproof as those of ducks.

Female phalaropes are bigger and brighter than the males; and they do not build the nest, they do not incubate the eggs, they do not even care for the young. Indeed the female is even the aggressor in the courtship, and it is a common sight over the prairie sloughs to see one small male pursued by two large, brightly colored females which swell out their necks and fill the air with curious grunts.

After the eggs have been laid and the males are doing the work of incubation, the females gather in flocks by themselves. They do not entirely lose the maternal instinct, however. I learned while studying a colony of Wilson's phalaropes in western Manitoba that whenever any disturbance flushed the males from the nest, the females would come flying in from the sloughs to learn the trouble.

At one nest where I had my photographic blind this seemed to irritate the male, and whenever the female approached within five or six feet he would set upon her, pound her head with his bill and drive her away.

The Wilson's phalarope is the only one of the three species that is restricted to the New World, wintering in southern Chile and Patagonia and passing the summers from central California to central Manitoba, where it is found about grassy ponds and prairie sloughs feeding almost entirely on aquatic insects. It has longer legs and a longer neck than the other species, and its toes are less broadly lobed, no doubt in consequence of its more terrestrial habits. The only call I have ever heard it give is a little grunt or quack.

Northern Phalarope

Lobipes lobatus
Average Length, Seven and Three-quarters Inches

One morning early in June, 1935, we peered over an embankment to the surface of a reservoir near Denver, Colorado, and to our amazement found it covered with what looked like tiny ducks all heading into the wind, except for a few near the shore which were whirling about in a dance, almost like whirligig beetles.

There were several thousand of these little birds, northern phalaropes, on their way to their Arctic breeding ground. They had been wintering off the coast of Peru and had just completed one leg of their 3,500-mile journey.

They seemed in no hurry that morning, despite the fact that some of their kind had probably already reached the nesting ground on Hudson Bay. Indeed it had been a year before almost to a day that I had watched the first arrival of their kind at Churchill on Hudson Bay. The following day, however, all were gone. Probably they had been resting for the day preparatory to their next night's flight of some 700 miles to Lake Winnipeg. All the shore birds are primarily night migrants.

These phalaropes are found throughout the Northern Hemisphere, nesting on the Northern Plains, and wintering on the open sea off the coasts of South America and Africa. Their stopping places in the interior of the country are rather local, but one often meets with flocks of them out of sight of land, resting on the sea or flying in close formation just above the water—a strange environment for a shore bird.

The northern phalarope is similar to the Wilson's in the reversal of the sexes as to size, color, and domestic relations; and the grassy nests and buff, spotted eggs placed in grassy hummocks, usually surrounded by water, are likewise common to the two species.

The only note I ever heard from this species was a simple *check* of alarm as the birds took flight. Their courtship pursuits are usually silent.

Red Phalarope

Phalaropus fulicarius
Average Length, Eight Inches

This is the most boreal of the three phalaropes, pushing even farther north than the northern, and seldom found south of the delta of the Yukon or Southampton Island in summer. It is likewise equally abundant from Iceland to eastern Siberia, and in winter is plentiful off the coasts of South America, Africa, and Arabia. It is the most maritime of the three phalaropes and is seldom found on our coasts or inland except when driven in by heavy storms at sea.

In winter plumage it is much grayer than the northern phalarope and is sometimes called the "gray phalarope." It is likewise easily distinguished by its much broader bill. In breeding plumage all three species are so distinct that there is little danger of confusing them. This species with its red underparts and white cheeks is particularly distinctive. Its simple note is the most metallic of the three, sounding like the striking together of two bits of steel.

The reversal of the coloration and marital relationships noted with the other species is even more pronounced with the red phalarope. The female, obviously head of the house, is much more showy in appearance than her consort, and she proves her authority by driving the male around to suit her pleasure.

THEY WALK ON STILTS ALONG THE SHORES OF WESTERN LAKES

The handsome **Avocet** (right in summer finery above downy chick, bird in winter plumage flying) shares marshy western bottom lands with the **Black-necked Stilt** (left, adult male and young female), a widely ranging species that postures and screams to divert attention from its nest.

Avocet

Recurvirostra americana
Average Length, Sixteen and One-half Inches

On September 15, 1909, I leveled my glasses on a distant flock of shore birds at the head of Cayuga Lake and there, among a variety of smaller sandpipers, I espied my first avocet. Likewise it was the first avocet to be recorded from New York State.

Four years later in October on the same shore I recorded the second avocet for New York State, but never since have I seen one east of the Mississippi River.

In the early part of the 19th century Alexander Wilson reported them as breeding on the New Jersey salt marshes, but such a striking bird is the avocet that apparently all eastern breeding colonies were extirpated and today there are none east of northern Iowa. From there westward to California, northward to southern Alberta and Manitoba, and southward to southern Texas and New Mexico, the avocet is not uncommon in suitable places, such as shallow marshes and flooded fields.

Like the stilt, the avocet protests loudly when its nesting grounds are invaded, circling about with an oft-repeated *yip-yip-yip*.

These showy birds feed peculiarly in shallow ponds. Singly, in pairs, or in flocks, they stalk through the water, swinging their heads from side to side in unison, as if they were mowing hay with a scythe. The flattened, thin-edged tips of their curiously upcurved bills are swung laterally through the surface film of water, or through the silt at the bottom, and mosquito wigglers, midge larvæ, and the like are sorted out with scarcely a ripple.

The avocets build nests similar to those of the stilts, depressions in the ground lined with grasses. Like the stilts they sometimes build up their nests when the waters rise.

Male and female avocets are alike in plumage and share the duties of incubation. One of a pair that I was photographing was much more timid than the other and always waited for its mate to go to the nest in front of the blind before it would dare to go itself. It always felt the urge to incubate, however, after its mate became settled on the nest and would come up to the brooding bird and bunt it with its head until the latter gave way.

In winter plumage the avocets lose the cinnamon on their heads, which is partly replaced by gray. They migrate to southern Texas, Mexico, and Guatemala.

Black-necked Stilt

Himantopus mexicanus
Average Length, Fifteen Inches

My first experience with black-necked stilts was unfortunate. I had been instructed by Dr. Frank Chapman to collect for the American Museum a few specimens of a rare duck (*Marila nationi*) which had been lost to science shortly after its discovery and which he had reason to believe could be found in the Cauca River marshes of Colombia. After numerous failures I had finally located a small flock of these ducks on a marsh near Cali and was sneaking down to the shore to stalk them when a pair of black-necked stilts spied me.

Then and there I might just as well have packed up my belongings and gone home. The deafening racket of the stilts was taken up by the jaçanas and the whole marsh was soon in a clamor. Up went the screamers, then the Muscovies, then the tree-ducks, and finally the scaups; and I left without obtaining the coveted specimens. Thanks to the stilts I was forced to return another day, and I have never felt quite the same toward them since.

The stilts are wide-ranging birds, for they nest all the way from Peru and Brazil through Mexico and the West Indies to northern Utah and central Colorado, wintering in the southern part of their breeding range.

In Florida when I was trying to find their nests, I searched for several hours before I discovered that the birds had flown a quarter of a mile to meet me and were diverting my attention from their home by making a big fuss a couple of hundred yards away. The nests, I finally realized, were in a rather scattered colony on an adjacent flooded field, the light olive-brown, heavily spotted eggs being inconspicuous on thin, flat beds of broken grasses.

In Utah when I was trying to find the nest of a long-billed curlew, the stilts, which also nested there, were trying to frustrate my purpose by spying on me and telling the curlews of my hide-out and how long I was going to stay.

In addition to their loud cries the stilts have other amusing tricks to attract one's attention to themselves and thus protect their eggs or young. As if not striking enough in their black and white plumage on their long, pink, stiltlike legs, they run out into the open water where there will be nothing to conceal them and then start bobbing, suddenly bending their legs and then straightening them again so that each time their snowy-white breasts strike the water.

If this trick is not sufficient to divert one's attention, they begin waving their wings, sometimes one at a time, sometimes in unison, and then go hobbling off in pitiful decrepitude. Meanwhile, to accompany these incidents, there is such an uproar from all the other stilts of the vicinity that one is thankful to be able to leave the locality.

Occasionally heavy rains cause the water to rise about their nests or mud hummocks and then they are busy pushing straws and sticks and weed stems under the eggs until sometimes they raise them six or eight inches—ludicrous Noah's arks if the waters again recede.

Mexican Jaçana

Jacana spinosa gymnostoma
Average Length, Eight and One-half Inches

This curious little tropical bog-trotter is really more closely related to the shore birds than to the rails, but in its appearance, habits, and environment it is more like the gallinules. It gains admittance to consideration here among the birds of the United States and Canada because of its occasional wanderings from Mexico into the lower Rio Grande Valley of Texas near Brownsville. Its real home is in Mexico, with closely allied subspecies in Central and South America.

Its four brownish, glossy eggs are laid in floating nests of debris. Scrawls and pen-like black scratches all over the surface make them unique though inconspicuous.

American Coot

Fulica americana americana
Average Length, Fifteen Inches

"Half duck and half chicken" well describes this clown of the rail family, which in many places is still very abundant and is known by such familiar names as "mud hen," "blue peter," "puldoo," and "crow duck."

With a wide distribution during the summer from central British Columbia to New Brunswick, and south regularly as far as New Jersey in the east and Mexico or even Nicaragua in the west, in winter it often stays as far north as it can find food and open water. In California, Texas, and Louisiana it is locally extremely abundant in winter about lakes, ponds, and marshes, and wherever protected becomes so tame as to be almost a nuisance.

The coot ordinarily gleans along the shore or "tips" in shallow water to feed on many kinds of leaves, buds, seeds, and aquatic insects, but it may dive to depths of 10 to 20 feet.

On Cayuga Lake in winter I have seen individuals diving with the canvasbacks to get the buds of wild celery, and one cold season a flock massed like scaups over the weed beds and apparently had little difficulty in procuring a livelihood even when marshes and country-side lay deep under ice and snow.

During the nesting season coots are noisy, giving vent to their feelings in a variety of explosive cacks, clucks, coos, and wails, to the accompaniment of much splashing, chasing, and wing waving. Their rather deeply hollowed nests of dried rushes are built at the edges of ponds, sometimes concealed in the reeds, sometimes quite conspicuous in the open, and anchored to only a few bulrushes.

Their eggs are light tan in ground color with numerous pinhead black specks. They lay from 6 to 15 eggs, and like the gallinule start incubating after laying only a few, so that at hatching time the male has to take the first comers off into the marsh to feed while the mother continues her duties as incubator.

Florida Gallinule

Gallinula chloropus cachinnans
Average Length, Thirteen and One-half Inches

The Florida gallinule or "water chicken," as it is sometimes called, is found in summer in most of our large marshes from Minnesota to southern Ontario and New England, south to the West Indies, Panama, and even the Galápagos Islands. Like the coot, however, it is somewhat local and may be scarce over considerable areas.

It is similar to the coot in most of its habits, though because its toes are not lobed it does less swimming and diving and seldom ventures very far from the protection of the cattails or rushes. Its long toes act like snowshoes in distributing its weight, and it is able to run over the lily pads almost as well as the jaçana.

It derives the name of "water chicken" not only from its bantamlike appearance but also from its variety of barnyardlike clucks and cackles, many of which are almost indistinguishable from those of the coot. It likewise has a *co-co-co-co-co* call that suggests the notes of the pied-billed grebe.

Its nest is similar to that of the coot, built of dead cattails or rushes with a runway of the same material leading up to it from the water, but it is usually built farther back from the open water. Its eggs are similar in ground color but the spots are larger, browner, and less regular. The downy young are black, with a few gray whiskers on their chins.

Our gallinules are the New World representatives of the Old World "moor hens," which are found throughout Europe.

Purple Gallinule

Ionornis martinica
Average Length, Thirteen Inches

This tropical representative of the gallinule tribe has extended its range from the South American marshes as far north as Texas, Louisiana, and South Carolina, and in some of the marshes it is an abundant bird. It is somewhat smaller than the Florida gallinule and frequents more open places where its brilliant plumage and bright yellow legs present an attractive picture among the deep-green "bonnets" or lily pads. In South America I have seen these birds sunning themselves on the tops of bushes at the edge of a marsh, but in Florida or Louisiana they seem to like to have their feet wet most of the time.

The only nests I have found were in rather open places such as coots select, especially among the pickerel weed, but this species is reported to nest sometimes several feet above the water in cattails or saw grass.

Though this bird normally is not found north of South Carolina, it is apparently given to wandering or is picked up by tropical storms, for there are many records of it as far north as Quebec, New Brunswick, and Nova Scotia.

"MUD HENS" AND "WATER CHICKENS" CACKLE AND SPLASH AMONG THE RUSHES

"Mud hen" is only one of the nicknames of the common **American Coot** (left, with a downy chick, and running over the water in background). The **Florida Gallinule,** or "water chicken" (center, young in background), frequents extensive marshes from Ontario to Panama. Southern States are usually "farthest north" for the black-necked **Mexican Jaçana** and the tropical **Purple Gallinule** (right).

289

California Clapper Rail

Rallus obsoletus obsoletus
Average Length, Seventeen and One-half Inches

In the salt marshes of San Francisco and Monterey Bays, in a habitat that is being rapidly restricted, lives the California clapper rail. Two hundred miles down the coast is found a subspecies, the so-called "light-footed rail" (*Rallus o. levipes*), named by Bangs, and still farther south in the mangrove swamps and salt marshes in the Cape district of Baja California is found still another variety, the Belding's rail (*Rallus o. beldingi*).

Farther east in the marshes of the lower Colorado River north of Yuma is still another variety, the Yuma clapper rail (*Rallus o. yumanensis*), a form which has the distinction of being the only clapper rail inhabiting a fresh-water marsh.

These clapper rails differ somewhat from those of our eastern coastal marshes. They get their name from calls which resemble the *cack-cack-cack* of old-fashioned clappers.

Their nests are built of dead vegetation, and their eggs are much paler than those of the eastern birds and less heavily marked.

Virginia Rail

Rallus limicola limicola
Average Length, Nine and One-half Inches

The most satisfactory way to get acquainted with rails is to find their nests in late May or early June and then stand quietly by, with or without a blind, and wait for the birds to appear. Sometimes they lose all fear in the presence of their eggs or young and I photographed one Virginia rail that would actually attack my hand if its eggs were touched.

The nests are built of dead rushes, rather deeply hollowed, and are placed just above the water. From 5 to 12 eggs of a cream-buff color with spots of reddish brown are laid, and occasionally two birds lay in the same nest. Almost before the Virginia rail starts her nest, she begins pulling down the tips of the surrounding sedges or rushes to make a roof over it, and she keeps this shelter always in place.

Male and female Virginia rails are practically indistinguishable and they take turns incubating, but, as in gallinules, the young may be hatching over a period of several days. When danger threatens, it is apparently the adults' common practice to pick up the youngsters and carry them off to safety.

The Virginia rail is found in summer in suitable marshes from southern British Columbia to New Brunswick, south to Baja California, Utah, southern Ohio, and eastern North Carolina, wintering from the southern part of its breeding range south to Florida, Mexico, and Guatemala. It is more numerous in the interior, while the sora is more abundant in New England and the Atlantic States.

Sora

Porzana carolina
Average Length, Eight and One-half Inches

The sora and the Virginia rails are our best known and most widely distributed marsh birds, their ranges being almost identical with the exception that the sora seems not to nest south of Maryland on the Atlantic coast. It extends its migrations somewhat farther, however, and regularly crosses the Caribbean to winter as far south as Venezuela and Peru.

Male and female soras are alike in appearance. In juvenile plumage the soras lack the black face markings, and are paler and yellower in general color, so that they are sometimes confused with the smaller yellow rail.

A loud whinny that is frequently given by the sora I have never heard the Virginia imitate, and, vice versa, a call of *ticket-ticket-ticket* or *racket-racket-racket* I believe is given only by the Virginia.

Yellow Rail

Coturnicops novaboracensis
Average Length, Seven Inches

So mouselike is the yellow rail in its habits and so difficult to flush, that no one really knows the limits of its distribution. It doubtless ranges widely over North America, for there are scattered summer records of it from California to northern Manitoba and eastward to Nova Scotia and New England, but the only nests that have been found are one in California and a number in North Dakota. In winter the bird has been taken throughout the Gulf States and many have been caught alive by bird dogs because they refused to fly.

Nests of the yellow rail have been found in grassy marshes and have been like the sora's, only smaller, and the eggs whiter with a capping of brown spots at the large end.

Black Rail

Creciscus jamaicensis stoddardi
Average Length, Five Inches

Despite its diminutive size, elusive habits, and limited distribution, the black rail is gradually becoming better known than its yellow cousin. In summer it frequents grassy marshes from Massachusetts to Florida and westward to Iowa, Kansas, and Minnesota, being most regular, however, in the coastal marshes where fresh water and salt mingle. In winter it usually goes south as far as Guatemala, though sometimes it remains in our Gulf States.

It is ordinarily as silent and elusive as a mouse, but during the breeding season the male calls *kik, kik, kik* or *kuk, kuk, kuk,* and the female answers *croo-cro-croo-o,* like the beginning of a song of a cuckoo. Its nest, like that of a meadowlark, is partly roofed over, and its 6 to 10 eggs are pinkish white, speckled with brown and gray.

STUBBY-TAILED MARSH DWELLERS SELDOM FLY, BUT SNEAK SWIFTLY THROUGH SHELTERING REEDS AND GRASSES

The big **California Clapper Rail** (adult and downy young, upper right) keeps company with four other rails—the well-known **Sora** (adult and immature, right foreground), the **Black Rail** (dark, speckled bird), the almost flightless **Yellow Rail** (left foreground), and the **Virginia Rail** (left background).

King Rail

Rallus elegans elegans
Average Length, Fifteen Inches

This large edition of the Virginia rail is found throughout the interior of the United States and southern Ontario from southern Minnesota to Massachusetts, southward to Florida and Texas and intermediate points. It winters in the southern part of its breeding range from New Jersey southward.

The king rail mainly is restricted to freshwater marshes as the clapper rail is to the salt water, and since the birds are about the same size and decidedly similar in color and markings, one can be almost as sure of one's identification by the type of marsh in which he finds his bird as by the markings of the bird itself. The king rail ventures into the open a little more than the Virginia rail and is more given to wandering, so that it is sometimes seen about dooryards or in hayfields at some distance from its home marsh.

The king rail usually arranges the vegetation over its nest in a canopy. The eggs are paler than the clapper rail's or the gallinule's and are rather sparingly spotted with brown.

The downy young are covered with thick, coal-black fuzz like young Virginias, with no particular ornaments such as are worn by soras or gallinules.

The calls of the king rail are a loud *brip, brip, brip, brip, brip* of about five seconds' duration, and a grunting *ump, ump, ump, ump* given more deliberately.

Limpkin

Ararnus pictus pictus
Average Length, Twenty-eight Inches

Never shall I forget the voice of the limpkin. One night when I was floundering in a Florida swamp it crashed on my ears in the most dumbfounding, hair-raising, heart-thumping wail that I had ever experienced: *Aow, aow, aow, aow, aoooooooooow!*

The sound reverberated from cypress to cypress and out across the marsh and back again as if an alligator had suddenly seized some wandering spirit by the leg and was pulling him under. Again the weird howl and the wail sent shivers along my spine.

This time it was answered across the lake by another seemingly lost spirit—a call like the voice of a wolf baying the moon. Others took up the cry until the din was deafening. It was as if I had suddenly been plunged into bedlam. Needless to say, all this clamor did nothing to help me out of my confusion.

Since then I have heard many limpkins and have enjoyed their concerts at Wakulla Springs clear through the night when they joined the serenade of the barred owls. We have photographed their voices on film, but never have I received such a thrill from any voice of the wild as I did that evening on Puzzle Lake.

The limpkin, or "crying bird," as it is sometimes called, is a tropical species that finds the northern limit of its breeding range in Florida and southern Georgia where its distribution corresponds with that of a large snail (*Pomacea*) upon which it feeds almost exclusively. Since the snail is largely nocturnal, coming out of deep water at night, the limpkin has adapted its habits accordingly. The limpkin is also found in Cuba, and allied forms occur in Mexico, Central America, and Haiti.

In most of the localities where it is found the limpkin builds a nest of rushes in the saw grass, but along the Wakulla it makes its nest of twigs and Spanish moss in the dense myrtle bushes and lower branches of the moss-laden cypress trees growing in the river. It lays from four or five to eight light-brown eggs that are rather obscurely spotted. The young limpkin is covered with smoky-gray down.

Clapper Rail

Rallus longirostris crepitans
Average Length, Fourteen and One-half Inches

A person living long enough in one place isolated from the rest of the world develops certain peculiarities, and the same holds true for nonmigratory birds. Sometimes these peculiarities appear as slight differences of color or length of bill, so that we can tell at a glance whence the birds have come. At other times the distinction may be only in insignificant difference of voice or mannerisms.

The clapper rail lives much to itself in a peculiar environment, the salt marsh; and south of New Jersey it is nonmigratory.

Little differences in the darkness of the upper parts or paleness of the under parts have developed locally so that now we recognize four subspecies in addition to the northern birds. These are Wayne's clapper rail of the salt marshes from North Carolina to New Smyrna; the Florida clapper rail from Jupiter Inlet southward and on the Gulf coast of Florida; the mangrove clapper rail of the Florida Keys; and the Louisiana clapper rail of the rest of the Gulf coast.

In former years clapper rails were extremely abundant on our coastal marshes, and Audubon speaks of a commercial egger on the New Jersey coast collecting as many as 100 dozen eggs in a single day.

In favored spots clapper rails are still common and their loud rattling calls are familiar sounds toward evening or on moonlit nights and off and on in daytime. Any sudden sound like the discharge of a gun is likely to start them cackling.

Their nests are placed in clumps of sedges and are usually arched over like the Virginias'. Their large eggs vary greatly in ground color and spotting but are normally darker and more heavily marked than those of the king rail. The downy young are uniformly black.

DESOLATE WAILS OF THE "CRYING BIRD" ECHO WEIRDLY OVER SOUTHERN SWAMPS

The tropical **Limpkin**, or "crying bird" (center and flying), ranges as far north as Florida and Georgia. The **King Rail** (left), a "large edition of the Virginia rail," is mainly a fresh-water species, while the **Clapper Rail** (right) clings to the salt-water marshes.

Whooping Crane

Grus americana

Average Length, Fifty Inches

Today the total number of whooping cranes seen each year by the army of bird observers interested in this noble bird is few in the limited range left to these birds. Each year a few are reported wintering in Texas or Louisiana, and an occasional bird or small group is seen migrating with sandhill cranes in Nebraska or Saskatchewan, going to or from their nesting ground in northern Saskatchewan or Mackenzie. But their days are numbered, and like the trumpeter swan and the ivory-billed woodpecker, unless they can have more real protection they will soon follow the passenger pigeon and the great auk into extinction.

Recent nests of the whooping crane described in print were found by Neil Gilmore and Fred Bradshaw in Saskatchewan in 1922. They were built in the center of large marshes with open water all about them and nothing to obscure the vision of the wary birds. The nests were 4 or 5 feet in diameter, made of rushes and sedges pulled up or nipped off near the nest, and built up 15 or 18 inches above the water and lined with dried grasses. The two oval eggs are about four inches long and somewhat darker and more heavily spotted than those of the sandhill crane.

Young whooping cranes are covered with buffy down and follow their parents from the nest to drier land soon after hatching. For the first year they are more or less mottled with cinnamon brown and white. Just how long it requires for them to attain the snow-white plumage of the adult is not known.

Sandhill Crane

Grus canadensis tabida

Average Length, Forty-four Inches

We are now faced with the near extinction of another species that formerly abounded from Alaska to Florida: the sandhill crane, which has been reduced to a pitiful remnant of its former population even in the far corners of its once extensive range.

The northern birds that formerly nested in great numbers from Alaska to Hudson Bay and wintered from California to Texas and southward into Mexico are considered a separate subspecies called the little brown crane (*Grus canadensis canadensis*) because of their smaller size and somewhat browner back. The birds, which are permanent residents of the Florida Peninsula and southern Georgia, are likewise smaller and darker gray, and are recognized as a distinct race—the Florida crane (*Grus canadensis pratensis*). The rest of the birds which formerly nested from British Columbia and Manitoba southward to California, Colorado, Nebraska, Illinois, and Ohio are the ones commonly called "sandhill cranes," and these have suffered most from the en-

croachments of civilization. In former years they wintered commonly from California to Louisiana and were numerous on migration along the Atlantic coast as far north as New England. Today they are extremely rare east of the Mississippi, except for a few nesting in Michigan, and they are extinct as breeding birds in the south half of their former range.

All three forms of sandhill cranes are so similar in appearance and habits that they cannot be distinguished in the field and they may, therefore, well be considered together.

In flight cranes differ from great blue herons, which are sometimes called "cranes," in that they carry their necks straight out instead of folded, their wing strokes are shorter, and their flight feathers more spread. They are, in reality, much larger also, though size is deceptive in a flying bird when there is no means of judging distance. In migration they fly in long lines or in V's like geese, calling loudly *gar-oo-oo-oo, gar-oo-oo-oo,* a cry heard even farther than the honking of similar flocks of geese. At times, when not migrating, they may circle higher and higher like turkey buzzards or wood ibises, seemingly just for the enjoyment of it, or to await the passing of some enemy on the prairie below.

One of the most distinctive habits of all members of the crane family the world over is their habit of dancing during the breeding season. These dances are occasionally indulged in during the fall and winter, and just what their actual relationship is to the procuring of mates is not well understood, for, even after they are mated and have their nests built and eggs laid, the giddy birds are sometimes seen bowing and hopping in a none too domestic manner. In the mating season several flocks of six to eight each will gather on a bare hilltop for what resembles an old-fashioned barn dance.

The nests of the sandhill cranes are usually large affairs of dead rushes and the like, resembling low nests of muskrats or alligators, four or five feet in diameter, built up a foot or more above the surface of the surrounding water in the center of a more or less extensive marsh. The two eggs are pale brownish, rather obscurely marked with darker brown. The newly hatched young are thickly covered with golden-brown down, and are capable of following their parents to dry land about the edge of the marsh where they spend most of their time until grown.

The cranes are perhaps our wariest birds, but even so they respond to kindness and lose their fear of man at times. A friend of mine, W. E. Browne, at his home called "Manywings" between two small lakes in northern Florida, has not only tamed most of his small bird neighbors, but has so beguiled a pair of wild Florida cranes that they bring their youngsters up to his back door for cornbread, which he cooks especially for them.

TO THE ILL-FATED WHOOPING CRANE—HAIL AND FAREWELL!

Apparently a doomed species, the towering **Whooping Crane** (right) is seldom observed today even in regions where, a century ago, its legions flew past by the hour. The ranks of the smaller **Sandhill Crane** (left, adult and young) have also been so seriously depleted that extinction threatens that species, too. Two subspecies, the northern **Little Brown Crane** (flying above) and the Florida crane, have been persecuted less than the true sandhills.

AVOCETS BOLT THEIR FOOD FASTER THAN NAUGHTY CHILDREN

This group near Pinneo, Colorado, flew into the wind for a short distance, then turned and came down to feed with their backs to the breeze, their bills stabbing into the water with almost incredible rapidity.

THE GULLS AND TERNS

The Myriad Birds That Fly About Ports Begging for Scraps Know Their Own Young

By T. Gilbert Pearson

A GRAY flattened ball of down lay among the pebbles at high-water mark and pulsated gently as the sea wind undulated its surface. As I watched it burst into life, first showing a tiny beak and a pair of bright eyes. Then uprearing on two unsteady legs, it advanced to meet a large white bird that had dropped to the ground.

But the little one did not receive the food it had expected; instead the old herring gull struck it to the earth and continued to peck it until it was dead. Then with raucous cries he announced his triumph over the weak. "Baby killers" the warden calls those occasional gulls that stalk about the breeding colony and slay their neighbor's young.

PARENT GULLS KNOW THEIR YOUNG

It would seem that in the confusion of this gull kingdom, no parent bird could tell which of the countless downy young are its own, yet I feel certain that each recognizes its offspring, although certainly the young do not know their own parents. I have seen gulls just back from foraging expeditions walk past many young ones before coming to a halt and feeding one of them. They were solicited by many, but they disregarded all advances until each found the one it sought.

I observed the habits of gulls and their young on one of the numerous islands dotting the coast of Maine from Kittypoint to the St. Croix River, which down east floods into the Channel of Grand Manan. It is known as Great Duck Island and may be reached in an hour's sail from Southwest Harbor. There are no human habitations there except at the seaward end where stands a tower with warning beam that guides homeward the plunging boats of the fishing fleet.

In winter eider ducks feed off the shore or ride the swells as if at anchor. Sometimes a few come on the beach to rest, and now and then a black-backed gull goes by, while icy gales sweep the bowlder-strewn upland and hurl bits of seaweed into the tossing limbs of the evergreen trees.

In April fresh grass appears, the buds of the raspberries swell, and life stirs in the little chickweed. It is then that herring gulls come from over the waves. They perch on dead trees or alight on the shore and cackle and chuckle from the tops of the big bowlders. Their numbers rapidly increase. Soon they are everywhere, flying and screaming, carrying grass and moss and seaweed, and now and then fragments of rotting wood.

Nests are built on the "mink dirt" where evergreens once stood, or amid the interminable jumble of the bowlder-covered beaches, or sometimes on a bushy tree. In the first week of May eggs begin to appear. These are scrawled with many spots and blotches of varying shades of brown.

Nests become more numerous, 2,000, perhaps 3,000 in number. After four weeks the eggs hatch, and as soon as the summer wind has dried the down on the little gull chicks life becomes to them an experience of great interest. Before they are a day old, they are ready to feed on the semi-digested food which the parent places before them. Soon they are out of the nest wandering about with other young ones. If a man comes near they crouch, often with only their heads concealed, for they trust their coloration to shield them from observation.

They are fed on squids and fish, although the diet may be varied with flies, moths, beetles, and other insects.

THEY MASTER AVIATION EARLY

It requires five or six weeks for a young herring gull to grow up and gain command of the air. Its parents then abandon it and the problems of life begin in earnest for the young gull hatched in the clamorous rookery on Great Duck Island. It is now about the size of its parent, but has very dark plumage and is the "gray sea gull" of which people speak. Before full development it must pass through several molting seasons —two each year. Adult plumage comes with the fourth year and a red spot now gleams on either side of its lower bill.

In August the herring gulls leave Great Duck Island. Some may linger in near-by waters, but the great majority drift southward to Marblehead, to Boston Harbor, to the waters about Providence and to Long Island Sound. For days they follow the ships leaving New York for Le Havre, for Southampton, and for ports of the Spanish Main. You may see them resting in the Charles River at Cambridge, or drinking fresh water from the reservoir in Central Park, or soaring above Manhattan.

They gather to feed where a certain sewer empties into the Harlem River, and contend with each other for scraps of food thrown from boats where the Washington Monument looks down on the waters of the Potomac. They eat dead fish cast up by the waves and gather about fishing vessels and wharves of fishing ports to feast on the refuse thrown overboard. They are truly the scavengers of the sea.

In February, 1934, the waters about Long Island, New York, became ice-bound, and men distributing grain for starving ducks found herring gulls feeding upon the remains of many which had died from lack of food. Gulls sometimes make depredations on young ducks. I once received a bill for $23 sent by an irate farmer who claimed that the "Audubon Societies' gulls" had killed and eaten 23 of his ducklings.

DROP CLAMS TO BREAK THEM

Herring gulls are fond of clams and often carry them aloft to drop in the hope of breaking them on the rocks or ground below. Some time ago I was told that a watchman at a bridge on a motor highway near the New Jersey coast was forced to sweep it several times a day to rid it of the broken shells of clams dropped there by herring gulls.

At Beaufort, North Carolina, I saw one of these birds drop the same clam 16 times in its endeavors to get the juicy morsel which the hard shell contained. Every time the mollusk fell on the soft mud, and at length the discouraged gull flew away. I was interested in noting that in each case the clam was dropped from a height of about 40 feet. Apparently, disappointing experiences taught this bird nothing.

Many herring gulls breed in the interior of North America. We may see them from the docks of Duluth and in the channel at Sault Ste. Marie, and following the thrashing whalebacks down the Lakes.

HERRING GULLS LONG-LIVED

This bird is one of Nature's successes. A robin may live to be six or eight years old if a cat or a hawk or a fatal disease does not claim its life, but the herring gull lives on and on for many seasons. Recently I photographed one that has been in captivity for 40 years.

We know that they have long inhabited North America, for their bones have been found in the Pleistocene deposits of Fossil Lake, Oregon.

Thirty years ago these birds were far less numerous than they are today. They had been shot in immense numbers because their feathers were in great demand for trimming women's hats. The Audubon Society brought about the passage of laws to make this illegal and, in order to enforce the measures against their destruction, employed special guards to watch their nesting colonies.

The gulls increased rapidly and there began to be complaints of their depredations on cultivated blueberry patches, on fields where fish scrap was scattered as fertilizer, and of their annoyance to owners of yachts and harbor craft. The National Association of Audubon Societies removed its guards.

There was no longer any commercial demand for feathers, and people of the coast country had become accustomed to thinking of these birds as a species that should not be disturbed. The gulls continued to prosper, but the more they increased the greater became the complaints against them.

At length the Maine State Conservation Department began to issue permits here and there to people who wished to use the shotgun to protect their property from the clouds of gulls that came inland to their farms.

In May, 1934, I was a guest in a party that visited several seabird colonies in Casco Bay. I was surprised to find that a Federal game warden who went along had instructions from the United States Bureau of Biological Survey to drill holes in all the gulls' eggs that he could find in a number of breeding colonies. This was an experimental effort in control. Several thousand eggs were thus destroyed.

Two months later in the Leadenhall Market in London I found that 250,000 gulls' eggs had this season been sold for food. Most of these were of the black-headed gull. Efforts have been made at times to develop a demand for herring gulls' eggs, for this bird is much disliked along the coasts of many countries of western Europe.

ONE GULL NAMED FOR A PRINCE

About a hundred years ago there lived in Philadelphia a princely naturalist, Charles Lucien Bonaparte; and it is for him that our French-Canadian neighbors called the daintiest of all of our gulls "le goéland de Bonaparte." This bird is small for a gull. Not only does it float buoyantly on the water, but also in the air it flies lightly with the grace of a tern.

It travels usually in flocks, apparently to enjoy the companionship of others possessing its own gentle nature. Few naturalists have seen its nest, which, in Alaska and northwestern Canada, decorates a tree or stump on the border of some wilderness lake or slough. In autumn it journeys southward and spreads along the Atlantic and the Pacific coasts to tropical America.

There are many instances where birds have appeared in unexpected places. In the forenoon of November 12, 1913, while following the track of a deer on the forested heights of the Santa Catalina Mountains of Arizona, I was amazed to see a Bonaparte's gull. It was flying through the thick woods, dropping or lifting now and then to avoid a limb, and was following the course of a stream scarcely ten feet in width. The day was cold, the ground covered with newly fallen snow. There was ice along the edges of the stream, and the altitude was more than a mile above sea level!

Once I left the dining-room of a hotel in Cocoa, Florida, with a handful of crackers. Through the window I had seen several lesser scaup ducks close to the dock a hundred feet away, and I thought that it would be amusing to feed them. These little swimmers, which had come from western Canada to spend the winter on the Indian River, were pets of the community and were accustomed to being fed.

Scarcely had they begun to enjoy my offerings when several Bonaparte's gulls appeared and contested for a share. They hovered and darted down and arose again with such swiftness that they secured a fair portion of the crackers. One even alighted on the back of a duck and seized the cracker from its bill.

When the food supply stopped, the gulls left in a straggling flock, not flying directly away, as if bound on some other mission, but rising, falling, and circling with light-hearted ease. Perhaps they would soon be catching minnows, which they consume in winter when they live in waters bordering the sea, although in their summer homes their regular diet consists of insects.

In habits of life they differ widely from the great herring gull. I always associate in my mind these two water birds of the Atlantic seaboard, the larger one, fierce, a feeder on carrion, and a confident rider of the freezing gales; the other gentle, dainty —and a living emblem of the more peaceful, milder phases of the sea.

MANY KINDS OF GULLS AND TERNS

There are 20 orders of North American birds. One of these, the Charadriiformes, is composed of ten families, of which three are discussed in this article. The birds mentioned belong to the Stercorariidae (jaegers), Laridae (gulls and terns), and Rynchopidae (skimmers).

Of the jaegers there are four species, inhabiting the northern seas and the Antarctic regions. These are the fierce "sea hawks" or "robbers of the sea." They have extraordinarily long wings which enable them to fly with great swiftness and to dart upon their prey with remarkable agility.

Their bills are strongly hooked at the tip, and the birds possess sharp falconlike claws; thus they differ from the other groups of sea birds with which they are classified. Besides robbing fish-eating birds, they destroy many birds' eggs, and their hooked beaks and curved claws enable them readily to tear the flesh of birds and small mammals upon which they often feed.

Of the gulls and terns about 85 species are known, divided about equally between the two groups. They are distributed throughout the world, 40 having been found in North America.

Most gulls are noticeably larger than terns. Their bills are somewhat hooked, while those of the terns are nearly straight. At sea they wander far from land where only a few terns are found. Nor do they possess long central tail feathers so characteristic of most jaegers. Their tails differ also from those of the terns in that they are square or rounded and are not forked, as are those of our terns. They feed largely upon dead fish and other animal life cast upon the shores.

Terns, as a rule, are much lighter in weight than gulls and are far more graceful in flight. The bill is noticeably long and slender and is often seen pointed downward when the birds fly about seeking the small fish upon which chiefly they prey.

There are three kinds of skimmers that dwell about the warmer seas, only one of which occurs in North America. Their flat knifelike bills, with the lower mandible longer than the upper, are characteristic of no other bird. These are useful in skimming their marine prey from the surface of the sea as the birds sweep along close to the water.

In their feeding habits they are both diurnal and nocturnal. Like most terns, the skimmers do not wander far from land, as do the gulls and jaegers.

HAT FASHIONS MENACED GULLS

There was a period when for many years fashion demanded birds' wings or even their entire skins as trimming for women's hats. Millions of birds in the United States and elsewhere were killed for this purpose. In summer vessels equipped with guns and ammunition cruised the coasts, and the hunters they carried shot gulls and terns on their breeding islands until some species were almost exterminated.

It was as a protest against the needless slaughter of wild birds that the Audubon Society was first formed in 1886, although nearly 30 years were to elapse before the Society's warfare on the feather trade was to bring about a cessation of this unfortunate business. Today, the terns again swarm along our coasts by untold thousands.

Bird Key, of the Dry Tortugas group, is a low, flat island of coral sand on which grow bay cedars, cacti, and a few palms. Late in April to this isolated spot, perhaps from vast regions of the Caribbean, come the noddy and sooty terns to fight, to mate, to build their nests, and to fill the sea winds with their shoutings.

The noddy nests in bushes and low trees, building for its one buff-colored egg a structure of sticks and seaweeds, sometimes decorating it with bits of coral or sea shells. About five weeks pass before the egg is hatched.

The sooty tern scratches a little cavity in the sand, sinks its breast into this and turns its body until the depression is smooth and round, when the nest is finished. It, too, lays a single egg.

The colony may contain 1,500 noddy terns and perhaps 13,000 or 20,000 sooties. These birds do not dive for their prey, but in full flight capture the minnows upon which they feed, when the little fish leap from the water or skim the surface in their attempts to avoid the onrushing schools of larger fish below.

SOOTIES' HOMING INSTINCT AMAZING

Professor John B. Watson wanted to learn whether or not birds could find their way back if removed a long distance from their nests. Therefore he caught some terns at the Tortugas and sent them by ship to points at various distances from Bird Key, and then allowed them to go free. Their feathers were marked with paint, and the location of the nest from which each one had been removed was recorded.

Three noddies and two sooties were taken to Key West and placed aboard a northward bound steamer. During the voyage they were supplied with water and minnows.

On the morning of June 15 they were set at liberty 12 miles from Cape Hatteras. Just five days later the two sooty terns returned to Bird Key and were found quietly sitting on their eggs. During their absence their mates had cared for the nests.

Professor Watson thus demonstrated the fact that the sooty terns, although liberated a thousand miles north of regions which they are known to frequent, were able to return past strange headlands, and over unknown waters, to their nests on that lonely key. He calculated that the birds had flown a distance of 1,081 miles to regain their island home. His estimate was based on the theory that, since these birds always roost on land at night they probably followed the shore-line rather closely on their return down the Atlantic from the Diamond Shoal off Hatteras Light.

Of the three noddies only one was ever known to return. It appeared several days after the sooties had arrived, but when its long heart-breaking flight over the sea was ended and it reached its nest and sought to alight, its former mate, now with a new companion, drove it away and it was not seen again.

In September the sooty and the noddy terns leave the Dry Tortugas. In flocks they wing southward to feed and rest about the shores of a thousand tropical islands lost in the tropic seas.

During the last forty years I have enjoyed the unusual privilege of visiting a great many breeding colonies of terns in North America and in Europe. As a rule these expeditions have been made for the purpose of discovering the location of colonies which might be of special ornithological interest, and also with the object of arranging to employ local men to guard them.

Such experiences are a pleasure of which I never tire. Even without referring to notes I can recall distinctly the place where I first came into personal contact with each of these charming birds.

Terns, with a few exceptions, lay their eggs on the sand or among the broken shells washed up on sand bars and lonely islands. At some places only small colonies have been found, at others the birds have been very numerous, often as the direct result of having received protection for many years.

Formerly their eggs were gathered in great numbers for food, and years ago I frequently ate them in hotels along the Atlantic seaboard. For a long time New Orleans was a market in which many were sold. Schooners would sometimes bring in thousands of them upon returning from egging expeditions to the islands of Mississippi Sound.

TRAFFIC IN BIRDS' EGGS ENDED

Today, the traffic in birds' eggs is at an end in the United States, although it is still carried on extensively in many other parts of the world.

Among the terns, the Arctic has attracted much attention because of its extraordinary migrations. Many raise their young along the Atlantic coast of North America, from Massachusetts to Ellesmere Island, far beyond the Arctic Circle. After the breeding season they go to the Antarctic regions.

One young that was banded in Labrador by O. L. Austin, on July 22, 1927, was picked up dead October 1 in the Department of Charente-Inférieure, France. Another was found in Natal, on the east coast of South Africa, three months and 22 days after it had been banded when a chick.

Since some time elapsed before the latter was old enough to fly, and since the distance on its line of migration from Labrador must have been 9,000 miles, not including a thousand side trips to catch food or to roost, it seems safe to assume that the bird made this prodigious journey at an average rate of 100 miles a day. This circuitous route of migrating southward is similar to that used by the little land bird known as the "wheatear," which passes the summer in Labrador and the winter in Africa.

Big Bird Island, lying in the shallow waters of Laguna Madre, about 32 miles southward from Corpus Christi, Texas, is a good example of one of the larger tern colonies of the country. I landed there once on May 23, 1920.

Part of the island was covered with grass in which I estimated that from 20,000 to 40,000 laughing gulls had built their nests. There were also 45 occupied nests of the brown pelican, 8 nests of the reddish egret, 11 of the Louisiana heron, and 20 of the Ward's heron. Of the Forster's terns, only about a score of eggs were seen.

TERNS' NESTS CLOSE TOGETHER

There were several egg fields of the Cabot's and royal terns. Both species had laid their eggs on the bare sand, and in each case the nests were just far enough apart so that a brooding bird could not be pecked by its nearest neighbors.

I measured these areas where the eggs were found in such great numbers, and counted the nests over certain measured spaces. By simple multiplication it appeared that there were at least 9,000 nests of the Cabot's tern and 35,000 nests of the royal tern.

By the very reasonable assumption that there were two adults for each nest I felt certain that from 125,000 to 150,000 birds were making their summer headquarters on this small sandy island. One can imagine the bewildering activity on those hot sands a few weeks later when all the young of the several species were mingled in endless confusion.

How a mother tern or gull must have had to search to find her own chick among the vast hosts of juvenile birds that thronged the water front or lay panting among the clusters of seared and trampled beach grass!

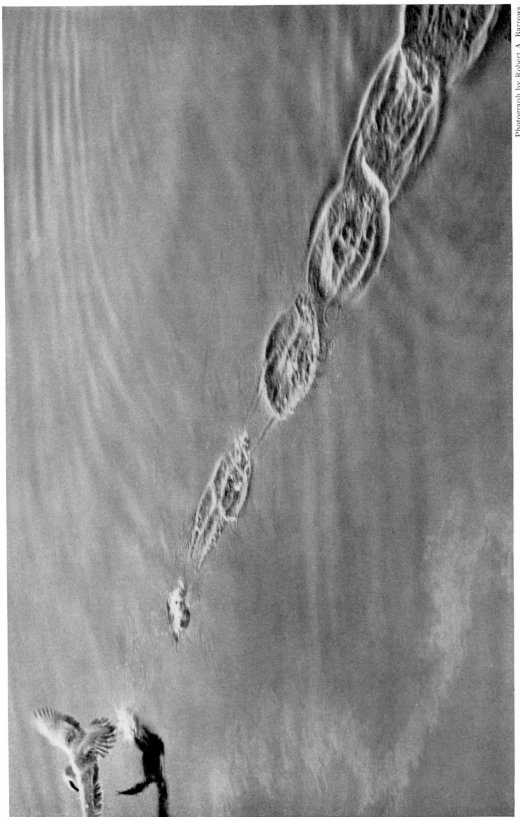

A PAUSE, A SWOOP, AND AWAY WITH A TWO-POUND MACKEREL

As a fisherman the herring gull excels. This bird is just rising from a capture, its prey tightly clutched. The photograph, which was published in the rotogravure section of the *New York Times*, October 8, 1933, was shown at the Seventy-eighth Annual Exhibition of the Royal Photographic Society of Great Britain in London.

Photograph by Robert A. Barrows

TO THE GULLS A BOAT MEANS POSSIBLE SCRAPS OF FOOD

This prize-winning amateur photograph from the salon of the 1936 Newspaper National Snapshot Awards shows the birds in characteristic flight attitudes. Little wonder that such flocks, seen from a distance, gave rise to early legends of sea serpents.

Long-tailed Jaeger

(Stercorarius longicaudus)

Average Length, Twenty-one Inches

The long-tailed jaeger is a seabird that is extremely agile and swift in its movements. Its summer home is in countries bordered by Arctic seas, extending over much of the very northern part of the continents of America, Europe, Asia, and adjacent islands.

Its nest is built in dry spots, often amid grassy, mossy areas of barren grounds. Its food consists of insects and their larvæ, crustaceans, fish caught by the bird itself, or picked up dead or stolen from gulls and terns—in fact, any flesh that is available.

It has a partial molt of feathers in spring and a complete molt after the breeding season. It may be distinguished from other birds of the northern seas by two long central tail feathers, which are held in an upright position when the bird is resting on the water.

During migration jaegers may be seen inland in North America, although most of them go southward by sea on their way to the coasts of Chile and Argentina for the winter.

Pomarine Jaeger

(Stercorarius pomarinus)

Average Length, Twenty-two Inches

In August when the schools of mackerel and bluefish are striking in along the New England coast, look for the pomarine jaegers. They are due to arrive about this time from their breeding grounds on the cliffs and tundras of Greenland and other Arctic regions. The large fish themselves do not attract the birds, but the small fry which they drive to the surface are caught by gulls and terns, which are then robbed of their prey by the swift-flying jaegers.

The pomarine may be identified by the form of the elongated central tail feathers. These are broadened at the end like a canoe paddle, and the blade is vertical, making a most useful rudder for the bird in the quick, sudden turns which it must take when pursuing other birds of the sea.

These jaegers occur in winter off the coast of Virginia, southward through the Gulf of Mexico, and in the South Atlantic. Those dwelling in the Pacific Ocean breed in Alaska and Siberia, and pass the winter in southern waters, wandering even as far below the Equator as Peru and Chile.

Parasitic Jaeger

(Stercorarius parasiticus)

Average Length, Seventeen Inches

This is a circumpolar species, nesting in the Arctic of both hemispheres, and as far southward as Scotland and southwestern Alaska. In the breeding season the birds inhabit the vast wet tundras, either near the coast, or inland about ponds and lakes.

This jaeger is a terror for the other birds of the region, preying upon their eggs and young. Eider ducks and gulls especially suffer from its depredations. At all seasons of the year it attacks terns and the smaller gulls for the purpose of forcing them to disgorge their last meal.

Parasitic jaegers are a fearful scourge to the wild ducks and geese that breed on the great wet Arctic prairies. In pairs or small groups they range far and wide, beating back and forth, searching the ground for the nests of the breeding waterfowl. Also they will pick up any other small animal life they find, such as mice and lemmings.

Terns, which probably have nothing in their stomachs to disgorge, may be chased for more than a mile before the relentless hawklike freebooter of the air desists in its attempts at robbery.

In watching these birds in their piratical raids on other flyers of the sea, I have often been amazed at their swiftness and astonishing dexterity. They will plunge, turn, and dart with such suddenness that few, if any, birds can escape their attacks.

The parasitic jaeger winters from Florida and California southward, along the Atlantic coast of Europe and Africa, and also in the Persian Gulf.

Northern Skua

(Catharacta skua)

Average Length, Twenty-two Inches

No other bird of the North Atlantic is so fierce and strong in flight or so boldly assertive as the master of all seabird pirates, the northern skua. Naturalists of the British Isles call it the "great skua." Men who earn their living on the ocean refer to it as the "sea hen."

The name skua comes from a fancied resemblance between the pronunciation of this word and the bird's cry when chasing other birds to rob them of their prey. The skua is 22 inches in length and powerfully built. Its feet and legs are very strong and its sharp claws are used to hold the food while it is being torn apart by the stout hooked beak.

The northern skua feeds upon dead fish or the carrion of sea mammals. It is constantly robbing other birds, pursuing them until they disgorge, in various stages of digestion, the fish which they have consumed. Often it catches such booty before it reaches the waves beneath.

Skuas lay their two eggs in nests built on the ground on islands from Davis Strait eastward through Iceland, Shetland, and the Orkneys. They winter rarely as far south as Massachusetts and Gibraltar. The Chilean skua (*C. chilensis*) occasionally reaches California in summer.

There are four known species of jaegers and skuas. Except in the nesting season, when they frequent the interior, they inhabit the ocean and are great wanderers.

WINGED RAIDERS OF THE ARCTIC COASTS

Summer residents of far northern ocean shores, these feathered freebooters often snatch food right out of the air—fish they have forced other birds to disgorge in flight. Most rapacious of sea-bird pirates, the **Northern Skua** (standing over the bird carcass) feeds on carrion or stolen fish. Two other bold buccaneers are the **Pomarine Jaeger** (left center), whose paddle-shaped tail rudder aids in making sudden turns, and the **Long-tailed Jaeger** (upper left). Tiered on the right are speedy **Parasitic Jaegers,** from top to bottom, respectively—the black phase, the light phase, the young (on the rock),

Glaucous Gull

(Larus hyperboreus)
Average Length, Twenty-eight Inches

In the far northern seas a large pale-plumaged gull known as the "burgomaster" comes to feed upon the refuse cast overboard by the whalers. Only one other gull of the Arctic and North Atlantic waters is comparable to it in size, and its ferocity in attacking other sea birds is equaled only by the great brown skua.

Besides being a famous scavenger of the waves, it captures and readily devours such small life as it finds. It has been known to swallow whole, without pausing to dismember them, species even as large as the golden plover. In turn, it falls a prey to the Eskimo, who eats its eggs and enjoys the meat from its great breast.

The glaucous gull makes its nest on rocky shoals or on great perpendicular cliffs by or near the sea. During the breeding season it inhabits the Arctic coasts and adjacent islands from northwestern Alaska and northern Greenland, to the Pribilof Islands, James Bay, and eastern Labrador.

In winter it wanders southward to California, the Great Lakes, and Long Island, New York. Sometimes it travels even farther, and specimens have been found in Bermuda, Missouri, the Hawaiian Islands, and elsewhere. In the Old World it goes as far south as Japan and the Mediterranean. The bird measures 28 inches in length.

Kittiwake

(Rissa tridactyla)
Average Length, Sixteen Inches

Living in the northern seas is a graceful little gull whose cries of *kitta-aa, kitti-aa* have given it the name of kittiwake. It is at home on the waves, often resting on the rolling waters far from land.

It preys upon fish or such other flesh as it can find either adrift or cast upon the shore. One of the great annoyances of its life is the presence of the glaucous gull, which relentlessly robs it of its food.

Such piracy is understandable when we recall the difference in size of the two birds. The kittiwake has a wing-spread of three feet, while the big glaucous, from wing-tip to wing-tip, measures fully five feet.

The kittiwake breeds along the coasts in North Atlantic regions as far south as the Gulf of St. Lawrence and northern France. With great delight I have watched hundreds of these dainty rangers of the sea gathered about their nests or sitting in irregular rows on the shelves that adorn the cliffs of one of the Farne Islands in the North Sea. In England as well as in northern North America the kittiwake is a great favorite of those who enjoy the beauties of a rugged coast.

In addition to the Atlantic kittiwake (*R. t. tridactyla*) the species includes the Pacific kittiwake (*R. t. pollicaris*). There is also the red-legged kittiwake (*R. brevirostris*).

Herring Gull

(Larus argentatus)
Average Length, Twenty-four Inches

The large gulls seen so commonly along the Atlantic and the Pacific coasts of Canada and the United States are herring gulls. They appear in two noticeably different plumages; one is a large white, the other a dark-gray bird. The dark one is the immature, the light one the adult. (See pages 297-298.)

There are three varieties of this species, distributed as follows: herring gull (*L. a. smithsonianus*) breeding from Alaska and Baffin Island southward to British Columbia, Wisconsin, and Massachusetts; Thayer's gull (*L. a. thayeri*) on the Arctic coast of America; and Vega gull (*L. a. vegae*) breeding on the north coast of Siberia. They all drift southward in winter, not only along the coasts, but also about inland lakes and rivers.

Great Black-backed Gull

(Larus marinus)
Average Length, Twenty-nine Inches

This great gull, with a wing sweep of five and one-half feet, may be identified not only by its large size, but by its very noticeable black back. "Saddle-back" is one of the names by which it is known.

Some years ago I visited a very large breeding colony of them on an island in Lake George, Nova Scotia. With this exception I have never found the black-backed engaged in domestic duties except on islands surrounded by the waters of the sea. Sometimes on a little ledge exposed but a few feet above the water a single nest may be located. Again one may find two, five, or as many as twenty pairs defending their nests on islands off the coast of Maine. While the birds often are disposed to build close to each other, this is in no sense a universal custom. On the same island I have noted nests of these giant gulls fully half a mile from those of their nearest gull neighbors.

This fierce bird often preys upon the young of terns, picking them up and carrying them away despite the screams of all the outraged adult terns of the neighborhood. It also destroys many eggs, of the eider duck.

This is a bird of the North Atlantic, and its nest of grasses and seaweeds may be found at many places from Iceland and southern Greenland southward to Nova Scotia, the British Isles, and northern Russia. Since 1932 several pairs have bred on rocky islands off the coast of Maine. In winter this gull ranges southward to the Mediterranean, the Azores, the Great Lakes, and Delaware Bay.

THE MAYOR OF THE SEA SCAVENGERS ALIGHTS AMONG NEIGHBORS

Nightmare of smaller birds is the great **Glaucous Gull** (upper left), known also as the "burgo-master." It devours the young of other birds (even adults of some species) and also accepts refuse cast overboard from fishing fleets and whalers. The familiar **Herring Gull** (lower left with young bird) is seen in every eastern harbor or river mouth, standing on the mud flats or following passing ships. The chubby **Kittiwake** (upper right-hand pair, young right) often sleeps floating on the waves, "rocked in the cradle of the deep." Icy northern waters are the habitat of the **Great Black-backed Gull** (lower right with young bird).

Short-billed Gull

(Larus canus brachyrhynchus)
Average Length, Seventeen Inches

This small gull is well known along the Pacific coast from Alaska to the Mexican border. In autumn, winter, and spring its flocks often associate with those of other gulls that come into the harbors or beat along the rocky shores.

It is a peculiar fact that this species, which is so fond of living about salt water, should retire inland to breed. In summer it inhabits the lakes, ponds, and sloughs of the tundra country of the far northwest, as well as forest-bordered lakes in the timbered regions.

Nests containing their two or three spotted eggs may be found on rocky shores, in marshes, and on stumps or in the tops of low trees near water. It breeds in Alaska and the western Provinces of Canada to northern Alberta and Saskatchewan.

Late in summer these interior nesting birds fly westward over prairies and mountains until they reach the sea.

Heermann's Gull

(Larus heermanni)
Average Length, Nineteen Inches

The "white-headed" gull breeds in large colonies on islands along the western coast of Mexico, and is especially abundant in the Gulf of California. The nests are simple affairs, those found in some regions being merely slight depressions in the ground.

It has a habit of migration practiced by no other water bird of North America. Egg-laying begins about the first of April, and by July the young are on the wing.

Soon after this the remarkable migration begins. Some move southward as far as Guatemala, but others, in large numbers, stream northward along the coast and are common winter birds of California, Oregon, Washington, and British Columbia.

Young in their second-summer plumage are often seen along the coast of the United States while the fully adult birds are breeding in the south. Not yet old enough to breed, they feel no urge as yet to return to more southern regions with their parents.

California Gull

(Larus californicus)
Average Length, Twenty-one and One-half Inches

So closely does this species resemble the herring gull that one is often mistaken for the other. Where both were supposed to be present, I have never been able to determine merely by watching which of the two gulls I saw. Unless the bird is taken and examined with care to identify it, one has to depend upon the yellowish legs, darker back, and the black spot in addition to the red on the bill to distinguish the California gull from its larger cousin.

In general it may be said that large gulls found breeding about lakes from the eastern edge of the great plains westward are California gulls, and those nesting east of such an arbitrary line are herring gulls.

California gulls nest in colonies, sometimes 1,000 or more nests being constructed on one small island. With an occasional exception, nests are placed on the ground. Although often seen in summer along the coast of Washington and southern Alaska, these birds breed throughout the interior from Great Slave Lake southward to northern California.

This is an abundant species, and the birds gather in large colonies during the nesting season. I have visited many of their populous summer cities. Among these I might mention islands in Chase and Devils Lakes, North Dakota; Yellowstone Lake, Wyoming; Pyramid Lake, Nevada; Klamath and Malheur Lakes in southern Oregon, and a large breeding colony in Great Salt Lake, Utah.

California gulls spread out over much of the interior country in search of food. At times they swarm in the newly plowed fields, often following closely the man and horse engaged in turning the soil. Here they gorge themselves on grubs and worms, and sit about waiting until the processes of digestion shall enable them again to enjoy the feast so bounteously provided. They eat grasshoppers and at times have been known to feed on the young of wild ducks.

Their spotted and blotched eggs are laid in nests made of weeds, grasses, moss, or, in fact, any easily gathered vegetable matter. Sometimes the nests are only an inch or two in thickness; again, they rise from the ground to a height of a foot and a half.

In winter these gulls wander as far south as Mexico and rarely to the Gulf coast of Texas. At this season they are found both along the coast and in the interior.

Western Gull

(Larus occidentalis)
Average Length, Twenty-five and One-half Inches

These large gulls are seen very commonly along the California coast, where they haunt the rocky shores, exposed reefs, and harbors. Besides being scavengers they are persistent destroyers of the eggs of many other species of sea birds whose nests they unhesitatingly rifle.

This species is divided into three forms: the western gull *(L. o. occidentalis)* breeds from Washington to the Farallon Islands, some thirty miles from the Golden Gate; Wyman's gull *(L. o. wymani)* ranges the coastal waters from Monterey County, California, and the Santa Barbara Islands to Asunción Island, Baja California; and the yellow-footed gull *(L. o. livens)* is a resident within the Gulf of California. This last-named variety is known to occur in the United States only as a casual visitor to southern California.

TWO OF THE COMMONEST PACIFIC GULLS BREED AROUND INLAND LAKES

The screaming **California Gull** (left foreground), which closely resembles the herring gull, and the shy little **Short-billed Gull** (adult and young on the rock) both nest far from salt water, the former throughout the western interior from Great Slave Lake southward to Utah, and the latter in Alaska and northwestern Canada. When neither "sea food" nor refuse is to be had, the **Western Gull** (right foreground with young) savagely devours eggs and nestlings of other sea birds. The indolent **Heermann's Gull** (on the wing), after breeding on the Mexican coast, may migrate either north or south for the winter.

Bonaparte's Gull

(Larus philadelphia)

Average Length, Fourteen Inches

This is one of the small black-headed gulls wandering far and wide in loose flocks over a large part of North America. Along the Atlantic coast in April and May, many may be seen moving leisurely northward before starting the long overland trip to their nesting grounds. Crustaceans and marine worms compose the bulk of their marine diet.

Their breeding habits have not been extensively studied, but we know that they raise their young about lakes in the wooded regions from Alberta and British Columbia to northwestern Alaska. So far as reported, it is evident that the nests, composed of sticks, are built usually in trees.

Gentle in demeanor and great destroyers of insects, which they gather in the air and on the marshes and prairies, they are among the most appealing of all the gull family about coastal waters from South Carolina southward, and around the Gulf coast to Texas and Yucatán. On the Pacific coast they winter from Washington to central Mexico.

Franklin's Gull

(Larus pipixcan)

Average Length, Fourteen Inches

The Franklin's gull is a bird of the prairie regions of the interior of North America, and is one of the most characteristic species met with about the shallow lakes and sloughs of Canada and western United States. Its food in summer consists often wholly of insects of which 15 species have been taken from the stomach of a single bird.

Dr. Thomas S. Roberts has recorded taking 327 nymphs of the dragon fly from the stomach of a Franklin's gull in Minnesota. In the late summer immense numbers of grasshoppers are eaten.

The nests are built in marshes. To form a foundation for them rushes are bent downward, or sometimes simply are laid on the mud or water, the structure thus free to rise and fall if the water level should change. On this platform is built a dry and substantial cup-shaped superstructure of fine rushes and grasses. Usually three eggs are laid.

The breeding range extends from Alberta and Manitoba to Utah and Minnesota. The bird winters from Louisiana to Chile and Patagonia.

Laughing Gull

(Larus atricilla)

Average Length, Sixteen and One-half Inches

The name which this gull bears was given to it because of the peculiar laughing character of its cries. It is the only gull breeding along the coast of the eastern United States south of Massachusetts. Furthermore, it is distinctly an inhabitant of salt-water bodies, never constructing its nest in the neighborhood of fresh water, as do certain of the western gulls.

Laughing gulls assemble in colonies when the nesting season arrives. Sometimes in a breeding community there are only a few pairs, and again they congregate by thousands.

The nests are often built in grassy marshes, although I have seen many on the dry ground. A substantial structure of grasses and dried seaweeds generally is assembled, but I have seen nests which contained very little of these materials, this variation being due undoubtedly to the scarcity of available vegetation.

In the last 35 years I have visited many breeding colonies of laughing gulls on islands off the coast of Maine, Massachusetts, Virginia, North Carolina, Florida, Mississippi, Louisiana, and Texas, which I believe are the only eastern States in which the birds are now known to nest successfully.

For a number of years they were extensively shot for their wings, which were used in the millinery trade. By 1900 they had become very scarce; but as a result of protection, aided by the change in fashion, the laughing gull has again become an abundant species, especially along our Atlantic coast.

This species breeds also south to the coast of Venezuela, and on some of the West Indies islands. In winter it ranges southward to Brazil and Chile.

Ring-billed Gull

(Larus delawarensis)

Average Length, Eighteen and One-half Inches

With the exception of the herring gull this is the most common of our North American gulls. Since the settlement of the country it, in common with other sea birds, has suffered greatly from the depredations of commercial egg-hunters, and being more timid than some birds, it has consequently retired from many of its former breeding places.

Today it breeds chiefly in the interior of the continent from James Bay to Alaska, and south to Oregon, Ontario, and the Gulf of St. Lawrence. It closely resembles the herring gull and, since at a distance the black spots on its bill cannot be seen, identification is often difficult. When these two species are observed together, the ring-bill may be known by its smaller size.

The food of the ring-billed gull is not confined wholly to fish, garbage, and other matter found floating on the water, cast up by the sea, or thrown on garbage dumps. In the prairie regions of the central United States, which they cross in migration, they have been seen circling about in the air, catching grasshoppers and beetles on the wing.

They winter about large bodies of water all over the United States, including both the Atlantic and the Pacific seacoasts.

A BLACK-HOODED "OLD SALT" HOBNOBS WITH INLAND INSECT EATERS

The handsome **Laughing Gull** (lower left with young) is the only gull breeding along the eastern coast of the United States south of Massachusetts. It never wanders far from salt water, a trait distinguishing it sharply from the small **Bonaparte's Gull** (flying center, young right), which breeds in the northwestern interior from Alberta to Alaska; the black-faced **Franklin's Gull** (top flying figure), a bird of the inland prairies of Canada and the western United States; and the common **Ring-billed Gull** (lower right, with young), which nests from the Gulf of St. Lawrence to British Columbia. All three inland breeders are avid insect eaters.

Photograph by Hugo H. Schroder

"BREAD CAST UPON THE WATERS" IS SOON PICKED UP

Avid for food, this laughing gull swoops down upon a titbit floating in Tampa Bay, Florida. Where such birds abound, they are efficient removers of waste.

Photograph by Herbert K. Job

ROYAL TERNS ARE GREGARIOUS BIRDS

Breeding in great colonies off the South Atlantic coast and the shores of the Gulf of Mexico, these birds nest so close together that it is difficult to walk through their breeding grounds without treading on the eggs. On a Louisiana reservation.

"GOING DOWN"

And it's a long way for a black-necked stilt when she gets ready to incubate.   Photographed in Florida.

Photographs by Arthur A. Allen

A BRAVE VIRGINIA RAIL TRIES TO PROTECT HER EGGS

Photographed near Ithaca, N. Y.

THEY RELISH THE COOLNESS OF THEIR HIGH-LATITUDE HOME

Rare in museums and in much of their range are the rosy-breasted **Ross's Gull** (upper left) and the **Aleutian Tern** (upper right). One of its scientific names, *Pagophila*, from the Greek for "ice" and "loving," reveals the polar range of the exquisite **Ivory Gull** (left center, young spotted), which perches more often on ice pans than on land. **Sabine's Gull** (right center, young right), with a summer address in Arctic America and a winter home in Peru, flirts a deeply forked tail. A sleek **Glaucous-winged Gull** (foreground, young left) is about to feed its clamorous offspring.

Ross's Gull

(Rhodostethia rosea)

Average Length, Thirteen and One-half Inches

One of the rarest gulls in museum collections is Ross's rosy gull. Comparatively few naturalists have ever seen one alive. It is strictly a bird of the Arctic, and extremely few nests have been found, with the exception of those in a small colony discovered some years ago on the tundras of eastern Siberia.

There the birds appeared about the first of June, and, being already paired, they soon began to nest. The eggs were laid either on the bare moss or in nests.

Ross's gulls were always associated with black-capped terns. Their food was found to consist of insects. Their chief enemies appeared to be the skuas and the Vega gulls, both of which preyed upon their eggs.

These discoveries were made by the Russian explorer, Dr. Sergius A. Buturlin. The rosy gull migrates to Alaska and to the west coast of Greenland. Rarely they have been known to wander to England, France, and Italy.

Aleutian Tern

(Sterna aleutica)

Average Length, Thirteen and One-half Inches

Another little-known Arctic sea bird is the Aleutian tern, so named because in June, 1868, two specimens and one egg were found on Kodiak Island, and it was mistakenly supposed that the tern inhabited the entire Aleutian chain of islands.

Dr. E. W. Nelson found two small colonies of the birds breeding near St. Michael, Alaska, in 1887, and the species is believed to be still occupying the territory. In Dr. Nelson's account of his discovery, he states that the birds "laid their eggs directly on the moss," which covered the rocks. This tern has been found also on the Bering seacoast of Siberia and is known to winter as far south as Japan.

Ivory Gull

(Pagophila alba)

Average Length, Seventeen Inches

Throughout the north polar seas the exquisite ivory gull makes its summer home. "Ice partridge" whalers call it, because it is seldom seen except where ice abounds, and it perches more often on ice cakes than on land.

As the great ice-cap advances in winter, the birds move before it. Sometimes they are shot at Battle Harbour when they "come with the ice and seals in November or December." In January, 1918, one appeared in the harbor at Portland, Maine.

Ivory gulls have been found breeding on Prince Patrick Island, Melville Island, northern Baffin Island, northern Greenland, Zemlya Fridtjof Nansen (Franz Josef Land), and Spitsbergen, and on Arctic islands of the Eastern Hemisphere. Now and then in autumn they come down to Point Barrow and stray specimens have been found in British Columbia and Manitoba.

Sabine's Gull

(Xema sabini)

Average Length, Thirteen and One-half Inches

This attractively colored bird, which greatly resembles Bonaparte's gull, was named for Captain Edward Sabine, who discovered it in the breeding season off the west coast of Greenland. An inhabitant of polar seas, it abounds along the northwest coast of Alaska and elsewhere around Bering Sea.

Of these Alaskan birds, Dr. E. W. Nelson has written that after arrival about the middle of May "they wander in company with the arctic tern, but by the last of May or the first of June, they congregate about the parts of the marshes selected for their own nesting grounds."

There are a few records of their occurrence in the Canadian Provinces, and they have been recorded about a half dozen times in New York and Massachusetts waters.

In autumn this gull migrates southward along the Pacific coast of North America, generally keeping to sea some miles from the land. It winters commonly along the coast of Peru. Only occasionally is it seen on the Atlantic coast of North America. There are records of its occurrence in Labrador, Maine, and New York, also, strangely enough, inland in such regions as Saskatchewan, Ohio, and Nebraska. A few have been seen in France and the British Isles.

Glaucous-winged Gull

(Larus glaucescens)

Average Length, Twenty-five Inches

This is the most numerous of the several kinds of gulls inhabiting the American coastline of the North Pacific. I have watched them as they followed our ship at intervals all the way from Seattle to Skagway, Alaska, and have seen them riding on log rafts being towed down Puget Sound, have noted them resting on numerous rocks jutting from the sea, and found them about the wharves of many towns along the northwest coast.

They breed in colonies, the nests being placed on sandy beaches, on turf-covered islands, and on ledges by the sea.

Their breeding range extends from certain of the Washington islands northward to Norton Sound. They inhabit islands in the Bering Sea and along the neighboring coast of Siberia. In winter they range from the Pribilofs to Baja California and Japan.

Like all other gulls of the sea, they are largely scavengers, feeding upon dead or disabled fish, animal life cast up by the breakers, and floating refuse.

"SEA SWALLOWS" STAGE AN AIR CIRCUS FOR THEIR CHILDREN

Terns hover and plunge for their food, rather than alight on the water to feed, gull-fashion. The amazing **Arctic Tern** (upper right) makes an annual round-trip flight between north and south polar regions. During the mating season, the breast of the **Roseate Tern** (adult, upper left, young, lower left) is faintly suffused with pink. Dark gray on the inner sides of the forked tail distinguishes the **Forster's Tern** (adult, left center, young, lower center) from the **Common Tern** (adult, right center, young, lower right).

Roseate Tern

(Sterna dougalli dougalli)

Average Length, Fifteen and One-half Inches

The name of this bird derives from the rosy tint that faintly overspreads the breast in the breeding season. The color is usually so slight that it is not readily seen in flight. I have watched closely birds flying about over me without being able to detect any reddish glow in the plumage of one of them.

Although the species is fairly numerous, it is not so common on the North American coast as it was fifty years ago. Today it may be found breeding locally from Sable Island, Nova Scotia, to the Dry Tortugas, which lie west of Key West, Florida.

The coast of Maine, and especially the coastal waters of Massachusetts, are the best places to find roseate terns. There they nest on small rocky or sandy islands in colonies with other terns, often concealing their nests in tall grass.

Their food consists largely, if not wholly, of small fishes. This species breeds in Bermuda, the Bahamas and other West Indies islands, and southward to Venezuela. It is also found in European, African, and Asiatic waters.

Arctic Tern

(Sterna paradisaea)

Average Length, Fifteen and One-half Inches

This bird occupies a very extensive territory throughout almost the entire Arctic regions. In North America it breeds from British Columbia northward about the Aleutian Islands in Alaska, eastward to the lower Slave River and northern Greenland, thence southward as far as Massachusetts.

These are the champion migratory birds, for they pass the period of the northern winter in the Antarctic Ocean. Like other terns they nest in colonies, often with the common tern, making their nests in the sand or on flat, exposed bedrock or shale.

The eggs number three or four, and are covered with many spots and blotches. At times the birds defend their nests with great vigor. On Stratten Island, Maine, one pierced my scalp with its bill when I approached its nest.

Forster's Tern

(Sterna forsteri)

Average Length, Fifteen Inches

One way to distinguish a Forster's tern from a common tern is by the color of the long tail. The inner sides of the fork are dark gray in the former, while in the latter this dark shading is on the outer sides of the fork. Even this difference is not noticeable unless the observer is very near the birds.

In California and in Virginia I have examined typical nests of this species made of weed stalks, grasses, and seaweeds, and hidden in the tall marsh grass. On the mud lumps off Pass a Loutre at the mouth of the Mississippi I have seen their eggs on the dried mud, where they were kept from rolling away by a very slight surrounding barrier of dried vegetation.

Although they assemble in colonies to breed, rarely have I seen their nests close together. Generally there is a space of several yards between them. Like other terns, the Forster's feeds chiefly on small fish.

This bird breeds in the interior as well as along the coast. In summer it is found from Washington through Utah, Nevada, Nebraska, Minnesota, and Ontario. It also breeds in Virginia, Louisiana, and Texas, wintering from California and South Carolina to Guatemala.

Common Tern

(Sterna hirundo hirundo)

Average Length, Fifteen Inches

The common tern is well named, for the United States at least, since here it is a very abundant species and is the tern most often seen along our Atlantic seaboard. In Massachusetts it is often called "mackerel gull." Lobstermen in Maine speak of it as the "medricks," and in the great sounds of North Carolina it is a "striker."

Mackerel, like bluefish, drive schools of small minnows to the surface where they attract the terns in great numbers. By watching the birds, fishermen know where to draw their nets. When feeding, these terns plunge headlong from the air.

The common tern breeds from Manitoba, Ontario, and the Gulf of St. Lawrence southward to North Dakota, Ohio, and North Carolina. It also breeds in the Bahamas, along the coast of the Gulf of Mexico, and in the Dutch West Indies. It is an inhabitant of Europe, western Asia, and northern Africa.

As is customary with the several species of terns, this one collects in colonies in the early summer. Usually several hundred, and at times many thousands of them, thus assemble in the breeding season. Near the extremity of some sandspit or on a small isolated island of sand oyster shells, or on rocky ledges they make their simple nests. They scratch slight depressions in the soil, smooth them by turning their bodies, and line the shallow cavities scantily with grass or bits of seaweed. Three or four heavily spotted eggs are laid.

The young are fed chiefly on minnows which frequently the old birds carry for long distances to their young. Many times I have watched these terns returning over the sea with small fish carried crosswise in their bills, when the island which was their destination was so far away that it could not be seen from the boat.

Common terns winter from Florida to the Strait of Magellan, as well as in southern Asia and Africa.

TERNS OF SOUTHERN SEAS FIND STRENGTH IN NUMBERS

On hot, sandy subtropical and tropic shores they collect in vast flocks to raise their young. With white-powdered forehead, the brown **Noddy Tern** (on the rock, left) is a courteous gentleman, greeting every stranger with a deep bow. The immense nesting colonies of the black-backed **Sooty Tern** (flying with young, upper left) are often raided by natives who gather thousands of the eggs for food. The white-tipped black bill of **Cabot's Tern** (upper right) identifies it in a crowd. Largest of terns are the **Royal Tern** (lower right), with its natty pompadour, and the **Caspian Tern** (left foreground with young).

Sooty Tern

(Sterna fuscata)

Average Length, Seventeen Inches

A sooty tern's nest was found in a tern colony on an island off the Louisiana coast in the summer of 1933. With the exception of this rare instance these birds have for many years been known to breed in the United States only on islands of the Dry Tortugas group off Florida. As far back as records exist, large numbers of them have assembled every summer on these little sandy keys.

The eggs, usually one to a nest, are laid in slight hollows scooped in the sand. The sooty is one of the "egg birds" of the Tropics, and thousands of its eggs are gathered for food by natives of numerous and little-known islands of the sea.

In the Bahamas and other West Indies islands, and about the tropical islands even as far as the South American coast, these birds collect in immense colonies to rear their young.

Two varieties of the sooty are recognized as belonging to the list of North American birds: the eastern sooty tern and the Socorro sooty tern, the latter inhabiting the Pacific coast of Mexico and Central America.

Cabot's Tern

(Thalasseus sandvicensis aculavidus)

Average Length, Sixteen Inches

The Cabot's tern is inclined to leave the quiet waters of inside bays and cruise along over the surf of ocean beaches. A distinguishing mark is its white-tipped black bill. Like most other terns it plunges headlong to secure the small fish upon which it preys. It gathers to breed in colonies, usually in company with the royal tern, and the nests of the two species are often very close to each other.

They lay two or rarely three handsomely spotted and blotched eggs, and the nests are placed very close together. The birds soon become accustomed to the presence of a man and will at times permit an observer to approach closely rather than leave the nest and expose the newly hatched young to the rays of the blazing summer sun.

Cabot's terns are known to nest on flat sandy islands from North Carolina southward and around the coast line of the Gulf of Mexico to Texas, Central America, and Brazil. They inhabit also the Bahamas and other islands of the West Indies group.

The sandwich tern, almost identical in appearance, is found in Europe and northern Africa.

Noddy Tern

(Anoüs stolidus stolidus)

Average Length, Ten and One-fourth Inches

Of all the North American terns only the noddy has the habit of building its nest in bushes and low trees. Some noddies are exceptions to this rule, however. In some places they enter crevices in rocks to lay their eggs, or even use the open ground for this purpose. The nests are substantial structures of twigs, grass, seaweed, and similar materials.

The birds' only known breeding place in the United States is on Bird Key at the Dry Tortugas. There several hundred pairs collect every summer to nest on a small island in proximity to a vast congregation of sooty terns. These birds breed also on the Bahamas and other islands of the West Indies group.

The eggs are pale buffy white marked sparsely with spots and lines of chocolate.

Royal Tern

(Thalasseus maximus maximus)

Average Length, Nineteen Inches

This and the next named species are the two great terns of this country.

Royal terns are inhabitants of warm seacoasts, breeding from Virginia southward to Texas, and in the Bahamas and the West Indies. Also they inhabit the Pacific coast of Mexico and in winter range in the South Atlantic to Argentina and Peru. They breed in dense colonies on hot, sandy islands and when they arise from their nests a vast "egg field" is disclosed.

It would be an unusual sight to find one on the Atlantic coast in winter, for they prefer to journey to warmer seas, even going as far south as Peru and Brazil.

Caspian Tern

(Hydroprogne caspia imperator)

Average Length, Twenty-one Inches

This is the largest of all our terns, exceeding in size several of the species of gulls which frequent the marshes and open waters of North America. Ternlike, it breeds in colonies, but when the birds are sitting on their eggs they are not clustered in such compact masses as is customary with the royal and Cabot's terns.

Their eggs apparently are not dropped at random on the sand, but are usually supported and surrounded by dried vegetation.

The birds are not confined to the coasts, but range inland, breeding in Great Slave Lake, Lake Michigan, Klamath Lake (a few years ago), central California and elsewhere.

I have found many of their nests on islands along the coasts of Louisiana and Texas, as well as on the great floating rafts of tules in lakes and ponds in the fresh-water areas of California. Some breed in Labrador. They winter to southern Mexico, both on the Atlantic and the Pacific coasts.

After feeding, long rows of them may often be seen standing on a sand bar or a beach by the sea, where the inexperienced observer may easily mistake them for large gulls.

THE STRANGE SKIMMER IS APTLY NAMED

Flying just above the water, the **Black Skimmer** (lower right and bird skimming the water, left background) scoops up unwary fish on its long, knife-shaped lower mandible. An inch shorter than a robin is the dainty little **Least Tern** (lower left with young). The **Gull-billed Tern** (on the log, left) feeds chiefly on insects and is the rarest tern breeding in the United States. In defense of its home, the **Black Tern** (upper right, flying above young on log) darts solicitously at any intruder. It nests in fresh-water marshes from eastern Alaska to Tennessee and California.

Gull-billed Tern

(Gelochelidon nilotica aranea)

Average Length, Fourteen and One-half Inches

The gull-billed tern, so named for its heavy beak, is the rarest tern breeding in the United States. For some unknown reason its numbers have been decreasing during the last thirty years, while other species of terns with which it associates have steadily increased.

Formerly there was a colony of several hundred gull-billed terns on Cobb Island, Virginia. While making a study of the bird life of that region in the summer of 1892, I examined a number of their nests on the salt marshes bordering the back of the island. By 1907 they had become so rare that Mr. Bent was able to find only four nests, these being situated on the higher parts of the sandy beach.

The food of these birds differs from that of most terns. Apparently it consists chiefly of insects caught from the air or taken from vegetation in the marshes.

The breeding range on the Atlantic coast today is restricted to the few islands of Virginia, and possibly Pamlico Sound, North Carolina. In limited numbers they are found on islands in Louisiana and Texas. Other breeding places are Cuba, the Bahama Islands, Salton Sea, California, and at the mouth of the Amazon.

Black Tern

(Chlidonias nigra surinamensis)

Average Length, Ten Inches

The black tern fluttering about over a lake always reminds me of a nighthawk engaged in feeding near the ground. The birds have also striking resemblance in form and size. Once while I was fishing from a boat in a small North Carolina lake, a black tern darted down and caught the minnows on my hook as I swung it through the air.

In the Southern States these terns appear as migrants as early as July, but soon pass on to the southward. They pass the winter from southern Mexico to Chile.

The black tern nests in fresh-water sloughs and marshes from eastern Alaska to California, and eastward to New York State and Tennessee. The nests consist of reeds and grasses, and are placed among rushes or marsh grass, often on clumps of dead vegetation or on old muskrat nests. The chocolate-spotted eggs are two or three in number.

Least Tern

(Sterna antillarum)

Average Length, Nine Inches

This, the smallest of our terns, attains a length of nine inches, being therefore one inch shorter than the robin. It is an exquisitely dainty little bird, which at times shows an amazing disregard for the presence of man. Its two spotted eggs are laid in slight hollows on the bare sand of spits and small islands.

In five of the South Atlantic and Gulf States I have found colonies of the species nesting on diminutive and temporary sand bars thrown up by dredges clearing out channels in salt water bays, sometimes within the limits of towns. Its food consists chiefly of small minnows caught when it skims low over the water, or makes headlong plunges from the air.

The least tern breeds on the Atlantic coast from Massachusetts to southern Florida, and along the Gulf coast to Mexico. It is also found in the Bahamas and other West Indies islands, Venezuela, and British Honduras. Some breed on bars in the Missouri and the Mississippi River systems. It passes the winter along the coast of Louisiana and southward as far as Venezuela and Peru. Brown's tern, a western form (S. a. browni), nests from central California to southern Mexico.

Black Skimmer

(Rynchops nigra nigra)

Average Length, Eighteen Inches

This peculiar bird, with a beak flattened like a knife blade, is a summer resident only along the coast of the United States from New York to a point near the Mexican border. It passes the winter in coastal waters, mainly from Louisiana to northern and eastern South America.

On November 8, 1932, I saw a flock of at least a thousand in the harbor at Beaufort, North Carolina.

The birds breed in colonies, laying their three or four heavily blotched eggs in slight depressions on island beaches or exposed bars of cast-up oyster shells. They often exhibit a stupid helplessness in guarding their nests. Their eggs are often kicked out of the nests or covered with sand by royal terns that want the territory for their own nests. After the breeding season they assemble in large flocks and often perform amazing evolutions in the air.

When seen at a distance they may appear as a mass of great long-winged black birds, but a moment later, when they turn in such a way as to expose their underparts, the flock becomes a regiment of snowy white.

Black skimmers feed both by day and by night. In gathering the fish and shrimps upon which they mainly subsist, they fly just above the water. Their long, razorlike under bills cut the surface, and up these narrow inclines the prey passes into their mouths.

Their unusual note is an assertive, petulant yap which at a distance sounds not unlike the bark of a dog. It is among the characteristic noises of the southern coastal waterways. Black skimmers usually travel about in small flocks.

Photograph by J. D. Rattar

SHOUT "HALLOO!" AND THE CLIFF INSTANTLY BLOSSOMS WITH WHITE AS MURRES
ABOUT-FACE

When the birds are incubating, their dark backs generally are turned toward the sea. If disturbed they face about as one, the myriads of white "shirt fronts" appearing in sudden contrast. When murres are frightened from their ledges their flight is often accompanied by a shower of eggs. Here their attention has been attracted by two men in a small boat, who are exploring the recesses under the cliffs at Noss, Shetland Islands. The birds on the rock in the foreground are murres; those flying are kittiwakes.

BIRDS OF THE NORTHERN SEAS

Auks, Auklets, Puffins, Murres, Murrelets, Guillemots, and Dovekies Are Clowns of the Bird World

By Alexander Wetmore

GRAY, misty fog over a restless sea, land concealed somewhere in the haze, an occasional clumsy, heavy-bodied bird indistinctly seen as it blundered away from our ship—this was my introduction to the Aleutian Islands of Alaska, and to one of the most interesting groups of sea fowl that I have known.

The revenue cutter *Tahoma* moved at half speed, with all hands watching for some landfall ahead that might direct our course through Unimak Pass. The air came damp and cold against our faces.

Suddenly the fog lifted to reveal Tigalda Island, the desired landmark, and on all sides endless thousands of birds scattered near and far to distant horizons.

Large-billed puffins in pairs sat near one another on the water, tiny auklets rested in flocks, and occasional groups of dark-backed murres swam over the lifting swell. As the ship bore down upon them, some, after momentary hesitation, dived with hastily beating wings and darted away in submarine flight. Others spattered off, striking the water with broad, webbed feet, until their heavy bodies had sufficient momentum to allow them to rise in the air, when the feet were drawn back beneath the tail and the birds flew swiftly away.

SHEEPLIKE, THEY FOLLOW THE LEADER

If one bird of a group started across our bow, its companions followed, this follow-the-leader course continuing until those in the rear were forced to dive to avoid striking the steel side of the ship.

In the background were huge, black cliffs, and towering, snow-capped mountains rising from rocky shores or grassy slopes of vivid green. In the thrill of anticipation of what lay before us, the momentary discomforts of the stormy passage that had brought us across the Gulf of Alaska were forgotten.

The auks, murres, and puffins (family Alcidae) are found only in the Northern Hemisphere and are most abundant in the subarctic area. Some range south into regions of temperate climate, principally in the Pacific Ocean, but none penetrates as far as the Tropics.

Twenty-three species are known, with 14 additional subspecies or geographic forms. Most of these various kinds are found at some season in North American waters, only a few being restricted entirely to the shores of the Old World. All are maritime and come to fresh water only by chance.

Without exception, members of the auk family have heavy bodies, small wings, and broadly webbed feet set far back on the body. The plumage is dense and waterproof, and the birds are among the most expert divers, using both wings and feet in progression beneath the water. Their food, taken entirely from the sea, includes small fish and crustaceans.

BODIES BUILT FOR DEEP-SEA DIVING

In search of food they often dive to considerable depths, where the heavy salt water of the sea subjects them to powerful pressure. To protect the vital organs against this, the lower margin of the breast bone is extended in a flat plate of bone and cartilage over the upper part of the abdomen to serve as a buckler.

Birds of this group are true mariners, and for much of the year they live at sea, feeding and sleeping on the water. Only in the nesting season do they resort regularly to land; then they frequently gather in extensive colonies.

Rocky coasts and lonely islands form their haunts at this time, as there they have a better chance to escape their natural enemies. The murres and guillemots nest on open ledges. Others, such as the puffins and auklets, prefer underground burrows, or crannies deep in piles of rock. Sometimes they nest in caves or under bushes.

Many of the auklets are nocturnal, and they may be so retiring that their abundance is often unsuspected by those who

© Hugo A. Bernatzik

THE TAKE-OFF! A "SLOW-MOTION MOVIE" IN A SINGLE
PICTURE

This unusual action shot shows four puffins at different stages of launching themselves from a ledge on the Norway coast. Heavy-bodied, they push off in a slanting dive to gain momentum before rising in full flight. Razor-billed auks at the right hold their ground. Overhead a neighbor flies homeward on swiftly beating wings, feet trailing behind.

thousands about their nesting grounds and are easily captured. Dovekies alight on projecting rocks in struggling masses, each individual intent on obtaining a perch without regard to its neighbors. A stone cast into such a group may kill half a dozen.

NATIVES NET THEM ON
THE WING

Netting is a more profitable means of pursuit, and, considering the number of birds taken, it is astonishing that any remain. With their heavy bodies and small wings, members of the auklet tribe cannot swerve quickly to avoid obstacles, though they fly with great rapidity. On certain days in early summer, hundreds and thousands of the birds are in restless flight over the rocky islands and headlands that form their breeding grounds. Native hunters lie concealed on points and ridges, and as puffins, auklets, or dovekies pass swiftly, thrust up long-handled nets into which the birds crash headlong. Quickly biting the head and neck with his strong teeth, the hunter kills the struggling bird and then is ready for the next one.

visit their breeding places only by day.

To the Eskimo and Aleut of the North, birds of this group are important because they furnish valuable additions to the food supply. The return of puffins and their cousin auklets to their breeding haunts on the rocky coasts of the North after the long winter is a time of rejoicing. Eggs, young, and adult birds, all are eaten, and the skins of the old birds, properly tanned with the short, dense feathers in place, are made into warm parkas and other articles of clothing.

Puffins and dovekies especially swarm in

The flesh of these birds is eaten fresh as a welcome addition to the monotonous diet of seal or other meat of winter, and hundreds are stored for use later.

It is only in the far north, where men are few, that murres, puffins, dovekies, and their kind can maintain their abundance under such conditions. With the coming of white men and the advance of white settlements along the southern edge of their range, the birds have been too greatly harassed and have not maintained themselves against specialized modern methods aimed at their destruction.

The great auk early became extinct. Razor-billed a u k s, murres, and others in southern parts of t h e i r range o n o u r northeastern coasts have been much reduced in numbers. In recent years they h a v e b e e n afforded protection through the Migratory Bird Treaty in effect between the United States and Canada and through other means, so once more there has been a slow increase among them.

BIZARRE PLUMES AND BRILLIANT BEAKS

Black, g r a y, and white are the predominating colors in the plumage of members of the auk group, with the markings often contrasted and highly attractive. Many, such as the t u f t e d puffin, and some of the auklets in breeding dress, have plumes and tufts of feathers about the head that give a bizarre appearance. These plumage oddities usually are ornaments of the breeding season and are shed in fall.

Photograph by J. D. Rattar

FOUR SOLEMN PUFFINS RULE A ROCKY ROOST

Puffins generally arrive there about the first of April and leave around the twenty-third of August. About the third week in May they lay a single egg in a hole from eighteen inches deep to beyond the reach of a man's arm. They often nest in rabbit burrows, which are numerous in the vicinity, but for the most part the birds dig the holes themselves with their strong claws.

Most species lack them in winter.

The bill of the puffin is one of the most curious and unusual among birds. In the nesting season it is large and brilliantly colored, giving the bird the appearance of a grotesque mask.

Birds of the auk group have their existence remote from the lives of most of us and are little known at first hand, even among naturalists. To see them one must usually go to northern seas or visit lonely places. But on a cold December morning, as I walked along the beach near Ocean City, Maryland, a bird with white breast and black back swam through the surf. I recognized it as a razor-billed auk, a northern species of rare occurrence so far south.

Without seeming to notice my presence, it moved, prostrate on its breast, by aid of wings and legs beyond the wash of the sea. After a moment, thinking that the auk was injured, I stepped forward to pick it up. To my astonishment it became suddenly alert and, with feet striking the sand, flew back to alight in the surf, where it rested buoyantly and swam steadily out to sea.

MILLIONS OF MURRE EGGS ONCE WERE SOLD IN SAN FRANCISCO MARKETS

Nature seems to have made them small at one end so that they will roll in a circle and not off flat nesting ledges. The ground color varies from white or cream to bright green and blue. Scrawls and blotches of gray, brown, and black form intricate patterns which evidently are the "trade-mark" of the individual, as eggs laid by any one bird are more or less alike from year to year. Murres lay only one egg for a set; these were deposited by five different Atlantic murres.

Photographs by Alfred O. Gross

THIS PUFFIN IS EIGHT YEARS OLD—HOW DO WE KNOW?

The aluminum band on its leg tells the story. Puffins bite and scratch so savagely that gloves need to be worn in handling them. The lighthouse keeper on a little Canadian island, where the bird was banded, says it has returned to the same nesting hole year after year. There are many such places, but that crevice is claimed and defended against all comers.

Photograph by Edward M. Weyer, Jr.

A HUNGRY ESKIMO BOY CATCHES ONE COURSE OF HIS DOVEKIE DINNER

The birds swarm past the crags along the sea in vast numbers, and fly so swiftly that they cannot easily dodge a net swung up suddenly in their path. Here at Cape York, Greenland, even the youngsters are marvelously adept at catching them. For an expert the "net-profit" is almost one hundred per cent. The "spare" is used in case the other net is broken.

Photograph by Alfred O. Gross

PRIDE AND PUGNACITY ARE REFLECTED IN THIS PUFFIN PORTRAIT

Several small fish can be caught and held side by side in the seemingly clumsy bill. Here it is slightly ajar, with the curious thickened tongue showing. Strong, heavy, and sharp-edged, the deeply ridged parrotlike beak makes a formidable weapon which can wound a man's hand severely. In summer the bill is colored yellow, grayish blue, and vermilion. After the nesting season the bright covering is shed in nine separate strips and the bill is more plainly colored and smaller.

Great Auk

(Plautus impennis)

Average Length, Twenty-nine Inches

In late May, 1534, the French voyager, Jacques Cartier, came to Funk Island, off the northeastern coast of Newfoundland, and found there a horde of birds so vast that "in less than half an hour," he wrote, "we filled two boats full of them." These were the great auks, whose destruction continued until, a little more than 300 years after Cartier's visit, the last one was gone.

Fishermen voyaged to Newfoundland waters near the close of the 15th century, and as early as 1517 forty Portuguese, French, and Spanish boats were engaged in the codfishery. Hakluyt informs us that in 1578 the fishing fleet included 400 vessels.

Many of these boats depended upon the great auk colony for their supplies of meat. The birds were killed with clubs and carried aboard ship, where some were eaten fresh and the remainder salted as provisions for the voyage. Eggs also were taken.

When the weather permitted, planks or sails were laid from the rocky shore of Funk Island to small boats, and the birds were literally herded aboard, floundering and scrambling, until no more could be located. They were so helpless and unwary that few if any escaped when men from a ship thus raided one of their nesting places. In addition to supplying food for the fishermen, it was said that the great auks were used for bait.

When Newfoundland was colonized, the great auks became a source of meat supply for the early settlers, who for years visited their breeding grounds to kill them and salt them for winter use. Richard Whitbourne, in considering this, wrote in 1622: "God made the innocencie of so poor a creature to become such an admirable instrument for the sustentation of man."

With white settlement of the New World there came demand for feathers to make feather beds. Men camped on Funk Island throughout the summer to kill and pluck the great auks. Stone corrals or compounds were constructed, into which the birds were driven. As needed, they were killed and thrown into kettles of hot water preparatory to removing the feathers.

Wood was scarce on this barren island, and the bodies of the auks themselves, covered with a thick layer of fat, were said to have been used as fuel to feed the flames for scalding their companions.

Against this commercial destruction the birds were helpless. Early in the 19th century the great auk had disappeared, and the large colonies in which it bred were no more.

The last great auks of which there is certain record were two captured alive on June 3, 1844, on the rocky islet of Eldey, on the southwest coast of Iceland. There is report of one seen on the Newfoundland Banks in 1852, and of one found dead in 1853 in Trinity Bay, Newfoundland, but neither account has been verified.

In the Old World the great auk, also known as the garefowl, nested in the Faeroe Islands, on Papa Westray in the Orkneys, and on rocky islands near Iceland. As recently as 1753 it came regularly in May to nest on the island of St. Kilda, and the last known in this general area, aside from Iceland, was one killed on St. Kilda in 1821.

Possibly in prehistoric times the great auk had a more extended range. Its bones have been found in deposits on the coast of Italy, and it is one of the species depicted by Stone Age artists on the walls of caves on the northern coast of Spain. In the United States its bones have been found abundantly in shell heaps remaining from ancient Indian feasts on the coast of Massachusetts. Other remains have been identified from shell mounds as far south as the east coast of Florida.

Though the great auk's wings were so small that it could not fly, it was strong and powerful in the water. On land it stood with the body erect, resting on the full length of the foot and tarsus, the leg being located rather far back on the body. It walked or ran with short steps and plunged from heights of 10 or 12 feet into the water.

The bird swam with neck drawn in and head lifted. Diving with ease and progressing beneath the water by means of wings and broad, webbed feet, it moved so swiftly that it was able to escape pursuit by rowboats. Though flightless, it seems to have performed extensive migrations by water.

Its notes were harsh and croaking. Although inoffensive, the birds bit savagely with their heavy bills when handled.

The great auk, despite the vast numbers that once covered the breeding places, was not exceptionally prolific. It laid only one egg, and that on bare ground or rock without a nest and without any protective surroundings. The shell was white or yellowish white, blotched, lined, and spotted with black, drab, and varying shades of brown.

According to present record, there have been preserved in museums and private collections 80 skins and 75 eggs of the great auk. The National Museum in Washington has a large collection of great auk bones obtained years ago on Funk Island, and bones are preserved in other museums.

Specimens are so much in demand that recently $3,500 was asked for a mounted bird. At an auction in London in 1934, six eggs were sold at prices ranging from $525 to $1,575 each, the amount depending on the condition of the egg. Two mounted birds brought $4,615.

THE LAST SURVIVING GREAT AUK PERISHED MORE THAN 80 YEARS AGO

Only in the artist's imagination does this bewildered, solitary bird remain to walk the bleak, rocky shores of little Funk Island, near Newfoundland, while wheeling gulls scream a requiem. "Here lies the victim of man's thoughtlessness," might read the epitaph of his clan, which once bred in amazing numbers here. Small-winged and flightless, penguinlike in their helplessness, the luckless **Great Auks** were slaughtered by the thousands for food and featherbeds—even for bait and fuel. Their eggs were stolen. Inevitably they became extinct, and today a mounted bird is worth thousands of dollars, while a dozen eggs would almost ransom a king.

Razor-billed Auk

(Alca torda)

Average Length, Sixteen and One-half Inches

In summer, in their northern breeding grounds, razor-billed auks may be found with murres resting on ledges or points of rock. At rest the razor-bill is marked by compact, thickset form and shortened neck. On the wing it travels swiftly, with rapid strokes, swaying slightly from side to side. The head is drawn in, and bill, body, and feet make a straight line.

In modern times, hunted for its flesh, eggs, and feathers, it has been much reduced. The birds now nest only on inaccessible cliffs.

The best-known colony of razor-bills on our northeastern coast today is that on Great Bird Rock, in the Gulf of St. Lawrence. Here, as elsewhere, the single egg is placed on a rock ledge, sometimes in the open, but more often in some cranny where it is sheltered by overhanging rock. No nesting material is used.

When the young are about three weeks old, the parents entice them from their cliff homes into the sea, sometimes pushing them off or carrying them when they are reluctant to take the leap. Many are killed by falling short and striking on the rocks.

After thirty days of incubation the eggs hatch.

The razor-billed auk nests from the coasts of New Brunswick to Greenland, Iceland, the British Isles, Norway, and Lapland. In winter it comes south to the middle United States and the Mediterranean Sea.

Murre

(Uria aalge)

Average Length, Sixteen Inches

The murre, named perhaps from its low, murmuring calls, is a common tenant of the large sea-bird colonies of the North.

Approach its cliff apartments in the nesting season and you will see lines of dark-backed birds resting in rows on narrow ledges, each one covering its single egg.

At an alarm all about-face quickly, their white breasts appearing in startling contrast to the somber color of the previous instant. They drop off their ledges in a steep slant to gain momentum, then rise in rapid flight.

The murre has suffered equally with other colonizing birds from the coming of the white man, and on our northeastern coasts many rookeries have been decimated or destroyed. Only with the protection afforded in recent years have these birds been able to maintain themselves.

It is reported that between 1850 and 1856 more than three million of the eggs of the western murres were brought to San Francisco markets from the immense colonies on the Farallon Islands. As delicacies they sold for from 12 to 20 cents a dozen. In 1886, two men are said to have gathered 108,000 eggs. In 1897 the Lighthouse Board barred the eggers.

The single egg, much larger than the ordinary hen's egg, varies remarkably in color and in marking. Ground colors range from blue, green, and buff to pure white; markings, from eggs that are entirely plain to those that are blotched and scrawled with intricate and overlapping patterns of gray, brown, and black. No two seem exactly alike.

No nest is made, the eggs being placed on bare rock or earth. All are strongly pointed at the small end.

When nearly grown, the young murres are enticed by their parents to scramble down over the rocks to the water.

Murres are agile and active in the water, diving with half-opened wings with which at once they begin subaqueous flight. Their swiftness beneath the surface is such that their food of fishes is obtained with ease.

The Atlantic murre *(Uria aalge aalge)* nests from southern Greenland to Nova Scotia and the Faeroe, Orkney, and Shetland Islands. In winter it ranges south to Maine and the coast of Morocco. The California murre *(Uria aalge californica)*, differing in larger size and in form of bill, is found from Bering Sea south to California and Kamchatka.

Brünnich's Murre

(Uria lomvia)

Average Length, Sixteen and One-half Inches

Thicker, shorter bill, darker head, and a light stripe at the base of the bill distinguish this species from the common murre.

It nests in large colonies on cliffs and rocky headlands, often with related species.

The large eggs of this murre are relished by natives, who also eat the birds, and on the northeastern coast of North America the species has suffered much destruction. In the Bering Sea area it is more abundant and in places has tremendous colonies.

Bogoslof Island, in Bering Sea, has been a regular breeding ground in spite of periodic volcanic eruptions that have at times submerged the entire island.

With the end of the nesting season Brünnich's murres retire to the open sea for the winter. Only the closing of the water by ice drives them south, and then they do not go far beyond the ice floes. Fish and small crustaceans are the food of these birds, and they feed entirely at sea.

Of the two forms of this species, the true Brünnich's murre *(Uria lomvia lomvia)* is found from Hudson Strait and adjacent islands, and Spitsbergen and Novaya Zemlya, to Long Island and the North Sea. The larger, western form, Pallas's murre *(Uria lomvia arra)*, ranges from Wrangel and Herald Islands through Bering Sea to Kodiak Island and Japan.

RAZOR-BILLED AUKS AND MURRES GO FISHING IN NATTY "FULL DRESS"

On the higher rock squats a full-grown **Razor-billed Auk** of the Atlantic in summer garb, while overhead flies its immature offspring in winter's whiter plumage. Sometimes parents teach chicks to swim by pushing them off cliffs. In the foreground, wearing summer attire, sits a **Murre,** so named from its murmuring call; and rising from the water is another in winter feathering. On the surface rests an immature **Brünnich's Murre** in cold-weather costume.

Puffin

(Fratercula arctica)
Average Length, Thirteen Inches

By their grotesque bills, suggesting the exaggerated noses of masquerade masks, the puffins are set apart from all other North American birds. The odd form of the common puffin is accentuated by its air of solemn gravity and by the brilliant colors of its bill and feet. Male and female are alike in markings.

In the air the puffin flies swiftly, with rapidly beating wings, veering at times from side to side like other members of its family. In the water it swims on the surface like a little duck. When alarmed it dives as often as it takes to the air, and flies beneath the surface with quickly beating wings, trailing the feet behind as in aerial flight. On land it ordinarily stands erect, ducklike, not resting back on the leg, as do murres and auks.

The puffin nests in burrows, which it digs in loose soil with its strongly clawed feet, or in crevices beneath stones. The single large egg, plain white, or faintly marked with lilac and brown, is placed in a slight nest of dried grass, herbage, and feathers.

Searching for eggs is fraught with some excitement. In occupied burrows one of the pair is always at home, and the usual indication that eggs or young may be found, as one explores with the hand the dark recess that may conceal them, is a savage bite from the sharp-edged bill of the parent. Seizure of the bird is accompanied by vigorous scratching with sharp claws.

The Atlantic puffin (Fratercula a. arctica) is found from Norway and southern Greenland to Maine, and in winter as far as New York. The larger large-billed puffin (F. a. naumanni) ranges from northern Greenland to Novaya Zemlya.

Black Guillemot

(Cepphus grylle)
Average Length, Thirteen Inches

From Maine to northern Greenland the guillemot is one of the common birds of the sea, being found in sheltered bays and about rocky headlands. Known as the "sea pigeon" from its trim and dovelike form, it rests buoyantly on the water.

As it flies, the black body, white-marked wings, and red feet make a bright pattern.

In nesting time, guillemots select their mates with somewhat clumsy antics and much display of red-lined mouths, then repair to some rocky island or cliff-bound headland to make a home.

Where nesting sites abound, the guillemot gathers in colonies, but elsewhere it may be scattered in pairs over a fairly large area.

Winter has no terrors for these hardy birds, and only when the seas are completely icebound are they driven south.

The nest is placed in a rock crevice, often difficult of access, the two eggs resting on the bare rock or soil, or on accumulations of small pebbles or shells. The eggs are white to greenish or cream-buff, handsomely and boldly marked with various shades of brown and lilac.

The food of this species is composed of small fish, crustaceans, and mollusks, obtained by diving, often to a considerable depth.

The black guillemot (Cepphus grylle grylle) breeds from Labrador and Norway to Maine and northern Scotland, coming in winter to Cape Cod and northern France. Mandt's guillemot (C. g. mandti) nests along the Arctic Ocean, coming in winter to Bering Sea and James Bay.

Dovekie

(Alle alle)
Average Length, Eight Inches

Occasionally, during terrific gales in winter, small black and white sea birds appear in numbers in the northeastern section of our country, cast up dead or bewildered on the beaches by the titanic waves, or driven far inland by the force of the winds. These are dovekies, Arctic sea birds no larger than quail, with thick, dense plumage and heavy, compact bodies.

Dovekies breed north to 78° North Latitude and have been recorded at 82°. They are found in almost incredible numbers, and return to their Arctic homes far in advance of other species that nest in these localities. To the northern Eskimo the dovekie means food.

The birds come to the rocky slopes where they nest in tremendous abundance, congregating on bowlders in fluttering crowds. Boys kill them with stones and, seizing them, literally eat the warm bodies out of the skins. Men and women armed with long-handled nets crouch in depressions among the rocks, and, as the dense flocks sweep past, scoop in bird after bird, often half a dozen at a time.

Thousands of dovekies are stored by the natives in frozen ground for winter. Foxes find in this bird their principal summer food. The eggs are devoured by Eskimos and foxes. Ravens and gulls eat the birds. In spite of these enemies, the dovekie survives and maintains its enormous numbers.

The nests are mainly in crevices and crannies amid the stones of talus slopes, above or near the sea. Where conditions are favorable the bird congregates by thousands. The single egg is plain bluish white, rarely with a few indistinct spots of brown about the large end. The food is mainly small crustaceans.

The dovekie flies readily and also dives, usually using its wings in progression beneath the water. Except in the nesting season, it is found at sea, far from land.

The dovekie nests on Arctic coasts from Greenland to Novaya Zemlya, in winter coming south to New York and the British Isles, casually farther. There are many records of storm-driven individuals in the interior.

THE SOLEMN PUFFIN HAS A HUGE, VIVID BEAK LIKE THE NOSE OF A CLOWN

After the summer breeding season the old **Puffin** on the rock will shed the bright bill covering and look like the one in winter plumage, flying. Red feet are a characteristic shared with the **Black Guillemot,** or "sea pigeon," one of which (left foreground) is a young bird, and the other (center) an adult in summer dress. Two more are flying low. The little quail-size **Dovekie** (right, showing summer and winter coats) is prized as food by Eskimos.

Tufted Puffin

(Lunda cirrhata)

Average Length, Fifteen Inches

In climbing the steep and slippery grass-covered slopes of a small island near the western end of the Alaska Peninsula, I found numerous holes as large as small rabbit burrows driven into the stony soil.

Exploring these one by one with a long arm, I was rewarded finally by a savage bite that gashed my fingers, and with some difficulty I seized and dragged out a struggling tufted puffin.

Flowing yellow plumes over the light-colored eyes, and a viciously heavy bill characterize this "sea parrot," also known as the "old man of the sea." Its bill and strong clawed feet command respect, and its capture by hand is attended by cuts and scratches.

To the fisherman of southeastern Alaska the boldly audacious tufted puffin is anathema. Fond of fish, it follows his boat and cleans his hooks of bait as fast as he can drop them into the water, even diving to considerable depths. Few lines escape.

The northern natives of the Alaskan and Siberian coasts, however, hail the coming of this puffin to its breeding grounds with delight, as puffin meat, though dark and heavy, is a welcome change from the seal and other foods of winter.

The birds gather in flocks and fly back and forth across the grassy banks of their nesting grounds. Although they travel swiftly, their short wings and heavy bodies make it difficult for them to turn or swerve quickly. Aleuts, hidden on the slopes, thrust up long-handled nets into which the puffins crash headlong, to be drawn rapidly in and killed by a bite on the head or neck or by a blow on the back.

The nest is composed of a few bits of herbage, ordinarily placed in a burrow, but occasionally, in the southern part of its range, beneath the shelter of bushes. The single large egg is white, plain or marked with a few spots or scrawls of gray and pale brown.

Where conditions are suitable, tufted puffins assemble in large colonies for breeding, often in company with other birds. In the south there are two broods in a season. The young birds feed voraciously and grow rapidly.

After the nesting season adults molt and in the winter plumage lack the white markings and plumes about the head. The covering of the bill also is shed and the bill is actually smaller than in summer. Adults and young range the open sea, far from land, until the next nesting season.

The tufted puffin is found from northern Alaska and northeastern Siberia south to the Santa Barbara Islands, California, and to Japan. Casual individuals have been reported from Greenland and Maine.

Horned Puffin

(Fratercula corniculata)

Average Length, Fourteen and One-half Inches

The horned puffin of the northwest coast is similar to the common puffin in pattern of color and general appearance. It differs from that species principally in having the cheeks white instead of gray, the impressed lines on the bill spaced and placed differently, and the black of the neck coming up on the throat.

The "horn" above the eye, which gives the bird its common name, is in reality merely an elongated, fleshy papilla that can be raised and lowered at will. A similar structure, of much smaller size, is found in the related species.

The horned puffin ranges usually about cliffs and small, rocky islands, where it digs its nesting burrow in the soil. From two to ten feet from the entrance there is a slight accumulation of herbage on which the spotted egg is laid. Beyond this point the tunnel ordinarily continues to the surface, so that the nest has two entrances.

These are hardy birds that spend the winter in northern seas, even in the stormy ice-bound waters of the southern part of Bering Sea. In May at the Pribilof Islands the horned puffins return to their nesting grounds though summer is still distant. They remain about their rookeries until some time in September when, accompanied by their young which are then able to fly, they repair once more to the open sea.

To see the parents carrying three, four, or five small, slender fishes, held side by side in the great bill, is laughable indeed. At the same time one wonders how, after one fish is caught, the others are captured.

Although I had seen pairs of horned puffins from the deck of our ship earlier, my acquaintance with the horned puffin really began at Chernofski, on the western end of Unalaska Island, when they were nesting on a rocky headland, and from here through the Aleutian chain these odd-appearing birds were seen in numbers.

At rest on a projecting rock near their nest tunnel they appear heavy and clumsy. They launch into flight in a downward sweep with spread feet and then with swiftly beating wings swing back again and again over the starting point.

Hunters familiar with this habit use it to shoot or net the birds as they return after being driven from their perches. Others are snared through little openings as they scuttle about under rock slides, or are pulled scratching and biting from their nests.

They dive with ease, traveling rapidly beneath the water by the aid of both wings and feet.

The horned puffin nests from the islands of Bering Sea and the adjacent Arctic Ocean south to Forrester Island, Alaska.

A ROBBER OF FISHLINES IS THE TUFTED PUFFIN, "OLD MAN OF THE SEA"

The weird **Tufted Puffin,** with its yellow plumes, light eyes, and heavy, colored beak, is dubbed "sea parrot" by Alaska fishermen, and often is called stronger names when, diving deep, it cleans their hooks. The young in first plumage (right) and adult in winter (left background) lack the tufts and white face. The formidable bill and claws can deal savage blows. In the foreground swims a full-grown **Horned Puffin** of the northwest coast in summer splendor. Its "horn" above the eye can be raised or lowered.

PROUD MURRE PARENTS LEAD THEIR OFFSPRING DOWN OVER THE ROCKS TO THE WATER

On lonely Walrus Island in the Pribilofs is heard the low, deep-throated "murre" of myriad birds and the higher-pitched note of the youngsters. Soon young and old will be swimming about together and heading for the open sea. These murres appear tame, but if the man should approach them too closely or make a sudden threatening move they would scatter quickly.

Photographs by Maynard Owen Williams

AT THE CONVENTIONAL RATE OF EIGHT BREASTS TO A PERSON, THIS GROUP NEEDED 48 BIRDS FOR A MEAL

Meat and eggs are eaten by these Etah, Greenland, natives, and the skins make warm shirts. When the little black and white dovekies come north in spring they seem to fill the sky.

RAW BIRD MEAT IS AN ESKIMO DELICACY—THE FEATHERS A NAPKIN

A native of Igloodahouny, Greenland, shows how the epicures of his people devour a dovekie. He eats the breast and throws the rest away. The dovekie is the most important bird of the far north.

SMALL, STRAIGHT-FLYING AUKLETS FALL EASY PREY TO ALEUTS AND ESKIMOS

Natives lie flat on the rocks and reach up long-handled nets into which the birds crash headlong. Quickly the hunter finishes them with a bite on the head and neck. Many northern birds are caught in this way, but specially relished is the **Crested Auklet** (sitting on the highest rock, and flying). The **Whiskered Auklet** at the right is rare and little known. Smallest of the family is the **Least Auklet** (center). The **Paroquet Auklet** in the foreground has a peculiar upturned bill. All are adults wearing their summer suits.

Crested Auklet

(Aethia cristatella)

Average Length, Ten and One-half Inches

Fallen rocks from the black cliffs of the headland at the entrance of Kiska Harbor, on Kiska Island, in the Aleutians, lay in bare, jumbled confusion above the rocky beach, with only occasional mats of grass pushing out over them where a little soil had accumulated.

As I clambered cautiously over this rough terrain, the scraping of my heavy hobnailed walking shoes brought forth harsh calls from birds concealed beneath my feet in subterranean crevices. I could not see them or reach them, and only when one shot out like a little bomb did I learn they were crested auklets.

Dark-plumaged birds, rough, black rock, and a leaden sea, with a haze of fog into which the auklets disappeared almost instantaneously— all this forms the background for my memory of this curious and interesting bird.

At sea the crested auklet usually is found in little flocks that rise from the water with celerity and fly swiftly away.

These birds breed on the coasts and islands of Bering Sea and the North Pacific. They nest always amid masses of stones and bowlders, laying one white egg.

Whiskered Auklet

(Aethia pygmaea)

Average Length, Seven and One-half Inches

This curious bird is little known, for it has been seen by few naturalists. Most of our knowledge of its mode of life comes from the observations of Dr. Leonhard Stejneger, who found it common many years ago about the Commander Islands.

The whiskered auklet feeds on small crustaceans obtained at sea. After nesting it spends its time in the open sea. It ranges to the Aleutian Islands and Japan.

Least Auklet

(Aethia pusilla)

Average Length, Six and One-half Inches

In the harbor of Kiska Island, one of the Aleutian Islands of Alaska, there suddenly appeared around our skiff little groups of small, heavy-bodied birds. They either rose with rapidly vibrating wings and darted about in swarms, or dived to "fly away" beneath the surface. These were least auklets.

Ashore, we found them nesting in crevices and crannies among cliffs and bowlders where their twittering, squealing calls came from beneath our feet, but where their eggs were entirely protected.

In suitable places the least auklet breeds in large colonies and, like others of its family, is captured in nets by the natives. Where stones are small enough to be moved aside, the single white egg may be discovered in some concealed crevice, while the birds scuttle away to safety in remote crannies, or fly quickly out when their cover is disturbed. No nest is made, the egg being placed on pebbles and stones without protection.

The food of this bird is composed of small crustaceans on which it thrives immensely.

Least auklets remain far north during the winter, but range at sea where they have slight contact with man. At this season the breast feathers are entirely white.

We can understand how the bodies of these and other northern sea birds, incased in feathers, skin, and heavy layers of fat, can endure the rigors of severe winter weather. But the bare feet and tarsi, immersed constantly in water that is only a few degrees above freezing and mercilessly cold to the human hand or body that penetrates it, offer a problem. The blood supply in the foot necessarily is slight.

We may suppose that a lack of the delicate nerves sensitive to cold that might cause crippling or discomfort, and the possession of a smooth, oily surface to which water does not adhere and freeze when the birds rise in flight, give these creatures their immunity. The least auklet nests on coasts and islands of Bering Sea, in winter passing to Japan.

Paroquet Auklet

(Cyclorrhynchus psittacula)

Average Length, Ten Inches

This auklet, marked by white breast and comparatively large size, is a summer inhabitant of Bering Sea and adjacent waters, where it lives about rocky cliffs and islands in company with its relatives.

In the Pribilof Islands the paroquet auklet arrives on its nesting grounds in early May. It lives unobtrusively, being quiet and rather solitary when compared with the least and crested species. Often it is seen resting on ledges, perhaps in little groups, and when startled flies circling to another perch or out to sea. The curiously upturned bill marks it instantly.

The single white egg is deposited in some rock crevice on bare stones or pebbles, usually in some inaccessible spot.

Paroquet auklets feed at sea on small crustaceans and the other animals that form the association of creatures known popularly as "whale food." Like the crested auklet, they have beneath the tongue a pouch or sac in which they store food for later consumption or to carry to their young.

In winter these auklets remain at sea and then travel southward through parts of the North Pacific. They have a wider range than the related species, coming at this time even to the northwestern coasts of the United States.

The paroquet auklet nests from the coasts and islands of Bering Sea to Kodiak and eastern Siberia. In winter it is found south to the Kurile Islands and California.

THE ANCIENT MURRELET TAKES ITS NAME FROM ITS "GRAY HAIR"

White head markings of the **Ancient Murrelet** (in flight) are fancifully supposed to resemble the hoary locks of age, hence the word "ancient." Numbers are killed by natives with clubs as they nest in the Aleutian and near-by islands. Sometimes found in company with them are **Kittlitz's Murrelet** (right, in winter plumage), and the alert, shy **Marbled Murrelet** (left, in winter dress; center, in summer).

Ancient Murrelet

(Synthliboramphus antiquus)

Average Length, Ten Inches

As our ship entered sheltered bays in the Aleutian Islands in early summer, we were certain to see little groups of these curious birds, resting quietly or swimming rapidly in line.

When I approached them in a small boat, they sometimes dived with a flirt of the wings and rowed away with quickly moving pinions beneath the surface, or rose in short flights.

Ordinarily they were tame and unsuspicious, and on close approach I never tired of admiring their beautifully contrasted markings. The name "ancient" is from a fanciful resemblance of the white head markings to gray hair.

The ancient murrelet gathers to breed on rocky islands, usually in company with other auklets and petrels. The birds are found in places in considerable numbers.

They nest in a variety of situations, ranging from crevices and crannies in rock to burrows in masses of tangled grass, where they sometimes penetrate for several feet to form a little chamber neatly lined with grass blades. Elsewhere the eggs are placed on bare rock or earth, or even on ice in some abandoned puffin burrow.

The eggs, of good size, are whitish to buffy brown, marked evenly with spots and lines of dark brown, lilac, and lavender.

Within a day or two after hatching, according to Professor Harold Heath, the young birds come down to the shore, enticed by the calls of their parents, and boldly plunge into the ocean. Through the surf, breaking heavily on rocky coasts, they swim and dive with ease.

About their breeding colonies these birds are most active at night. Natives visit the rookeries for food and kill the birds with clubs. They also gather the eggs, in all stages of incubation, and the young.

Though I found the ancient murrelet in quiet bays in the Aleutian Islands, elsewhere they range the roughest waters and in winter live entirely at sea. At this season they migrate considerably, coming south to the coast of California. Here they may be found feeding on small crustaceans and other aquatic creatures.

Off our northwestern coasts in winter they frequent sheltered coves or the open sea indifferently, though little noticed except by observant naturalists, since they remain in the water and seldom fly. At this season they are entirely quiet, though noisy and calling frequently in summer.

This species nests from the Aleutian Islands to Kodiak, the Queen Charlotte Islands, Forrester Island, and northern Japan. In winter it ranges to Baja California and Japan, occurring casually at interior points in the United States.

Kittlitz's Murrelet

(Brachyramphus brevirostris)

Average Length, Nine and One-half Inches

Though abundant in certain areas, Kittlitz's murrelet is so local in its range in American waters that few persons have seen it.

Specimens have been obtained in the Aleutian Islands, where in certain localities it is fairly common, and scattered individuals may be found in summer along the Pacific shores of the Alaska Peninsula. In Glacier Bay, Alaska, it is abundant.

This species is frequently found in company with the ancient and marbled murrelets, but is wilder and more difficult to approach. It flies and dives very swiftly.

To nest, the Kittlitz's murrelet flies inland and places its single egg on bare rock amid patches of snow on the high mountains. The egg, olive or buff, spotted with brown, was not discovered until 1913.

It nests from Bering Strait to Japan and the Alaska Peninsula, in winter retreating to Asiatic waters.

Marbled Murrelet

(Brachyramphus marmoratus)

Average Length, Nine and Three-quarters Inches

Traveling up the inside passage to Alaska, the sharp-eyed observer may see small black and white birds flying swiftly just above the water. They are shy and alert, and ordinarily take wing before the ship is near.

These are the marbled murrelets, common and widely distributed along our western coasts, but birds of mystery so far as much of their life is concerned.

The marbled murrelet feeds mainly on small fish, taken skillfully by diving, and also eats small mollusks. In the water it is quick and graceful, diving with ease and often traveling some distance under the surface. It rises on the wing with equal facility and darts away swiftly, attaining high speed immediately.

In the Queen Charlotte group on the coast of British Columbia, nests have been reported 200 feet above the sea in burrows six feet deep or in deep crevices in rock, where the single egg rested on dry grass and leaves.

An unlaid egg, taken from a bird captured near Prince of Wales Island by George G. Cantwell and now in the National Museum, is pale yellow, spotted rather finely with black.

It appears that these murrelets may make their nests amid inland forests. Marbled murrelets have been seen at dusk headed inland high above the water, but in the darkness it has not been possible to follow them. After nesting, this murrelet flies south.

It ranges in summer from Unalaska and Kodiak to northern California; in winter, from Bering Sea to southern California.

THE RHINOCEROS AUKLET WEARS ITS "HORN" ONLY FOR ORNAMENT

After the nesting season the strange **Rhinoceros Auklet** (left foreground) sheds the bill protuber-
ance, along with its nuptial plumes. Beyond, its young rests on the water like a block of wood, but can
dive in a flash if alarmed. The **Pigeon Guillemot** of the Northwest (right) also is an excellent diver.
Behind the somber old one in summer dress hides a downy nestling. Farther away are a guillemot in
cold-weather clothes (right) and its young in its first winter coat.

Rhinoceros Auklet

(Cerorhinca monocerata)

Average Length, Seventeen Inches

Even in a group of birds that seems to specialize in peculiarities of the beak, the rhinoceros auklet is strange and unusual.

The bill is fairly strong and arched, while from the base, like the front sight on a gun, projects a narrow, compressed plate than can have no other function than that of ornament. This is shed at the close of the nesting season, to grow again as the bird assumes its nuptial plumes the following spring.

Only for part of the year, therefore, does this strange bird warrant its name.

The rhinoceros auklet rests on the water like a block of wood, with neck drawn in and head on a line with the body, presenting a most curious appearance. Approach it by boat, and ordinarily it dives like a flash, traveling far beneath the water before showing itself again at the surface. Only seldom does it fly.

Through most of the year rhinoceros auklets are solitary and feed at some distance from shore. In the breeding season they gather in populous colonies, among which may be mentioned Destruction Island, on the coast of Washington, and Forrester Island, at Dixon Entrance, on the southern boundary of Alaska. Thousands of pairs come to nest in company on these steep-sided islands. About its colonies the rhinoceros auklet is active mainly at night, and the birds are seldom seen by day except when taken from their burrows.

They are reported to arrive at their breeding grounds en masse. One evening in spring the island may be silent, while on the next there is steady commotion as birds blunder heavily to the ground through the branches of trees and bushes, or, when safely landed, call and wail about the affairs of love that bring them thither.

They nest in burrows excavated from 8 to 20 feet through the earth, often ending at some depth in a chamber a foot long by seven or eight inches in diameter, lined with whatever vegetation may be at hand. From the main tunnel there are usually one or more short lateral passages, the use of which is not known. The large egg is white, sometimes plain, but more often spotted with brown, gray, and lavender.

Birds and eggs are eaten by Indians.

On Destruction Island the natives are said to thrust a wad of grass to the length of the arm down the nesting hole at dusk. As the birds arrive after dark and scuttle into their burrows, they are caught in this trap and hauled forth to be killed.

The food of this auklet consists of fishes and crustaceans. Though some forage near their colonies, others travel 60 miles or more to favorable feeding grounds.

The rhinoceros auklet nests from the Aleutian Islands to Washington and Japan, in winter ranging to Baja California.

The auks as a whole seem to occupy in the North the place taken by the penguins of Antarctic regions, but the similarity lies merely in habit and in manner of life, as the two groups are only remotely related.

Pigeon Guillemot

(Cepphus columba)

Average Length, Thirteen and One-half Inches

As a western representative of the black guillemot, the present species is distinguished in life mainly by the wedge-shaped bar of black extending into the prominent white patch on the wing.

In the hand it is found to be larger, to have the under wing-coverts brownish gray instead of white, and to possess 14 tail feathers instead of the 12 of the black guillemot of the Atlantic coast.

Throughout the rocky coasts of southwestern Alaska, from Unga to far-distant Attu, I saw the pigeon guillemot along rough shores and in every harbor that we entered. Pairs or small companies rested on the water or perched on rocks.

As I came near, they rose with whistled calls and swung away in quick flight, deceiving in its rapidity. On land they stood upright, or relaxed to rest on the breast. The dark plumage, red feet, and bright red-lined mouth made a pleasing contrast of color.

The nests of this species may be placed in caves, crevices, or crannies, or, where waves have cut caverns that penetrate beyond the reach of light, on open ledges. Elsewhere they utilize secure retreats beneath rough stones above the beaches, or may excavate burrows in clay banks above the water. The sites selected are secure and ordinarily may be reached, if at all, with difficulty. The two eggs vary from green to white and are marked boldly or finely with black, brown, and lilac.

Both parents assist in incubation, which is said to last three weeks. The young come into the world completely covered with soft down, black above and brown below.

When the plumage of fall is attained the young birds have white heads, and the adults are white instead of black below.

This species nests in company with other sea birds, living with all peacefully and in harmony. When approached on the water it often flies in a circle around a boat, traveling rapidly near the surface of the water.

Its note is a low whistle that does not carry for any distance.

Small fish taken by diving form the principal food. The birds are as expert beneath the surface as any of their companion species, flying under water with rapidly rowing wings and with red feet held straight out behind.

This species ranges from Bering Sea to Japan and southern California.

HUNGRY HAWKS TAKE HEAVY TOLL OF THESE LITTLE WEST COAST MARINERS

Xantus's Murrelet, shown below with a downy chick, finds the best way to escape the marauders is by flying straight out to sea at terrific speed.   These are more southerly members of the generally subarctic auk tribe.   After severe storms, California beaches are sometimes littered with the bodies of **Cassin's Auklet,** pictured at the top with a fluffy offspring.

Xantus's Murrelet

(Endomychura hypoleuca)

Average Length, Eight and One-half Inches

This interesting bird is named for the Hungarian naturalist, John Xantus (also known as Louis de Vesey), who found the first recorded individual at Cape San Lucas, Baja California, in 1859, while collecting specimens for the Smithsonian Institution. In recent years this murrelet has become better known and its metropolis has been found to be in the islands off the coast of southern California.

These birds are active about their nesting grounds only at night, when their twittering notes are heard. At other times they are seen only when frightened out. They fly with tremendous velocity straight to sea, as there they can escape the duck hawks that seem to be their worst enemies about their breeding grounds.

Nests of this bird are placed in caves, in rock crevices, or in hollows under stones. Two eggs are laid, which vary widely in color, ranging from those with light-blue background and a few spots of brown to others so heavily marked that they present an almost uniform chocolate color.

The young, as soon as hatched, are active and alert, and within four days are led down the steep slopes by their parents to tumble finally into the sea. Here they swim and dive, being able when they first reach the water to travel several yards beneath the surface, and even to elude the rushing attacks of large fishes.

It seems marvelous that such tiny creatures can withstand the buffeting of the open seas. Yet young only a few days old have been found swimming with their parents several miles from land.

The adult birds suffer much on land from falcons, and on some islands cats have destroyed them. They are about their nesting grounds for several months in spring and summer, and it is believed that two broods of young are reared each year. After breeding the adults remain mainly at sea, but the majority do not wander far.

Xantus's murrelet is found along the western shores of Baja California, and on coastal islands of southern California north to Anacapa. Stragglers have been taken as far north as Mendocino County.

Cassin's Auklet

(Ptychoramphus aleuticus)

Average Length, Nine Inches

Landing on North Coronado Island, Mexico, southwest of San Diego, one morning in early May, I climbed the steep slopes and found a family of well-grown duck hawks huddled in a little hollow at the base of a rock near the summit. The parent falcons wheeled overhead, cackling angrily at my intrusion.

Meanwhile, other members of our party had scattered over the slopes below, where there were populous colonies of Cassin's auklets.

Disturbed, these birds began flying out of their burrows to dash swiftly down to the sea. Instantly one of the duck hawks was after them, hurtling down from above and venting its anger by striking one after another until a dozen auklets had been killed before I could move away and leave the falcons undisturbed.

On the coastal islands of California Cassin's auklet is one of the most common birds. It gathers in large colonies to nest and places its single egg in any cover that may offer, from a burrow specially excavated for the purpose, to a crevice in rock or a hollow beneath a board or stone. On its nesting grounds the bird normally is active at night, possibly to avoid hawks and similar dangers, so that one may look over slopes known to house many without seeing a single one.

At nightfall all this changes and the auklets come and go swiftly. The partners of each pair change places on the nest, and there is a constant buzzing and croaking from hosts of birds at rest.

Since the nesting season is considerably prolonged, it is probable that more than one family is reared each year, accounting thus for the abundance of this species. After nesting the birds do not seem to travel far, for they are common in the vicinity of their breeding grounds. They seem, however, to remain mainly at sea.

Their flight is swift and at a low elevation whether over land or water. They seem to have little skill in avoiding obstacles, and when they arrive at their breeding grounds, after flying in at night from the sea, they continually crash into buildings. Partly stunned, the birds fall to the ground, and then, recovering, scuttle about in search of the nesting burrow.

Though silent at other seasons in their rookeries, these birds call in chorus throughout the night in loud and doleful tones that rise and fall in ear-filling cadence.

In early days many of these auklets were eaten by Indians, who found them fat and of good flavor.

Cassin's auklets suffer heavily during tempests. After severe storms hundreds may be found cast up, dead or dying, on southern California beaches.

This auklet nests from the Aleutian Islands to Baja California. In winter it is found north to Puget Sound.

A related species, Craveri's murrelet *(Endomychura craveri)* is found along the coast of southern Baja California. It has the under wing-coverts brownish gray instead of white, and is grayer and browner above than the related form.

ONE HUNDRED THOUSAND PELICANS ON ONE OF THE GUANO ISLANDS OF PERU

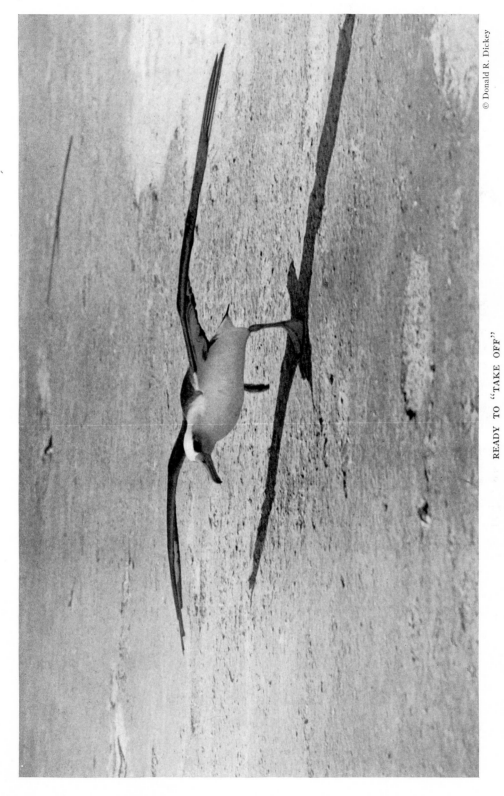

READY TO "TAKE OFF"

If any bird has an important aviation lesson to teach us, it is the albatross, for its soaring grace intrigued the thoughts of man long before he dreamed of human flight. After centuries, it remains, perhaps, the best example of specialized adjustment to the complex of air current, mass, and gravity.

347

© Donald R. Dickey

THE SPIRIT OF LIGHT

The quiet curiosity of the love tern is in striking contrast to the screaming threat of other terns. One of the sailors of the *Tanager* actually had one of these gentle birds alight on his outstretched, motionless hand. This incident is evidence of that rare bird comradeship which remains to Dr. Alexander Wetmore as his most intimate memory of Laysan Island, Hawaii.

INDEX TO VOLUME I

NATIONAL GEOGRAPHIC SOCIETY

GEOGRAPHIC ADMINISTRATION BUILDINGS

SIXTEENTH AND M STREETS NORTHWEST, WASHINGTON, D. C.

ORGANIZED FOR "THE INCREASE AND DIFFUSION OF GEOGRAPHIC KNOWLEDGE"

To carry out the purposes for which it was founded in 1888, the National Geographic Society publishes the NATIONAL GEOGRAPHIC MAGAZINE monthly. All receipts are invested in The Magazine or expended directly to promote geographic knowledge.

Immediately after the terrific eruption of the world's largest crater, Mt. Katmai, in Alaska, a National Geographic Society expedition was sent to make observations of this remarkable phenomenon. Four expeditions have followed and the extraordinary scientific data resulting given to the world. In this vicinity an eighth wonder of the world was discovered and explored—"The Valley of Ten Thousand Smokes," a vast area of steaming, spouting fissures. As a result of The Society's discoveries this area has been created a National Monument by proclamation of the President of the United States.

The Society coöperated with Dr. William Beebe in a deep-sea exploration of underseas life off Bermuda, during which a world record depth of 3,028 feet was attained August 15, 1934.

The Society also had the honor of subscribing a substantial sum to the expedition of Admiral Peary, who discovered the North Pole, and contributed $100,000 to Admiral Byrd's Antarctic Expeditions.

The Society granted $25,000, and in addition $75,000 was given by individual members, to the Government when the congressional appropriation for the purpose was insufficient, and the finest of the giant sequoia trees in the Giant Forest of Sequoia National Park of California were thereby saved for the American people.

The Society's notable expeditions to New Mexico have pushed back the historic horizons of the southwestern United States to a period nearly eight centuries before Columbus crossed the Atlantic. By dating the ruins of the vast communal dwellings in that region, The Society's researches have solved secrets that have puzzled historians for three hundred years.

On November 11, 1935, in a flight sponsored jointly by the National Geographic Society and the U. S. Army Air Corps, the world's largest balloon, *Explorer II*, ascended to an officially recognized altitude record of 72,395 feet. Capt. Albert W. Stevens and Capt. Orvil A. Anderson took aloft in the gondola nearly a ton of scientific instruments, and obtained results of extraordinary value.

The Society, coöperating with the United States Navy, sent an eclipse expedition to Canton Island, Pacific Ocean, June 8, 1937, which brought back natural color photographs and a fund of new information.

In Mexico, in the State of Vera Cruz, Matthew W. Stirling, director of an expedition sponsored jointly by The Society and the Smithsonian Institution, January 16, 1939, discovered the oldest work of man in the Americas, for which we have a date. This slab of stone (stele) is engraved in Mayan characters with a date which means November 4, 291 B. C. It antedates by nearly 200 years anything heretofore dated in America, and reveals a great center of early American culture, previously unknown.

AUTHORITATIVE PUBLICATIONS OF THE NATIONAL GEOGRAPHIC SOCIETY

THE following books—as well as the maps and pictures listed in back of Vol. II— are available to members of the National Geographic Society, and may be obtained only from The Society's headquarters, 16th and M Streets, N. W., Washington, D. C. *Prices listed apply only in United States and Possessions; elsewhere, 50c additional for the two-volume books, 75c for each bound volume of National Geographic Magazines, and 25c each for all other items. To minimize expense and reduce costs, it is requested that remittances accompany orders. All postage is prepaid.*

Books of Permanent Reference and Educational Value

The Book of Birds
Edited by Gilbert Grosvenor and Alexander Wetmore; the first book ever published portraying all major species of birds on the North American Continent north of Mexico *in full color.* Two volumes, indexed with approximately 3,000 specific references; 748 pages; 232 photographs; 204 pages of full-color plates showing 950 birds painted by Major Allan Brooks; 633 bird biographies; 37 fascinating articles; 17 maps disclosing remarkable new developments in the study of bird migration. Royal Octavo (10¼ x 7 in.).
Green Cloth Binding......$5 the set of two volumes

The Book of Wild Flowers
Color plates and biographies of 250 representative species, including familiar grasses, together with a chapter on Our State Flowers. 243 pages, including 27 photographs, a composite drawing of types and parts of flowers, 128 pages of flower paintings in accurate full color, and vivid text on ways and mysteries of plant life. Royal Octavo (10 x 7 in.).
Forest Green Cloth Binding....$3.00

Our Insect Friends and Foes and Spiders
500 insects and spiders in exact color; 161 monochrome illustrations; informative stories of bee, ant, beetle, bug, fly, butterfly, moth, and spider life; 252 pages. Royal Octavo (10 x 7 in.).
Tan Cloth Binding...........$2.50

The Book of Fishes
By John Oliver La Gorce and other authorities; presents an informative life story of the most important of American game and food fishes and strange citizens of ocean shores, lakes, and rivers; illustrated with many full-color paintings from life. A new and revised edition ready September 1939.

Wild Animals of North America
127 full-color portraits; many monochrome engravings and track sketches; 254 pages. Royal Octavo (10 x 7 in.).
Mulberry Cloth Binding......$2.00

Horses of the World
24 full-color pages; 72 monochrome engravings; 118 pages. Royal Octavo (10 x 7 in.).
Blue Cloth Binding..........$1.50

Hunting Wild Life with Camera and Flashlight
This unusual work by George Shiras, 3d—who was the first to take photographs of wild animals in their natural habitats, who originated flashlight photography of wild animals, and whose unique photographs have been awarded highest honors at home and abroad—is the record of 65 years' visits to the woods and waters of North America. Two volumes; 950 pages; illustrated with 950 of the author's photographs taken by flashlight and daylight. Royal Octavo (10¼ x 7 in.).
Blue Cloth Binding.......$5 the set of two volumes

Cattle of the World
45 subjects in full color; 94 monochrome illustrations; 142 pages. Royal Octavo (10 x 7 in.).
Molloy-made Binding........$1.50

The Valley of Ten Thousand Smokes
The first adequate account of the eruption of Mt. Katmai and of The Society's discovery of The Valley of Ten Thousand Smokes; 233 engravings and color plates; 9 specially drawn maps; 340 pages. Royal Octavo (10 x 7 in.).
Blue Cloth Binding.........$2.00

Cumulative Index to National Geographic Magazines from 1899 to 1938, Inclusive
This Cumulative Index to the NATIONAL GEOGRAPHIC MAGAZINE (1899-1936 inclusive), with Supplement covering 1937-38, contains 14,600 references to topical headings, nature subjects, places, maps, authors, titles, and pictures. It unlocks the wealth of material in 480 numbers of THE GEOGRAPHIC; illustrated foreword by Gilbert Grosvenor describes the history of The Society and its Magazine; 490 pages. Royal Octavo (10 x 7 in.).
Brown Cloth Binding, with 1937-38 Supplement...$1.25

Bound Volumes of Geographic Magazines
A limited number of bound volumes of THE NATIONAL GEOGRAPHIC, beginning with 1924, are available. Six numbers, with index, to the volume, two volumes to the year.
Half Morocco Binding....$5 per volume

PRICES LISTED APPLY ONLY IN UNITED STATES AND POSSESSIONS. FURTHER DETAILS AT TOP OF PAGE.

NATIONAL GEOGRAPHIC SOCIETY » » Washington, D. C.

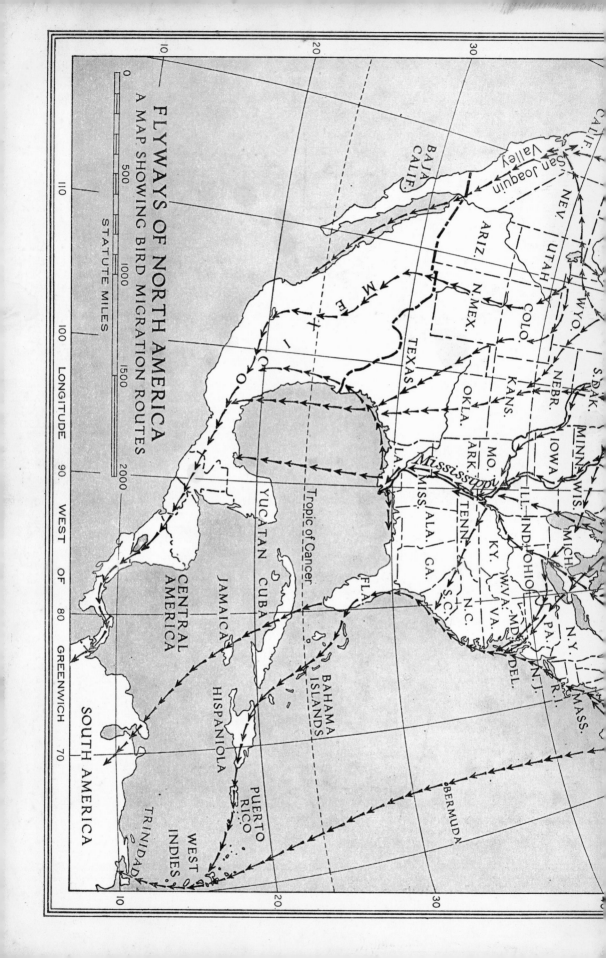